Soul Stirring

SONGS & HYMNS

REVISION EDITORS

Dr. Curtis Hutson
Dr. John Reynolds

COMPILERS

Dr. John R. Rice
Joy (Mrs. Roger) Rice Martin

"Speaking to yourselves in psalms and hymns and spiritual songs, singing and making melody in your heart to the Lord."

—Ephesians 5:19

Revised Edition: 1989

SWORD OF THE LORD PUBLISHERS
224 Bridge Avenue, Box 1099
Murfreesboro, Tennessee 37133

Printed in U.S.A.

TABLE OF CONTENTS

I. THE CROSS 1-30

II. THE RESURRECTION 31-38

III. HEAVEN 39-68

IV. SECOND COMING 69-84

V. COMFORT AND GUIDANCE 85-124

VI. ASSURANCE 125-154

VII. PRAISE 155-170

VIII. LOVE 171-189

IX. JOY AND SINGING 190-206

X. TESTIMONY 207-250

XI. SALVATION 251-268

XII. INVITATION 269-291

XIII. CONSECRATION 292-335

XIV. HOLY SPIRIT 336-350

XV. PRAYER 351-362

XVI. THE BIBLE 363-369

XVII. SOUL WINNING AND SERVICE 370-403

XVIII. CHRISTIAN WARFARE 404-419

XIX. CHRISTMAS 420-434

XX. PATRIOTIC 435-438

XXI. THANKSGIVING 439-442

XXII. CHOIR AND SPECIAL 443-479

FOREWORD

God has indeed been gracious to us in giving us the heavenly benefit of music. Many of the songs and hymns in this collection either quote or paraphrase Scripture. God-fearing, Christ-honoring, gifted men and women have been used of the Lord to pen poetry and melody that uplift our souls and challenge us to renewed dedication in serving the Lord.

This anthology includes several songs written by Dr. John R. Rice, our beloved founder, editor of THE SWORD OF THE LORD for many years, and author of more books than most people read in a lifetime. You will learn more of Dr. Rice's ardent study of the Word of God and of his fervent dedication to Christ through his songs.

SOUL STIRRING SONGS & HYMNS has been well received since its first publication in 1972. We are happy you like the selections and trust they will continue to be a blessing to you and to many of God's people who will yet be introduced to them.

We have given the book a "face-lift." Most of the songs are still the same, but they are now more readable and a bit more classic in appearance. We believe you will appreciate the new look.

May the Lord bless each of these songs and hymns to our hearts. May we be inspired to love the Lord more, to win more souls, to study our Bibles more, to pray more, through the moving messages in poetry and song. And may we, in the fellowship of others of God's children who would unite their voices with ours in singing together the praises of Zion, realize "a foretaste of Glory divine"!

The Publishers

REVISION EDITORS
Dr. Curtis Hutson
Dr. John Reynolds

COMPILERS
Dr. John R. Rice
Joy (Mrs. Roger) Rice Martin

Jesus, I My Cross Have Taken

1

HENRY F. LYTE

Ascribed to WOLFGANG A. MOZART
Arr. by Hubert P. Main

1. Je - sus, I my cross have tak - en, All to leave, and fol - low Thee;
2. Let the world de - spise and leave me, They have left my Sav - iour, too;
3. Man may trou-ble and dis-tress me, 'Twill but drive me to Thy breast;
4. Haste thee on from grace to glo - ry, Armed by faith, and winged by pray'r;

Des - ti-tute, de - spised, for-sak - en, Thou from hence, my all shall be.
Hu - man hearts and looks de-ceive me, Thou art not, like man, un - true.
Life with tri - als hard may press me, Heav'n will bring me sweet-er rest.
Heav'n's e-ter - nal day's be-fore thee, God's own hand shall guide thee there.

Per - ish ev - 'ry fond am-bi - tion, All I've sought, and hoped, and known;
And, while Thou shalt smile up-on me, God of wis - dom, love, and might,
O 'tis not in grief to harm me, While Thy love is left to me;
Soon shall close thy earth- ly mis - sion, Swift shall pass thy pil - grim days,

Yet how rich is my con-di - tion, God and Heav'n are still my own!
Foes may hate, and friends may shun me; Show Thy face, and all is bright.
O 'twere not in joy to charm me, Were that joy un - mixed with Thee.
Hope shall change to glad fru - i - tion, Faith to sight, and pray'r to praise.

Favorite song of Dr. John R. Rice and Dr. Arthur DeMoss.

2 Glory to His Name

ELISHA A. HOFFMAN

JOHN H. STOCKTON

1. Down at the cross where my Sav-iour died, Down where from cleans-ing from
2. I am so won-drous-ly saved from sin; Je - sus so sweet-ly a-
3. O pre-cious foun-tain that saves from sin; I am so glad I have
4. Come to this foun-tain so rich and sweet; Cast thy poor soul at the

sin I cried, There to my heart was the blood ap-plied; Glo - ry to His
bides with-in, There at the cross where He took me in; Glo - ry to His
en-tered in; There Je - sus saves me and keeps me clean; Glo - ry to His
Sav-iour's feet; Plunge in to-day and be made com-plete; Glo - ry to His

name. Glo - ry to His name, Glo - ry to His name;

There to my heart was the blood ap-plied; Glo - ry to His name.

Jesus Paid It All

ELVINA M. HALL

JOHN T. GRAPE

1. I hear the Sav-iour say, "Thy strength in-deed is small, Child of
2. Lord, now in - deed I find Thy pow'r, and Thine a - lone, Can
3. For noth - ing good have I Where - by Thy grace to claim— I'll
4. And when, be-fore the throne, I stand in Him com-plete, "Je - sus

weak - ness, watch and pray, . Find in Me thine all in all."
change the lep - er's spots, And melt the heart of stone.
wash my gar-ments white In the blood of Cal-v'ry's Lamb.
died my soul to save," My lips shall still re - peat.

Je - sus paid it all, All to Him I owe;

Sin had left a crim - son stain, He washed it white as snow.

4 The Way of the Cross Leads Home

JESSIE B. POUNDS

CHARLES H. GABRIEL

1. I must needs go Home by the way of the cross, There's no oth - er
2. I must needs go on in the blood-sprinkled way, The path that the
3. Then I bid fare - well to the way of the world, To walk in it

way but this; I shall ne'er get sight of the Gates of Light, If the
Sav - iour trod, If I ev - er climb to the heights sub-lime, Where the
nev - er - more; For my Lord says, "Come," and I seek my Home, Where He

way of the cross I miss.
soul is at Home with God.
waits at the o - pen door.

The way of the cross leads

Home, The way of the cross leads Home; It is
leads Home, leads Home;

sweet to know as I on - ward go, The way of the cross leads Home.

When I Survey the Wondrous Cross 5

ISAAC WATTS

Arranged by Lowell Mason

1. When I sur - vey the won - drous cross, On which the
2. For - bid it, Lord! that I should boast, Save in the
3. See, from His head, His hands, His feet, Sor - row and
4. Were the whole realm of na - ture mine, That were a

Prince of Glo - ry died, My rich - est gain I
death of Christ my God: All the vain things that
love flow min - gled down: Did e'er such love and
pres - ent far too small; Love so a - maz - ing,

count but loss, And pour con - tempt on all my pride.
charm me most, I sac - ri - fice them to His blood.
sor - row meet, Or thorns com - pose so rich a crown?
so di - vine, De - mands my soul, my life, my all.

Favorite song of Dr. Bill Rice and composer John W. Peterson.

6 Beneath the Cross of Jesus

ELIZABETH C. CLEPHANE

FREDERICK C. MAKER

1. Be - neath the cross of Je - sus I fain would take my stand, The
2. Up - on that cross of Je - sus Mine eye at times can see The
3. I take, O cross, thy shad - ow For my a - bid - ing place; I

shad - ow of a might - y Rock With - in a wea - ry land; A
ver - y dy - ing form of One Who suf - fered there for me; And
ask no oth - er sun-shine than The sun - shine of His face; Con -

home with-in the wil - der - ness, A rest up - on the way, From the
from my smit-ten heart with tears, Two won - ders I con- fess: The
tent to let the world go by, To know no gain nor loss, My

burn - ing of the noon-tide heat, And the bur - den of the day.
won - ders of His glo - rious love, And my own worth-less - ness.
sin - ful self my on - ly shame, My glo - ry all the cross!

I Gave My Life for Thee

FRANCES R. HAVERGAL

PHILIP P. BLISS

1. I gave my life for thee, My pre-cious blood I shed, That thou might'st ran-somed be, And quick-ened from the dead; I gave, I gave My life for thee, What hast thou giv'n for Me? I gave, I gave My life for thee, What hast thou giv'n for Me?

2. My Fa-ther's house of light, My glo-ry-cir-cled throne I left for earth-ly night, For wan-d'rings sad and lone; I left, I left it all for thee, Hast thou left aught for Me? I left, I left it all for thee, Hast thou left aught for Me?

3. I suf-fered much for thee, More than thy tongue can tell, Of bit-t'rest ag-o-ny, To res-cue thee from Hell; I've borne, I've borne it all for thee, What hast thou borne for Me? I've borne, I've borne it all for thee, What hast thou borne for Me?

4. And I have brought to thee, Down from My Home a-bove, Sal-va-tion full and free, My par-don and My love; I bring, I bring rich gifts to thee, What hast thou brought to Me? I bring, I bring rich gifts to thee, What hast thou brought to Me?

8   I Am Coming to the Cross

WILLIAM McDONALD

WILLIAM G. FISCHER

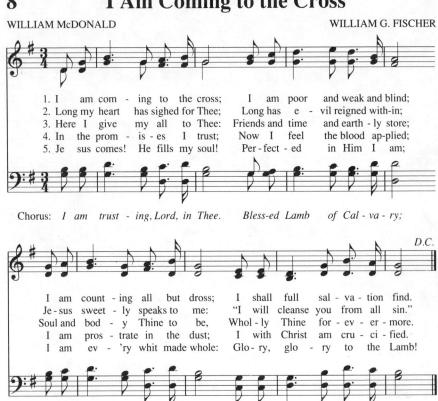

1. I am com - ing to the cross;   I am poor   and weak and blind;
2. Long my heart   has sighed for Thee;   Long has e - vil reigned with-in;
3. Here I give   my all   to Thee: Friends and time   and earth - ly store;
4. In the prom - is - es   I trust;   Now I   feel   the blood ap-plied;
5. Je - sus comes!   He fills my soul!   Per - fect - ed   in Him I am;

Chorus: *I am trust - ing, Lord, in Thee.*   *Bless-ed Lamb   of Cal - va - ry;*

D.C.

I am count - ing all but dross;   I shall full   sal - va - tion find.
Je - sus sweet - ly speaks to me: "I will cleanse you from all sin."
Soul and bod - y Thine to be,   Whol - ly Thine   for - ev - er - more.
I am pros - trate in the dust;   I with Christ am cru - ci - fied.
I am ev - 'ry whit made whole: Glo - ry, glo - ry to the Lamb!

Hum-bly   at   Thy cross I   bow.   *Save me, Je - sus, save me now.*

9   Room at the Cross for You

IRA F. STANPHILL

IRA F. STANPHILL

1. The cross up-on which Je - sus died   Is a shel - ter in
2. Though mil-lions have found Him a Friend   And have turned from the
3. The hand of my Sav - iour is strong,   And the love of my

10 Near the Cross

FANNY J. CROSBY

WILLIAM H. DOANE

1. Je - sus, keep me near the cross, There a pre - cious foun - tain
2. Near the cross, a trem - bling soul, Love and mer - cy found me;
3. Near the cross! O Lamb of God, Bring its scenes be - fore me;
4. Near the cross I'll watch and wait, Hop - ing, trust - ing ev - er,

Free to all — a heal - ing stream, Flows from Cal - v'ry's moun - tain.
There the Bright and Morn - ing Star Sheds its beams a - round me.
Help me walk from day to day, With its shad - ows o'er me.
Till I reach the gold - en strand, Just be - yond the riv - er.

In the cross, in the cross, Be my glo - ry ev - er;

Till my rap - tured soul shall find Rest be - yond the riv - er.

He Died for Me

JOHN NEWTON

EDWIN O. EXCELL

1. I saw One hang-ing on a tree, In ag-o-ny and blood; He
2. Sure, nev-er, till my lat-est breath, Can I for-get that look: It
3. My con-science felt and owned the guilt, And plunged me in de-spair; I
4. A-las! I knew not what I did, But now my tears are vain: Where
5. A sec-ond look He gave, which said, "I free-ly all for-give: This

fixed His lan-guid eyes on me, As near His cross I stood.
seemed to charge me with His death, Though not a word He spoke.
saw my sins His blood had spilt And helped to nail Him there.
shall my trem-bling soul be hid? For I the Lord have slain.
blood is for thy ran-som paid, I die that thou may'st live."

Oh, can it be, up-on a tree The Sav-iour died for me?

My soul is thrilled, my heart is filled, To think He died for me!

12   Blessed Redeemer

AVIS B. CHRISTIANSEN

HARRY D. LOES

1. Up Cal-v'ry's moun - tain, one dread-ful morn, Walked Christ my
2. "Fa - ther, for - give them!" thus did He pray, E'en while His
3. O how I love Him, Sav-iour and Friend, How can my

Sav - iour, wea-ry and worn; Fac-ing for sin - ners death on the
life - blood flowed fast a - way; Pray-ing for sin - ners while in such
prais - es ev-er find end! Through years un-num - bered on Heav-en's

cross, That He might save them from end-less loss.
woe — No one but Je - sus ev - er loved so. Bless-ed Re-
shore, My tongue shall praise Him for - ev - er - more.

deem - er! pre-cious Re - deem - er! Seems now I
Bless-ed Re-deem - er! bless-ed Re-deem - er!

see Him on Cal - va - ry's tree; Wound-ed and

14 Kneel at the Cross

CHAS. E. MOODY

CHAS. E. MOODY

1. Kneel at the cross, Christ will meet you there, Come while He waits for you;
2. Kneel at the cross, There is room for all Who would His glo-ry share;
3. Kneel at the cross, Give your i-dols up. Look un-to realms a-bove;

List to His voice, Leave with Him your care, And be-gin life a-new.
Bliss there a-waits, Harm can ne'er be-fall Those who are an-chored there.
Turn not a-way, To life's sparkling cup, Trust on-ly in His love.

Kneel at the cross, Leave ev-'ry care;
Kneel at the cross, Kneel at the cross, Leave ev-'ry care, Leave ev-'ry care;

Kneel at the cross, Je-sus will meet you there.
Kneel at the cross, Kneel at the cross, meet you there.

bleed - ing, for sin-ners plead - ing— Blind and un-
Wound-ed and bleed - ing, for sin-ners plead - ing—

heed - ing— dy - ing for me.
Blind and un - heed - ing—

Must Jesus Bear the Cross Alone? 13

THOMAS SHEPHERD

GEORGE N. ALLEN

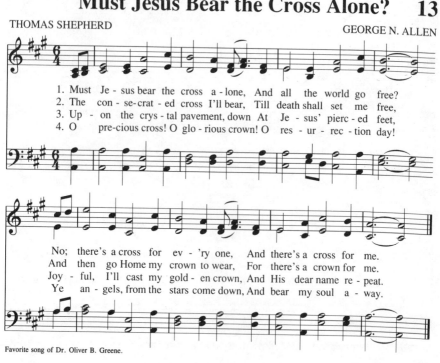

1. Must Je - sus bear the cross a - lone, And all the world go free?
2. The con - se - crat - ed cross I'll bear, Till death shall set me free,
3. Up - on the crys - tal pavement, down At Je - sus' pierc - ed feet,
4. O pre-cious cross! O glo - rious crown! O res - ur - rec - tion day!

No; there's a cross for ev - 'ry one, And there's a cross for me.
And then go Home my crown to wear, For there's a crown for me.
Joy - ful, I'll cast my gold - en crown, And His dear name re - peat.
Ye an - gels, from the stars come down, And bear my soul a - way.

Favorite song of Dr. Oliver B. Greene.

Lead Me to Calvary

15

JENNIE E. HUSSEY

WILLIAM J. KIRKPATRICK

1. King of my life, I crown Thee now, Thine shall the glo - ry be;
2. Show me the tomb where Thou wast laid, Ten - der-ly mourned and wept;
3. Let me like Ma - ry, through the gloom, Come with a gift to Thee;
4. May I be will - ing, Lord, to bear Dai - ly my cross for Thee;

Lest I for - get Thy thorn-crowned brow, Lead me to Cal - va - ry.
An - gels in robes of light ar - rayed Guard-ed Thee whilst Thou slept.
Show to me now the emp - ty tomb, Lead me to Cal - va - ry.
E - ven Thy cup of grief to share, Thou hast borne all for me.

Lest I for-get Geth - sem - a-ne; Lest I for-get Thine ag - o-ny;

Lest I for-get Thy love for me, Lead me to Cal - va - ry.

16   Majestic Sweetness Sits Enthroned

SAMUEL STENNETT   THOMAS HASTINGS

1. Ma - jes - tic sweet - ness sits en-throned Up - on the Sav - iour's
2. No mor - tal can with Him com-pare, A - mong the sons of
3. He saw me plunged in deep dis - tress, And flew to my re -
4. To Him I owe my life and breath, And all the joys I

brow; His head with ra - diant glo - ries crowned, His
men; Fair - er is He than all the fair Who
lief; For me He bore the shame - ful cross, And
have; He makes me tri - umph o - ver death, And

lips with grace o'er - flow, His lips with grace o'er - flow.
fill the heav'n-ly train, Who fill the heav'n-ly train.
car - ried all my grief, And car - ried all my grief.
saves me from the grave, And saves me from the grave.

Favorite song of Dr. Robert G. Lee.

17   One Day!

J. WILBUR CHAPMAN   CHARLES H. MARSH

1. One day when Heav - en was filled with His prais - es, One day when
2. One day they led Him up Cal - va-ry's moun - tain, One day they
3. One day they left Him a - lone in the gar - den, One day He
4. One day the grave could con - ceal Him no long - er, One day the
5. One day the trum - pet will sound for His com - ing, One day the

sin was as dark as could be, Je-sus came forth to be
nailed Him to die on the tree; Suf-fer-ing an - guish, de-
rest - ed, from suf-fer-ing free; An-gels came down o'er His
stone rolled a - way from the door; Then He a - rose, o - ver
skies with His glo-ries will shine; Won-der-ful day, my be -

born of a vir - gin: Dwelt amongst men, my ex - am-ple is He!
spised and re-ject - ed: Bear-ing our sins, my Re - deem-er is He!
tomb to keep vig - il; Hope of the hope - less, my Sav-iour is He!
death He had con-quered; Now is as-cend - ed, my Lord ev - er-more!
lov-ed ones bring-ing; Glo-ri - ous Sav - iour, this Je-sus is mine!

Liv-ing, He loved me; dy - ing, He saved me; Bur-ied, He

car - ried my sins far a-way; Ris-ing, He jus - ti-fied,

cresc. > > > > *rit.* > > >

free-ly for-ev - er; One day He's com - ing, O glo-ri - ous day!

Favorite song of Dr. Glen H. Schunk.

18　Take the Name of Jesus With You

LYDIA BAXTER

WILLIAM H. DOANE

1. Take the name of Je - sus with you, Child of sor-row and of woe;
2. Take the name of Je - sus ev - er, As a shield from ev - 'ry snare;
3. O the pre-cious name of Je - sus! How it thrills our souls with joy,
4. At the name of Je - sus bow-ing, Fall - ing pros-trate at His feet,

It will joy and com-fort give you, Take it, then, wher-e'er you go.
If temp-ta-tions'round you gath - er, Breathe that ho - ly name in prayer.
When His lov - ing arms re-ceive us, And His songs our tongues em-ploy!
King of kings in Heav'n we'll crown Him, When our jour - ney is com-plete.

Pre-cious name, O how sweet! Hope of earth and joy of Heav'n;

Pre-cious name, O how sweet!

Pre-cious name, O how sweet! Hope of earth and joy of Heav'n.

Pre-cious name, O how sweet, how sweet!

There Is a Fountain

19

WILLIAM COWPER

EARLY AMERICAN MELODY

1. There is a foun-tain filled with blood Drawn from Im-man - uel's veins;
2. The dy - ing thief re - joiced to see That foun - tain in his day;
3. Dear dy - ing Lamb, Thy pre-cious blood Shall nev - er lose its pow'r,
4. E'er since, by faith, I saw the stream Thy flow - ing wounds sup - ply,
5. Then in a no - bler, sweet - er song, I'll sing Thy pow'r to save,

And sin - ners, plunged be-neath that flood, Lose all their guil - ty stains:
And there may I, though vile as he, Wash all my sins a - way:
Till all the ran - somed church of God Be saved, to sin no more:
Re - deem - ing love has been my theme, And shall be till I die:
When this poor lisp - ing, stam-m'ring tongue Lies si - lent in the grave:

Lose all their guil - ty stains, Lose all their guil - ty stains;
Wash all my sins a - way, Wash all my sins a - way;
Be saved, to sin no more, Be saved, to sin no more;
And shall be till I die, And shall be till I die;
Lies si - lent in the grave, Lies si - lent in the grave;

And sin - ners, plunged be-neath that flood, Lose all their guil - ty stains.
And there may I, though vile as he, Wash all my sins a - way.
Till all the ran-somed church of God Be saved, to sin no more.
Re - deem - ing love has been my theme, And shall be till I die.
When this poor lisp - ing, stam-m'ring tongue Lies si - lent in the grave.

Favorite song of Dr. Tom Malone and Dr. Harold Sightler.

20   When I See the Blood

JOHN FOOTE   J. G. FOOTE

1. Christ our Re-deem-er died on the cross, Died for the sin-ner,
2. Chief-est of sin-ners, Je-sus can save, As He has prom-ised,
3. Judg-ment is com-ing, all will be there, Who have re-ject-ed,
4. O what com-pas-sion, O bound-less love! Je-sus hath pow-er,

paid all his due; All who re-ceive Him need nev-er fear,
so will He do; O sin-ner, hear Him, trust in His Word,
who have re-fused. O sin-ner, has-ten, let Je-sus in,
Je - sus is true; All who be-lieve are safe from the storm,

Yes, He will pass, will pass o - ver you.
Then He will pass, will pass o - ver you. When I see the
Then God will pass, will pass o - ver you.
O He will pass, will pass o - ver you. When I

blood, When I see the blood, When I see the
see the blood, When I see the blood, When I

blood, I will pass, I will pass o - ver you.
see the blood, o - ver you.

What a Wonderful Saviour!   21

ELISHA A. HOFFMAN   ELISHA A. HOFFMAN

1. Christ has for sin a - tone-ment made, What a won - der - ful Sav - iour!
2. I praise Him for the cleans-ing blood, What a won - der - ful Sav - iour!
3. He cleansed my heart from all its sin, What a won - der - ful Sav - iour!
4. He gives me o - ver - com - ing pow'r, What a won - der - ful Sav - iour!
5. To Him I've giv - en all my heart, What a won - der - ful Sav - iour!

We are re-deemed! The price is paid! What a won - der - ful Sav - iour!
That rec - on - ciled my soul to God; What a won - der - ful Sav - iour!
And now He reigns and rules there - in; What a won - der - ful Sav - iour!
And tri - umph in each try - ing hour; What a won - der - ful Sav - iour!
The world shall nev - er share a part; What a won - der - ful Sav - iour!

What a won - der - ful Sav - iour is Je - sus, my Je - sus!

What a won - der - ful Sav - iour is Je - sus, my Lord!

22   Are You Washed in the Blood?

ELISHA A. HOFFMAN   ELISHA A. HOFFMAN

1. Have you been to Je - sus for the cleans-ing pow'r? Are you washed in the
2. Are you walk - ing dai - ly by the Sav - iour's side? Are you washed in the
3. When the Bride-groom com-eth will your robes be white? Are you washed in the
4. Lay a - side the gar-ments that are stained with sin, And be washed in the

blood of the Lamb?   Are you ful - ly trust-ing in His grace this hour? Are you
blood of the Lamb?   Do you rest each mo-ment in the Cru - ci - fied? Are you
blood of the Lamb?   Will your soul be read-y for the man-sions bright, And be
blood of the Lamb?   There's a foun-tain flow-ing for the soul un - clean, O be

washed in the blood of the Lamb?
washed in the blood of the Lamb?   Are you washed   in the blood,
washed in the blood of the Lamb?   Are you washed   in the blood,
washed in the blood of the Lamb?

In the soul-cleans-ing blood of the Lamb?   Are your gar-ments
of the Lamb?

spot-less? Are they white as snow? Are you washed in the blood of the Lamb?

There Is Power in the Blood

LEWIS E. JONES   LEWIS E. JONES

1. Would you be free from your bur-den of sin? There's pow'r in the blood,
2. Would you be free from your pas-sion and pride? There's pow'r in the blood,
3. Would you be whit-er, much whit-er than snow? There's pow'r in the blood,
4. Would you do serv-ice for Je-sus your King? There's pow'r in the blood,

pow'r in the blood; Would you o'er e-vil a vic-to-ry win? There's
pow'r in the blood; Come for a cleans-ing to Cal-va-ry's tide; There's
pow'r in the blood; Sin-stains are lost in its life-giv-ing flow; There's
pow'r in the blood; Would you live dai-ly His prais-es to sing? There's

won-der-ful pow'r in the blood. There is pow'r, pow'r, Won-der-work-ing pow'r
won-der-ful pow'r in the blood.
won-der-ful pow'r in the blood. there is
won-der-ful pow'r in the blood.

In the blood of the Lamb; There is pow'r, pow'r,
In the blood, of the Lamb; there is

Won-der-work-ing pow'r In the pre-cious blood of the Lamb.

24   And Can It Be That I Should Gain?

CHARLES WESLEY

THOMAS CAMPBELL

1. And can it be that I should gain An in - t'rest in the Sav - iour's blood? Died He for me, who caused His pain? For me, who Him to death pur - sued? A - maz-ing love! how can it be That Thou, my God, should'st die for me? A - maz - ing love! how

2. He left His Fa - ther's throne a - bove, So free, so in - fi - nite His grace; Emp-tied Him-self of all but love, And bled for A - dam's help-less race; 'Tis mer-cy all, im - mense and free; For, O my God, it found out me. A - maz-ing love! how

3. Long my im-pris - oned spir - it lay Fast bound in sin and na - ture's night; Thine eye dif - fused a quick-'ning ray, I woke, the dun - geon flamed with light; My chains fell off, my heart was free; I rose, went forth, and fol - lowed Thee. A - maz-ing love!

can it be   That Thou, my   God, should'st die for   me?
How   can it be   That Thou, my God,

Wounded for Me   25

W. G. OVENS and
GLADYS W. ROBERTS

W. G. OVENS

1. Wound - ed   for   me,   wound-ed   for   me,   There   on   the   cross
2. Dy - ing   for   me,   dy - ing   for   me,   There   on   the   cross
3. Ris - en   for   me,   ris - en   for   me,   Up   from   the   grave
4. Liv - ing   for   me,   liv - ing   for   me,   Up   in   the   skies
5. Com - ing   for   me,   com - ing   for   me,   One   day   to   earth

He   was   wound - ed   for   me;   Gone   my   trans - gres - sions, and
He   was   dy - ing   for   me;   Now   in   His   death   my   re -
He   has   ris - en   for   me;   Now   ev - er - more from death's
He   is   liv - ing   for   me;   Dai - ly   He's   plead - ing   and
He   is   com - ing   for   me;   Then   with   what   joy   His   dear

dim.

now   I   am   free,   All   be-cause Je - sus was wound-ed for   me.
demp-tion I   see,   All   be-cause Je - sus was   dy - ing   for   me.
sting   I   am   free,   All   be-cause Je - sus has   ris - en   for   me.
pray-ing for   me,   All   be-cause Je - sus is   liv - ing   for   me.
face   I   shall   see,   O   how I   praise Him! He's com-ing for   me.

26 Hallelujah for the Cross!

HORATIUS BONAR, arr.

JAMES McGRANAHAN

1. The cross it stand - eth fast, Hal - le - lu - jah, hal - le - lu - jah! De-
2. It is the old cross still, Hal - le - lu - jah, hal - le - lu - jah! Its
3. 'Twas there the debt was paid, Hal - le - lu - jah, hal - le - lu - jah! Our

fy - ing ev - 'ry blast, Hal - le - lu - jah, hal - le - lu - jah! The
tri - umph let us tell, Hal - le - lu - jah, hal - le - lu - jah! The
sins on Je - sus laid, Hal - le - lu - jah, hal - le - lu - jah! So

winds of Hell have blown, The world its hate hath shown, Yet it
grace of God here shone Through Christ the bless - ed Son, Who
round the cross we sing Of Christ our of - fer - ing, Of

is not o - ver - thrown, Hal - le - lu - jah for the cross!
did for sin a - tone, Hal - le - lu - jah for the cross!
Christ our liv - ing King, Hal - le - lu - jah for the cross!

27   The Old Rugged Cross

GEORGE BENNARD   GEORGE BENNARD

1. On a hill far a-way stood an old rug-ged cross, The em-blem of suf-f'ring and shame; And I love that old cross where the Dear - est and Best For a world of lost sin-ners was slain.

2. O, that old rugged cross so de-spised by the world, Has a won-drous at - trac-tion for me; For the dear Lamb of God left His glo - ry a-bove, To bear it to dark Cal-va - ry.

3. In the old rugged cross, stained with blood so di-vine, A won - drous beau-ty I see; For 'twas on that old cross Je-sus suf - fered and died, To par - don and sanc-ti - fy me.

4. To the old rugged cross I will ev - er be true, Its shame and re-proach glad-ly bear; Then He'll call me some-day to my Home far a - way, Where His glo - ry for - ev - er I'll share.

So I'll cher - ish the old rug-ged cross, the old rug - ged cross, Till my tro-phies at last I lay down; I will cling to the old rug-ged cross,

Favorite song of Dale Evans Rogers.

29
At the Cross

ISAAC WATTS
Refrain: RALPH E. HUDSON

RALPH E. HUDSON

1. A - las, and did my Sav - iour bleed? And did my Sov-'reign die?
2. Was it for crimes that I have done, He groaned up - on the tree?
3. Well might the sun in dark - ness hide, And shut His glo - ries in,
4. But drops of grief can ne'er re - pay The debt of love I owe;

Would He de-vote that sa - cred head For such a worm as I?
A - maz - ing pit - y! grace un-known! And love be - yond de - gree!
When Christ, the might - y Mak - er, died For man the crea-ture's sin.
Here, Lord, I give my - self a-way, 'Tis all that I can do!

At the cross, at the cross where I first saw the light, And the

bur-den of my heart rolled a-way, (rolled a-way,) It was there by faith

I re-ceived my sight, And now I am hap-py all the day!

old rug-ged cross,   And ex-change it some-day for a   crown.
cross,   the   old rug-ged cross,

Alas! and Did My Saviour Bleed? 28

ISAAC WATTS   HUGH WILSON

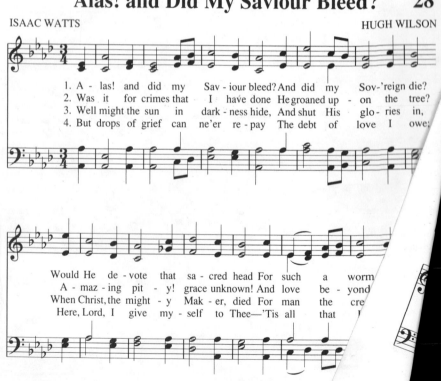

Nothing But the Blood

ROBERT LOWRY

ROBERT LOWRY

30

1. What can wash a - way my sin? Noth-ing but the blood of Je - sus;
2. For my par - don this I see— Noth-ing but the blood of Je - sus;
3. Noth - ing can for sin a - tone— Noth-ing but the blood of Je - sus;
4. This is all my hope and peace— Noth-ing but the blood of Je - sus;

What can make me whole a - gain? Noth-ing but the blood of Je - sus;
For my cleans-ing, this my plea— Noth-ing but the blood of Je - sus;
Naught of good that I have done— Noth-ing but the blood of Je - sus;
This is all my right-eous-ness— Noth-ing but the blood of Je - sus;

O pre - cious is the flow That makes me white as snow;

No oth - er fount I know, Noth-ing but the blood of Je - sus.

31　　　　　He Lives

ALFRED H. ACKLEY　　　　　　　　　　　　　　　　ALFRED H. ACKLEY

1. I serve a ris - en Sav - iour, He's in the world to - day; I
2. In all the world a - round me I see His lov - ing care, And
3. Re - joice, re - joice, O Chris - tian, lift up your voice and sing E -

know that He is liv - ing, what - ev - er men may say; I
though my heart grows wea - ry I nev - er will de - spair; I
ter - nal hal - le - lu - jahs to Je - sus Christ the King! The

see His hand of mer - cy, I hear His voice of cheer, And
know that He is lead - ing, through all the storm - y blast, The
Hope of all who seek Him, the Help of all who find; None

just the time I need Him He's al - ways near.
day of His ap - pear-ing will come at last.
oth - er is so lov-ing, so good and kind.

He lives, He lives, Christ Je-sus lives to-day! He

He lives, He lives,

walks with me and talks with me a - long life's nar - row way. He

lives, He lives, sal - va - tion to im - part! You

He lives, He lives,

ask me how I know He lives? He lives with-in my heart.

Favorite song of Evangelist Bud Lyles.

32 He Lives on High

B. B. McKINNEY

From a Hawaiian Folk Song
Arranged by B. B. McKinney

1. Christ the Sav - iour came from heav-en's glo - ry, To re-deem the lost from sin and shame; On His brow He wore the thorn-crown go - ry, And up-on Cal-va-ry He took my blame.
2. He a - rose from death and all its sor - row, To dwell in that Land of joy and love; He is com - ing back some glad to-mor - row, And He'll take all His chil-dren Home a-bove.
3. Wea-ry soul, to Je - sus come con-fess - ing, Re - demp-tion from sin He of - fers thee; Look to Je - sus and re-ceive a bless - ing, There is life, there is joy and vic - to - ry.

He lives on high, He lives on high, Tri - um - phant o-ver sin and all its stain; He lives on high, He lives on high, Some-day He's com-ing a-gain.

Christ the Lord Is Risen Today

33

CHARLES WESLEY

Arranged from *Lyra Davidica*

1. Christ the Lord is ris'n to-day, Al - le - lu - ia!
2. Lives a-gain our glo-rious King: Al - le - lu - ia!
3. Love's re-deem-ing work is done, Al - le - lu - ia!
4. Soar we now, where Christ has led, Al - le - lu - ia!

Sons of men and an - gels say: Al - le - lu - ia!
Where, O death, is now thy sting? Al - le - lu - ia!
Fought the fight, the bat - tle won; Al - le - lu - ia!
Fol-l'wing our ex - alt - ed Head: Al - le - lu - ia!

Raise your joys and tri - umphs high, Al - le - lu - ia!
Dy - ing once, He all doth save: Al - le - lu - ia!
Death in vain for - bids Him rise; Al - le - lu - ia!
Made like Him, like Him we rise; Al - le - lu - ia!

Sing, ye heav'ns, and earth re - ply. Al - le - lu - ia!
Where thy vic - to - ry, O grave? Al - le - lu - ia!
Christ has o-pened Par - a-dise. Al - le - lu - ia!
Ours the cross, the grave, the skies. Al - le - lu - ia!

34 I Know That My Redeemer Liveth

JESSIE B. POUNDS   JAMES H. FILLMORE

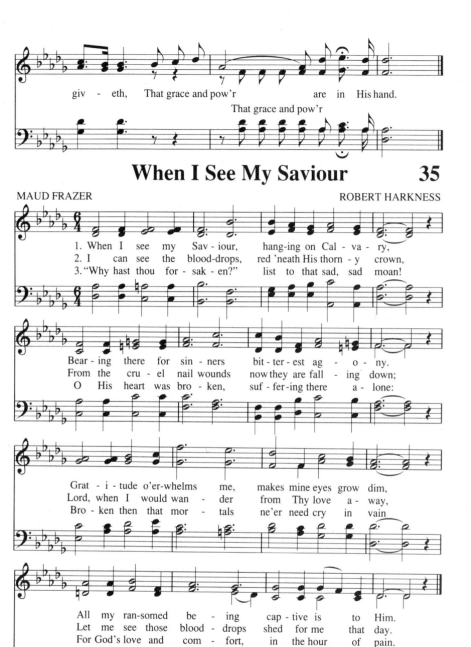

giv - eth, That grace and pow'r are in His hand.

That grace and pow'r

When I See My Saviour 35

MAUD FRAZER ROBERT HARKNESS

1. When I see my Sav - iour, hang-ing on Cal - va - ry,
2. I can see the blood-drops, red 'neath His thorn - y crown,
3. "Why hast thou for - sak - en?" list to that sad, sad moan!

Bear - ing there for sin - ners bit - ter - est ag - o - ny.
From the cru - el nail wounds now they are fall - ing down;
O His heart was bro - ken, suf - fer-ing there a - lone:

Grat - i - tude o'er-whelms me, makes mine eyes grow dim,
Lord, when I would wan - der from Thy love a - way,
Bro - ken then that mor - tals ne'er need cry in vain

All my ran-somed be - ing cap - tive is to Him.
Let me see those blood - drops shed for me that day.
For God's love and com - fort, in the hour of pain.

36 Christ Arose!

ROBERT LOWRY   ROBERT LOWRY

1. Low in the grave He lay— Je - sus my Sav - iour! Wait - ing the
2. Vain - ly they watch His bed— Je - sus my Sav - iour! Vain - ly they
3. Death can-not keep his prey— Je - sus my Sav - iour! He tore the

com- ing day— Je - sus my Lord!
seal the dead— Je - sus my Lord!
bars a - way— Je - sus my Lord!

Faster

Up from the grave He a -

rose, with a might - y tri-umph o'er His foes; He a-

He a-rose, He a-rose!

rose a Vic - tor from the dark do - main, And He lives for - ev - er with His

saints to reign. He a-rose! He a-rose! Hal-le - lu -jah! Christ a-rose!

He a-rose! He a-rose!

There'll Be No Dark Valley

WILLIAM O. CUSHING

IRA D. SANKEY

1. There'll be no dark val-ley when Je-sus comes, There'll be no dark val-ley when Je-sus comes; There'll be no dark val-ley when Je-sus comes To
2. There'll be no more sor-row when Je-sus comes, There'll be no more sor-row when Je-sus comes; But a glo-rious mor-row when Je-sus comes To
3. There'll be no more weep-ing when Je-sus comes, There'll be no more weep-ing when Je-sus comes; But a bless-ed reap-ing when Je-sus comes To
4. There'll be songs of greet-ing when Je-sus comes, There'll be songs of greet-ing when Je-sus comes; And a joy-ful meet-ing when Je-sus comes To

gath-er His loved ones Home. To gath-er His loved ones Home, (safe Home,) To gath-er His loved ones Home; (safe Home;) There'll be no dark val-ley when Je-sus comes To gath-er His loved ones Home.

38   Hallelujah, We Shall Rise

J. E. THOMAS   J. E. THOMAS

1. In the res - ur - rec - tion morn-ing, When the trump of God shall sound,
2. In the res - ur - rec - tion morn-ing, What a meet-ing it will be,
3. In the res - ur - rec - tion morn-ing, Bless-ed thought it is to me,
4. In the res - ur - rec - tion morn-ing, We shall meet Him in the air,

We shall rise,   we shall rise!

Hal - le - lu - jah!

Then the saints will come re-joic-ing
When our fa-thers and our moth-ers,
I shall see my bless-ed Sav-iour,
And be car - ried up to Glo - ry,

And no tears will e'er be found,
And our loved ones we shall see, We shall rise,   we shall rise.
Who so free-ly died for me,
To our Home so bright and fair,

Hal - le - lu - jah! in that morn-ing we shall rise.

Hal - le - lu - jah!   A - men! We shall rise!

We shall rise!   we shall rise!   Hal - le - lu -jah!

In the res - ur - rec - tion morn-ing, When death's pris - on bars are

broken, We shall rise, we shall rise.

Hal - le - lu - jah!

How Beautiful Heaven Must Be 39

Mrs. A. S. BRIDGEWATER

A. P. BLAND

1. We read of a place that's called Heav-en, It's made for the pure and the free;
2. In Heav-en no droop-ing nor pin - ing, No wish-ing for else-where to be;
3. Pure wa - ters of life there are flow-ing, And all who will drink may be free;
4. The an - gels so sweet-ly are sing-ing, Up there by the beau-ti - ful sea;

These truths in God's Word He hath giv - en, How beau-ti - ful Heav-en must be.
God's light is for - ev - er there shin - ing, How beau-ti - ful Heav-en must be.
Rare jew-els of splen-dor are glow - ing, How beau-ti - ful Heav-en must be.
Sweet chords from their gold harps are ring - ing, How beau-ti - ful Heav-en must be.

How beau-ti - ful Heav-en must be, (must be,) Sweet home of the hap - py and free;

Fair ha - ven of rest for the wea - ry, How beau-ti - ful Heav-en must be.

40   No Disappointment in Heaven

F. M. LEHMAN   F. M. LEHMAN

1. There's no dis-ap-point-ment in Heav-en, No wear - i - ness, sor-row or pain; No hearts that are bleed-ing and bro-ken, No song with a mi-nor re-frain; The clouds of our earth-ly ho - ri-zon Will nev - er ap-pear in the sky, For all will be sun-shine and glad-ness, With nev - er a sob nor a

2. We'll nev - er pay rent for our man-sion, The tax - es will nev-er come due; Our gar-ments will nev-er grow thread-bare, But al -ways be fade-less and new; We'll nev - er be hun-gry nor thirst-y, Nor an-guish in pov-er - ty there, For all the rich boun-ties of Heav-en His sanc - ti-fied chil-dren will

3. There'll nev - er be crepe on the door-knob, No fu - ner - al train in the sky; No graves on the hill-sides of Glo-ry, For there we shall nev-er-more die; The old will be young there for-ev-er, Trans-formed in a mo-ment of time; Im - mor - tal we'll stand in His like-ness, The stars and the sun to out-

41

Sweet By and By

SANFORD F. BENNETT   JOSEPH P. WEBSTER

1. There's a land that is fair - er than day, And by faith we can
2. We shall sing on that beau - ti - ful shore The mel - o - di - ous
3. To our boun - ti - ful Fa - ther a - bove, We will of - fer our

see it a - far; For the Fa - ther waits o - ver the way, To pre -
songs of the blest, And our spir - its shall sor - row no more, Not a
trib - ute of praise, For the glo - ri - ous gift of His love, And the

pare us a dwell - ing-place there.
sigh for the bless - ing of rest.   In the sweet   by and
bless - ings that hal - low our days.   In the sweet

by,   We shall meet on that beau - ti - ful shore;   In the
   by and by,   by and by,

sweet   by and by,   We shall meet on that beau - ti - ful shore.
   In the sweet   by and by,

My Latest Sun Is Sinking Fast

42

J. HASCALL

WILLIAM B. BRADBURY

1. My lat - est sun is sink - ing fast, My race is near - ly run;
2. I know I'm near the ho - ly ranks Of friends and kin - dred dear,
3. I've al - most reached my heav'n-ly Home, My spir - it loud - ly sings;
4. O bear my long - ing heart to Him, Who bled and died for me;

My strong - est tri - als now are past, My tri - umph is be - gun.
For I hear the waves on Jor - dan's banks, The cross - ing must be near.
Thy ho - ly ones, be - hold, they come! I hear the noise of wings.
Whose blood now cleans - es from all sin, And gives me vic - to - ry.

O come, an - gel band, Come and a - round me stand; O

bear me a - way on your snow - y wings To my e - ter - nal Home; O

bear me a - way on your snow - y wings To my e - ter - nal Home.

43   We're Marching to Zion

ISAAC WATTS

ROBERT LOWRY

march-ing up-ward to Zi - on, the beau - ti - ful Ci - ty of God.
Zi - on, Zi - on,

We'll Work Till Jesus Comes

44

ELIZABETH MILLS

WILLIAM MILLER

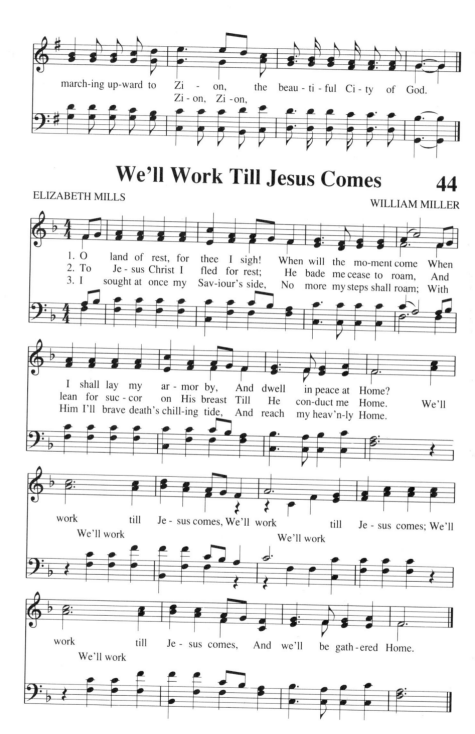

1. O land of rest, for thee I sigh! When will the mo-ment come When
2. To Je - sus Christ I fled for rest; He bade me cease to roam, And
3. I sought at once my Sav-iour's side, No more my steps shall roam; With

I shall lay my ar - mor by, And dwell in peace at Home?
lean for suc - cor on His breast Till He con-duct me Home. We'll
Him I'll brave death's chill-ing tide, And reach my heav'n-ly Home.

work till Je - sus comes, We'll work till Je - sus comes; We'll
We'll work We'll work

work till Je - sus comes, And we'll be gath - ered Home.
We'll work

45   When I Can Read My Title Clear

ISAAC WATTS

J. C. LOWRY

1. When I can read my   ti - tle clear   To man-sions in the skies,
2. Should earth a-gainst my   soul en-gage,   And fi - ery darts be hurled,
3. Let cares, like a   wild   del-uge come, And storms of sor-row fall!
4. There shall I bathe my   wea-ry soul   In seas of heav'n-ly rest,

I'll   bid fare-well to   ev - 'ry fear, And wipe my   weep-ing eyes.
Then   I can smile at   Sa-tan's rage, And face a   frown-ing world.
May   I but safe -ly   reach my Home, My God, my   Heav'n, my all.
And   not a wave of   trou-ble roll, A - cross my   peace-ful breast.

And wipe my weep - ing   eyes,   And wipe my weep-ing eyes,
And face a frown - ing   world,   And face a frown-ing world,
My God, my Heav'n, my   all,   My God, my Heav'n, my all,
A - cross my peace - ful   breast,   A - cross my peace-ful breast,

I'll   bid fare-well to   ev - 'ry fear, And wipe my   weep-ing eyes.
Then   I can smile at   Sa-tan's rage, And face a   frown-ing world.
May   I but safe -ly   reach my Home, My God, my   Heav'n, my all.
And   not a wave of   trou-ble roll, A - cross my   peace-ful breast.

My Saviour First of All

FANNY J. CROSBY

JOHN R. SWENEY

1. When my life-work is end-ed, and I cross the swell-ing tide, When the
2. O the soul-thrill-ing rap-ture when I view His bless-ed face, And the
3. O the dear ones in Glo-ry, how they beck-on me to come, And our
4. Through the gates to the Cit-y in a robe of spot-less white, He will

bright and glo-rious morn-ing I shall see; I shall know my Re-deem-er when I
lus-ter of His kind-ly beam-ing eye; How my full heart will praise Him for the
part-ing at the riv-er I re-call; To the sweet vales of E-den they will
lead me where no tears will ev-er fall; In the glad song of a-ges I shall

reach the oth-er side, And His smile will be the first to wel-come me.
mer-cy, love, and grace, That pre-pare for me a man-sion in the sky.
sing my wel-come Home; But I long to meet my Sav-iour first of all.
min-gle with de-light; But I long to meet my Sav-iour first of all.

I shall know
I shall know Him,
Him, I shall know Him, And re-deemed by His side I shall

stand; I shall know
I shall know
Him, I shall know Him By the print of the nails in His hands.

47 Let the Sun Shine Again in My Heart

JOHN R. RICE   JOHN R. RICE

1. I re-mem-ber the time when I first knew the Sav-iour, When the sun-light of bless-ing so flood-ed my heart. O the sweet-ness of "first love," with Je-sus so near me, and I thought such de-vo-tion would nev-er de-part.

2. Then how sweet were the Scrip-tures, they spoke to me dai-ly, How they guid-ed my steps; but my zeal did not last. And the sweet place of pray'r where I met with my Sav-iour, I ne-glect-ed, and so soon my joys were all past. Let the sun shine a-gain, Let the

3. O, I loved well to walk in the way with God's chil-dren, When we met with glad heart in a fel-low-ship sweet. But the pull of the flesh and some world-ly com-pan-ions In the paths of sin's pleas-ure at-tract-ed my feet.

4. Lord, I come now a-gain for for-give-ness and bless-ing, As Thy pen-i-tent child I am seek-ing Thy peace. For the blood paid my debt and Thy Spir-it with-in me Bids me come to my Fa-ther, my wan-d'ring to cease.

flow'rs bloom a - gain; Stir the em - bers of love in my heart!

Ho - ly Spir - it re - prove, then em - brace me a -

gain; Let the sun shine a - gain in my heart!

I'll Be So Glad 48

Anonymous

I'll be so glad when day is done, I'll be so glad when vic-t'ry's won;

There'll be no sor - row in God's to-mor-row, I'll be so glad when Je-sus comes.

49 Meet Me There

H. E. BLAIR

WILLIAM J. KIRKPATRICK

1. On the hap - py, gold - en shore, Where the faith - ful part no more, When the
2. Here our fond - est hopes are vain, Dear - est links are rent in twain; But in
3. Where the harps of an - gels ring, And the blest for-ev - er sing, In the

storms of life are o'er, Meet me there; Where the night dis-solves a - way
Heav'n no throb of pain, Meet me there; By the riv - er spark-ling bright
pal - ace of the King, Meet me there; Where in sweet com-mun-ion blend

In - to pure and per-fect day, I am go - ing home to stay, Meet me there;
In the Ci - ty of de-light, Where our faith is lost in sight, Meet me there;
Heart with heart and friend with friend, In a world that ne'er shall end, Meet me there;

Meet me there, Meet me there, Where the tree of life is
Meet me there, Meet me there,

bloom-ing, Meet me there; Meet me there; When the storms of life are o'er, On the

happy, golden shore, Where the faithful part no more, Meet me there. Meet me there.

Peace, Perfect Peace 50

EDWARD H. BICKERSTETH

GEORGE T. CALDBECK
Altered by Charles J. Vincent

1. Peace, per - fect peace, in this dark world of sin? The
2. Peace, per - fect peace, with sor-rows surg - ing round? On
3. Peace, per - fect peace, our fu - ture all un - known? Je -
4. Peace, per - fect peace, death shad-owing us and ours? Je -
5. It is e - nough: earth's strug-gles soon shall cease, And,

blood of Je - sus whis - pers peace with - in.
Je - sus' bos - om naught but calm is found.
sus we know, and He is on the throne.
sus has van-quished death and all its powers.
Je - sus, call us to Heav'n's per - fect peace. A - men.

51 Where We'll Never Grow Old

JAMES C. MOORE

JAMES C. MOORE

1. I have heard of a land on the far - a-way strand, 'Tis a
2. In that beau - ti - ful Home where we'll nev - er-more roam, We shall
3. When our work here is done and the life - crown is won, And our

beau - ti - ful Home of the soul; Built by Je - sus on high, there we
be in the sweet by and by; Hap-py praise to the King, through e-
trou-bles and tri-als are o'er; All our sor - row will end, and our

nev - er shall die, 'Tis a land where we nev - er grow old.
ter - ni - ty sing, 'Tis a land where we nev - er shall die.
voic - es will blend With the loved ones who've gone on be - fore.

Nev-er grow old, nev-er grow old, In a land where we'll nev-er grow old;
Where we'll

Nev-er grow old, nev-er grow old, In a land where we'll nev-er grow old.
Where we'll

Zion's Hill

JAMES A. CRUTCHFIELD

JAMES A. CRUTCHFIELD
Arranged by Haldor Lillenas

1. There waits for me a glad to-mor-row, Where gates of pearl swing open wide,
2. Some-day I'll hear the an-gels sing-ing, Be - yond the shad-ows of the tomb;
3. Some-day my la-bors will be end-ed, And all my wand'rings will be o'er;
4. Some-day the dark clouds will be rift-ed, And all the night of gloom be past,

And when I've passed this vale of sor-row, I'll dwell up - on the oth - er side.
And all the bells of Heav-en ring-ing, While saints are singing, "Home sweet Home."
And all earth's bro-ken ties be mend-ed, And I shall sigh and weep no more.
And all life's bur-dens will be lift-ed, The day of rest shall dawn at last.

Some - day be-yond the reach of mor - tal ken. Some - day, God

on - ly knows just where and when, The wheels of mor-tal life shall

all stand still, And I shall go to dwell on Zi - on's hill.

53 Beulah Land

EDGAR PAGE STITES

JOHN R. SWENEY

1. I've reached the land of joy di-vine, And all its rich-es free-ly mine;
2. My Sav-iour comes and walks with me, And sweet com-mun-ion here have we;
3. A sweet per-fume up-on the breeze Is borne from ev-er - ver-nal trees
4. The zeph-yrs seem to float to me Sweet sounds of Heav-en's mel - o-dy,

Here shines un-dimmed one bliss-ful day, For all my night has passed a-way.
He gen-tly leads me by His hand, For this is Heav-en's bor-der-land.
And flow'rs that nev-er fad-ing grow, Where streams of life for - ev - er flow.
As an-gels with the white-robed throng Join in the sweet Re - demp-tion song.

O Beu-lah Land, sweet Beu-lah Land! As on thy high-est mount I stand,

I look a-way a - cross the sea, Where man-sions are pre-pared for me,

And view the shin-ing glo - ry shore— My Heav'n, my Home for-ev - er-more.

O That Will Be Glory

CHARLES H. GABRIEL

CHARLES H. GABRIEL

1. When all my la-bors and tri-als are o'er, And I am safe on that beau-ti-ful shore, Just to be near the dear Lord I a-dore, Will through the a-ges be glo-ry for me.

2. When, by the gift of His in-fi-nite grace, I am ac-cord-ed in Heav-en a place, Just to be there and to look on His face, Will through the a-ges be glo-ry for me.

3. Friends will be there I have loved long a-go; Joy like a riv-er a-round me will flow; Yet, just a smile from my Sav-iour, I know, Will through the a-ges be glo-ry for me.

O that will be glo-ry for me, Glo-ry for me, glo-ry for me; When by His grace I shall look on His face, That will be glo-ry, be glo-ry for me.

O that will be glo-ry for me, Glo-ry for me, glo-ry for me;

55 When the Roll Is Called Up Yonder

JAMES M. BLACK

JAMES M. BLACK

1. When the trum-pet of the Lord shall sound, and time shall be no more, And the
2. On that bright and cloud-less morn-ing when the dead in Christ shall rise, And the
3. Let us la-bor for the Mas-ter from the dawn till set-ting sun, Let us

morn-ing breaks, e-ter-nal, bright and fair; When the saved of earth shall gath-er
glo-ry of His res-ur-rec-tion share; When His cho-sen ones shall gath-er
talk of all His won-drous love and care; Then when all of life is o-ver,

o-ver on the oth-er shore, And the roll is called up yon-der, I'll be there.
to their Home be-yond the skies, And the roll is called up yon-der, I'll be there.
and our work on earth is done, And the roll is called up yon-der, I'll be there.

When the roll is called up yon - der, When the
When the roll is called up yon - der, I'll be there,

roll is called up yon - der, When the roll is called up
When the roll is called up yon-der, I'll be there, When the roll is called up

yon - der, When the roll is called up yon - der, I'll be there.

When We All Get to Heaven 56

ELIZA E. HEWITT

EMILY D. WILSON

1. Sing the won-drous love of Je-sus, Sing His mer - cy, and His grace;
2. While we walk the pil - grim path-way, Clouds will o - ver - spread the sky;
3. Let us then be true and faith-ful, Trust-ing, serv-ing ev - 'ry day;
4. On-ward to the prize be - fore us! Soon His beau-ty we'll be-hold;

In the man-sions bright and bless - ed, He'll pre-pare for us a place.
But when trav-'ling days are o - ver, Not a shad-ow, not a sigh.
Just one glimpse of Him in Glo - ry, Will the toils of life re - pay.
Soon the pear-ly gates will o - pen, We shall tread the streets of gold.

1. pare for us a place.

When we all get to Heav-en, what a day of re-joic-ing that will be!
When we all What a day of re-joic-ing that will be!

When we all see Je - sus, We'll sing and shout the vic-to-ry.
When we all and shout the vic-to-ry.

57 When They Ring the Golden Bells

DION DE MARBELLE

DION DE MARBELLE

1. There's a land beyond the riv-er, That we call the sweet for-ev-er, And we
2. We shall know no sin nor sor-row, In that ha-ven of to-mor-row, When our
3. When our days shall know their num-ber, When in death we sweet-ly slum-ber, When the

on - ly reach that shore by faith's de-cree; One by one we'll gain the portals, There to
barque shall sail be-yond the sil-ver sea; We shall on - ly know the bless-ing Of our
King com-mands the spir - it to be free; Nev-er-more with an-guish la-den, We shall

dwell with the immortals, When they ring the gold-en bells for you and me.
Fa-ther's sweet caressing, When they ring the gold-en bells for you and me.
reach that love-ly Ai-den, When they ring the gold-en bells for you and me.

you and me.

Don't you hear the bells now ring-ing? Don't you hear the an- gels sing-ing? 'Tis the

glo-ry hal-le-lu-jah Ju - bi - lee (Ju-bi - lee). In that far - off sweet for-ev-er, Just be-

yond the shin-ing riv-er, When they ring the gold-en bells for you and me.

you and me.

He the Pearly Gates Will Open   58

FRED BLOM
Translated by Nathaniel Carlson

ELSIE AHLWEN

1. Love Di-vine, so great and won-drous, Deep and might-y, pure sub-lime!
2. Like a dove when hunt-ed, fright-ened, As a wound-ed fawn was I;
3. Love Di-vine, so great and won-drous, All my sins He then for-gave!
4. In life's e-ven-tide, at twi-light, At His door I'll knock and wait;

Com-ing from the heart of Je-sus, Just the same through tests of time.
Bro-ken-heart-ed, yet He healed me, He will heed the sin-ner's cry.
I will sing His praise for-ev-er, For His blood, His pow'r to save.
By the pre-cious love of Je-sus I shall en-ter Heav-en's gate.

He the pear-ly gates will o-pen, So that I may en-ter in;

For He pur-chased my re-demp-tion And for-gave me all my sin.

59 Caught Up Together

JOHN R. RICE   JOHN R. RICE

1. I sing hal - le - lu - jah that Je - sus is com-ing, And O what a
2. We wait for the com-ing of Je - sus our Sav-iour, Ex - pect-ing the
3. We'll rise in - cor-rupt - i - ble when sounds the trum-pet; O Grave, where the
4. Come up, all ye saints of the past to that meet-ing, From A - bel to

rais - ing of life from the dead; The graves burst - ing o - pen to
rap - ture, caught up in the clouds; The world has its sor - rows, we'll
vic - to - ry long you have known? All changed then the liv - ing, and
Mo - ses, from Dav - id to Paul; Come up, all ye mar - tyrs, soul

give up God's chil-dren, Those bod-ies long mold-ered in grave's dust - y bed.
leave them so glad-ly, We'll wipe all our tears when the trum - pet calls loud.
all go to - geth-er, And O what a gath-'ring to Christ of His own.
win-ners, Christ lov-ers, All un - der the blood of our Sav - iour, come all.

Caught up to greet Him to - geth - er, to - geth - er, Caught up with

Je - sus and nev - er to part; Changed in a mo - ment to

be with my Sav-iour, Caught up to-geth-er and nev-er to part.

Face to Face 60

CARRIE E. BRECK

GRANT C. TULLAR

1. Face to face with Christ, my Sav-iour, Face to face—what will it be?
2. On - ly faint-ly now I see Him, With the dark-ling veil be-tween,
3. What re-joic-ing in His pres-ence, When are ban-ished grief and pain;
4. Face to face! O bliss-ful mo-ment! Face to face—to see and know;

When with rap-ture I be-hold Him, Je-sus Christ who died for me.
But a bless-ed day is com-ing, When His glo-ry shall be seen.
When the crook-ed ways are straight-ened, And the dark things shall be plain.
Face to face with my Re-deem-er, Je-sus Christ who loves me so.

Face to face I shall be-hold Him, Far be-yond the star-ry sky;

Face to face in all His glo-ry, I shall see Him by and by!

61 We'll Never Say Good-bye

JOHN R. RICE   JOHN R. RICE

1. We say good-bye in part-ing With loved ones here be-low; We
2. Our chil-dren leave the home nest For school or wed-ding bells; Or
3. We greet and part with dear ones; We say hel-lo, good-bye; And
4. O hap-py, glad Home-com-ing With Je-sus in the sky; For

al-ways hope to meet a-gain, As on our way we go. But
coun-try's call or mis-sion field May take them far as well. Now
let-ters bind our fel-low-ship, We miss them, though we try To
some-times He seems far a-way, Though al-ways if we try, We

oft our hearts are griev-ing For those we nev-er meet. We'll
wed-ding bells are hap-py, And God's way al-ways right. And
feel them al-ways near us, And fol-low them with prayer. But
find Him near to help us, His Spir-it dwells with-in. But

say good-bye in sor-row Till we meet at Je-sus' feet.
ab-sent ones, we'll greet them In the Cit-y al-ways bright.
part-ing days are end-ed When we meet them in the air.
on-ly per-fect un-ion When we Heav-en en-ter in.

We'll nev-er say good-bye in Glo-ry, In the morn-ing, o-ver yon-der;

We'll nev - er say good-bye in Glo-ry; We'll nev-er say good-bye up there.

Saved by Grace   62

FANNY J. CROSBY

GEORGE C. STEBBINS
Altered by Seymour Swets

1. Some-day the sil - ver cord will break, And I no more as now shall
2. Some-day my earth - ly house will fall, I can-not tell how soon 'twill
3. Some-day, when fades the gold-en sun Be-neath the ro - sy - tint - ed
4. Some-day: till then I'll watch and wait, My lamp all trimmed and burn - ing

sing; But O the joy when I shall wake With-in the pal - ace of the
be; But this I know— my All in All Has now a place in Heav'n for
west, My bless-ed Lord will say, "Well done!" And I shall en - ter in - to
bright, And when my Sav - iour opes the gate, My soul to Him will take its

King! And I shall see Him face to face, And tell the sto-ry Saved by
me. shall see to face,
rest.
flight.

grace; And I shall see Him face to face, And tell the sto-ry Saved by grace.
shall see to face,

63   What a Day That Will Be

JIM HILL   JIM HILL

1. There is com-ing a day when no heart - aches shall come, No more
2. There'll be no sor-row there, no more bur - dens to bear, No more

clouds in the sky, no more tears to dim the eye; All is
sick - ness, no pain, no more part - ing o - ver there; And for -

peace for-ev-er-more on that hap - py gold-en shore, What a
ev - er I will be with the One who died for me, What a

day glo-ri-ous day that will be.
day glo-ri-ous day that will be.

What a day that will be when my

Je - sus I shall see, And I look up-on His face, the One who

saved me by His grace; When He takes me by the hand, and leads me

through the Prom-ised Land, What a day, glo-ri-ous day that will be.

Favorite song of Dr. Ron Schaffer.

Shall We Gather at the River? 64

ROBERT LOWRY

ROBERT LOWRY

1. Shall we gath-er at the riv - er, Where bright an - gel feet have trod;
2. On the bos-om of the riv - er, Where the Sav-iour-King we own,
3. Ere we reach the shin-ing riv - er, Lay we ev -'ry bur -den down;
4. Soon we'll reach the shin-ing riv - er, Soon our pil-grim-age will cease;

With its crys-tal tide for -ev - er Flow-ing by the throne of God?
We shall meet and sor-row nev - er, 'Neath the glo -ry of the throne.
Grace our spir -its will de -liv - er, And pro-vide a robe and crown.
Soon our hap -py hearts will quiv -er With the mel -o - dy of peace.

Yes, we'll gath - er at the riv - er, The beau - ti-ful, the beau-ti-ful riv - er,

Gath-er with the saints at the riv - er That flows by the throne of God.

65 Just Over in the Glory Land

JAMES W. ACUFF

EMMET S. DEAN

1. I've a Home pre - pared where the saints a - bide, Just o - ver in the glo - ry land; And I long to be by my Sav - iour's side, Just o - ver in the glo - ry land.

2. I am on my way to those man - sions fair, Just o - ver in the glo - ry land; There to sing God's praise and His glo - ry share, Just o - ver in the glo - ry land.

3. What a joy - ful thought that my Lord I'll see, Just o - ver in the glo - ry land; And with kin - dred saved, there for - ev - er be Just o - ver in the glo - ry land.

4. With the blood-washed throng I will shout and sing, Just o - ver in the glo - ry land; Glad ho - san - nas to Christ, the Lord and King, Just o - ver in the glo - ry land.

Just o - ver in the glo - ry land, I'll join the hap - py
o - ver, o - ver join, yes, join
an - gel band, Just o - ver in the glo - ry land; Just

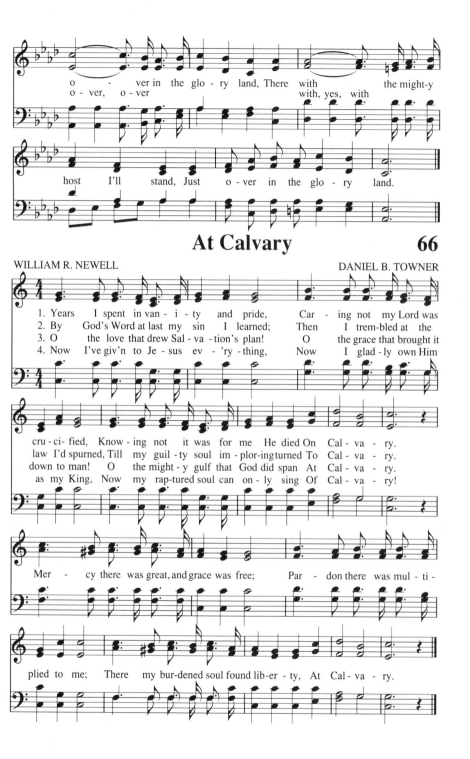

o - ver in the glo - ry land, There with the might-y
o - ver, o - ver with, yes, with

host I'll stand, Just o - ver in the glo - ry land.

At Calvary 66

WILLIAM R. NEWELL

DANIEL B. TOWNER

1. Years I spent in van - i - ty and pride, Car - ing not my Lord was
2. By God's Word at last my sin I learned; Then I trem-bled at the
3. O the love that drew Sal - va - tion's plan! O the grace that brought it
4. Now I've giv'n to Je - sus ev - 'ry - thing, Now I glad - ly own Him

cru - ci - fied, Know - ing not it was for me He died On Cal - va - ry.
law I'd spurned, Till my guil - ty soul im - plor - ing turned To Cal - va - ry.
down to man! O the might - y gulf that God did span At Cal - va - ry.
as my King, Now my rap-tured soul can on - ly sing Of Cal - va - ry!

Mer - cy there was great, and grace was free; Par - don there was mul - ti -

plied to me; There my bur-dened soul found lib - er - ty, At Cal - va - ry.

67 The Pearly White City

ARTHUR F. INGLER

ARTHUR F. INGLER

Moderato

1. There's a ho - ly and beau - ti - ful Cit - y, Whose build - er and
2. No sin is al - lowed in that Cit - y, And noth - ing de -
3. No heart-aches are known in that Cit - y, No tears ev - er
4. My loved ones are gath - er - ing yon - der, My friends too are

rul - er is God; John saw it de-scend-ing from Heav-en, When
fil - ing or mean; No pain and no sick-ness can en - ter, No
moist-en the eye; There's no dis - ap-point-ment in Heav-en, No
pass-ing a - way; And soon I shall join their bright num - ber, And

Pat - mos, in ex - ile, he trod; Its high, mas-sive wall is of
crepe on the door-knob is seen; Earth's sor-rows and cares are for -
en - vy and strife in the sky; The saints are all sanc - ti - fied
dwell in e - ter - ni - ty's day; They're safe now in Glo - ry with

jas - per, The Cit - y it - self is pure gold; And
got - ten, No tempt - er is there to an - noy; No
whol - ly, They live in sweet har - mo - ny there; My
Je - sus, Their tri - als and bat - tles are past; They

when my frail tent here is fold-ed, Mine eyes shall its glo - ry be-hold.
part-ing words ev-er are spo-ken, There's noth-ing to hurt or de-stroy.
heart is now set on that Cit - y, And some-day its bless-ings I'll share.
o-ver-came sin and the tempt-er, They've reached that fair Cit-y at last.

Slowly

In that bright Cit - y, pear - ly white Cit - y, I have a

man-sion, a harp, and a crown; Now I am watch-ing, wait-ing and

rit.

long - ing, For the white Cit - y that's soon com-ing down.

68 Remembering in Heaven

JOHN R. RICE

JOHN R. RICE

1. Should I, up in Heav-en, Re-mem-ber the heart-ache, All the
2. Or if, on the gold streets I think of earth treas-ures, Of the
3. Should I, in the Glo-ry Re-mem-ber a loved one, One who
4. O then, spread the mes-sage, The work He has giv-en, Nev-er

pain and the cross, All the shame and the loss, The re-proach of the
things I had bought, Of the fame dear-ly sought; I'd smile in my
walked by my side, But is lost and out-side; If I'd nev-er
mind the world's praise, Nor pos-ses-sions men crave. But O! for the

Sav-iour I'd borne in earth's con-flicts; In Heav-en I'd laugh at the
man-sion, my gem-stud-ded man-sion, In Heav-en I'd smile, "They are
begged him to trust in the Sav-iour, In Heav-en I'd sit down and
Sav-iour, bring souls in-to Heav-en, And joy through E-ter-ni-ty's

cost!"
naught!"   Je-sus' blood paid my ran-som, and I'm bound for Heav-en. But
cry.
day!

what will I think when re-mem-b'ring in Heav-en?

We Shall Shine as the Stars

J. W. VAN DeVENTER

J. W. VAN DeVENTER

1. We may tar-ry a while here as strang-ers, Un-no-ticed by those who pass by;
2. We may nev-er be rich in earth's treas-ures, Nor rise on the lad-der of fame;
3. We may live in a tent or a cot-tage, And die in se-clu-sion a-lone;

But the Sav-iour will crown us in Glo-ry, To shine as the stars in the sky.
But the saints will at last be re-ward-ed, Made rich in Im-man-u-el's name.
But the Fa-ther who see-eth in se-cret, Re-mem-bers each one of His own.

We shall shine as the stars of the morn-ing, With Je-sus the Cru-ci-fied One;

We shall rise to be like Him for-ev-er, E-ter-nal-ly shine as the sun.

70 Will Jesus Find Us Watching?

FANNY J. CROSBY

W. H. DOANE

1. When Je - sus comes to re - ward His ser-vants, Wheth - er it be
2. If, at the dawn of the ear - ly morn-ing, He shall call us
3. Have we been true to the trust He left us? Do we seek to
4. Bless - ed are those whom the Lord finds watch-ing, In His glo - ry

noon or night, Faith - ful to Him will He find us watch-ing,
one by one, When to the Lord we re - store our tal-ents,
do our best? If we o-bey all the Lord com-mands us,
they shall share; If He shall come at the dawn or mid-night,

With our lamps all trimmed and bright? Will He ans - wer thee—"Well done"?
Will He ans - wer thee—"Well done"?
We shall then be tru - ly blest.
Will He find us watch - ing there? O can we say we are

read-y, broth-er? Read-y for the soul's bright Home? Say, will He find you and

me still watch-ing, Wait-ing, wait-ing when the Lord shall come?

There's a Great Day Coming

WILL L. THOMPSON

WILL L. THOMPSON

71

1. There's a great day com-ing, A great day com-ing, There's a great day
2. There's a bright day com-ing, A bright day com-ing, There's a bright day
3. There's a sad day com-ing, A sad day com-ing, There's a sad day

com-ing by and by;   When the saints and the sin-ners shall be part-ed right and
com-ing by and by;   But its bright-ness shall on-ly come to them that love the
com-ing by and by;   When the sin-ner shall hear his doom, "De-part, I know ye

left, Lord, Are you read-y for that day to come?   Are you read-y?
not,"

Are you read-y? Are you read-y for the judg-ment day?

Are you read-y? Are you read-y for the judg-ment day?

72   Is It the Crowning Day?

GEORGE WALKER WHITCOMB   CHARLES H. MARSH

1. Je - sus may come to - day,   Glad   day! Glad day!   And I would
2. I   may go Home to - day,   Glad   day! Glad day!   Seem-eth I
3. Why should I anx - ious be?   Glad   day! Glad day!   Lights ap-pear
4. Faith-ful I'll be to - day,   Glad   day! Glad day!   And I will

see   my Friend;   Dan - gers and trou - bles would end   If
hear their song;   Hail to   the   ra - di - ant throng!   If
on   the shore,   Storms will af - fright nev - er - more,   For
free - ly tell   Why I should love Him so well,   For

Je-sus should come to - day.
I should go Home to - day.
He is "at hand" to - day.   Glad day! Glad day!   Is   it the crown - ing
He is my all to - day.

day?   I'll   live for to-day, nor anx-ious be,   Je - sus, my Lord, I

rit.

soon shall see; Glad   day!   Glad day!   Is   it the crown - ing day?

© Copyright 1910 by Praise Publishing Co. Renewed 1938 (extended),
The Rodeheaver Co., owner. Used by permission.

Some Golden Daybreak

73

CARL A. BLACKMORE

CARL A. BLACKMORE

1. Some glo-rious morn-ing sor-row will cease, Some glo-rious morn-ing
2. Sad hearts will glad-den, all shall be bright, Good-bye for-ev-er
3. O what a meet-ing, there in the skies, No tears nor cry-ing

all will be peace; Heart-aches all end-ed, school-days all done,
to earth's dark night; Changed in a mo-ment, like Him to be,
shall dim our eyes; Loved ones u-nit-ed e-ter-nal-ly,

Heav-en will o-pen — Je-sus will come.
O glo-rious day-break, Je-sus I'll see. Some gold-en day-break,
O what a day-break, that morn will be.

Je-sus will come; Some gold-en day-break, bat-tles all won, He'll shout the

vic-t'ry, break through the blue, Some gold-en day-break, for me, for you.

74 Christ Returneth

H. L. TURNER

JAMES McGRANAHAN

1. It may be at morn, when the day is a - wak- ing, When sun - light through dark - ness and shad - ow is break - ing, That Je - sus will come in the full - ness of glo - ry, To re-ceive from the world "His own."

2. It may be at mid - day, it may be at twi-light, It may be per - chance, that the black - ness of mid - night Will burst in - to light in the blaze of His glo - ry, When Je - sus re - ceives "His own."

3. O joy! O de - light! should we go with- out dy - ing, No sick -ness, no sad - ness, no dread and no cry - ing, Caught up through the clouds with our Lord in - to glo - ry, When Je - sus re - ceives "His own."

O Lord Je - sus, how long, how long Ere we shout the glad song, Christ re - turn - eth! Hal - le -

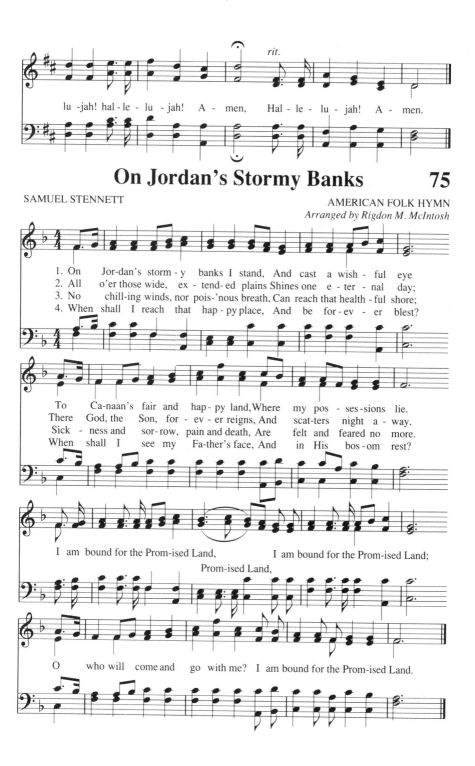

On Jordan's Stormy Banks   75

SAMUEL STENNETT

AMERICAN FOLK HYMN
Arranged by Rigdon M. McIntosh

1. On   Jor-dan's storm-y   banks I stand, And cast a wish-ful   eye
2. All   o'er those wide, ex - tend-ed plains Shines one e - ter - nal   day;
3. No   chill-ing winds, nor pois-'nous breath, Can reach that health-ful shore;
4. When shall I reach that hap-py place, And   be for-ev - er blest?

To   Ca-naan's fair and hap-py land, Where my pos - ses-sions lie.
There God, the Son, for - ev - er reigns, And   scat-ters night a - way.
Sick - ness and sor-row, pain and death, Are felt and feared no more.
When shall I see my Fa-ther's face, And   in His bos-om rest?

I am bound for the Prom-ised Land,   I am bound for the Prom-ised Land;

Prom-ised Land,

O   who will   come and   go with me? I am bound for the Prom-ised Land.

76 What if It Were Today?

LEILA N. MORRIS

LEILA N. MORRIS

1. Je - sus is com-ing to earth a-gain, What if it were to - day?
2. Sa - tan's do - min-ion will then be o'er, O that it were to - day!
3. Faith-ful and true would He find us here If He should come to - day?

Com-ing in pow - er and love to reign, What if it were to - day?
Sor-row and sigh-ing shall be no more, O that it were to - day!
Watch-ing in glad-ness and not in fear, If He should come to - day?

Com-ing to 'claim His cho-sen Bride, All the re-deemed and pu - ri-fied,
Then shall the dead in Christ a-rise, Caught up to meet Him in the skies,
Signs of His com - ing mul - ti-ply, Morn-ing light breaks in east-ern sky,

rit. *a tempo*

O - ver this whole earth scat-tered wide, What if it were to - day?
When shall these glo - ries meet our eyes? What if it were to - day?
Watch, for the time is draw-ing nigh, What if it were to - day?

Glo - ry, glo - ry! Joy to my heart 'twill bring;
Joy to my heart 'twill bring;

Glo - ry, glo - ry! When we shall crown Him King;
When we shall crown Him King;

Glo - ry, glo - ry! Haste to pre - pare the way;
Haste to pre - pare the way;

rit.

Glo - ry, glo - ry! Je - sus will come some - day.

Behold, He Comes! 77

ELEANOR S. MURRAY

ELEANOR S. MURRAY

Be-hold, He comes! Be-hold, He comes! Be-hold, He comes! Be-hold, He comes! And

ev - 'ry eye shall see Him! Friend, will you be read - y when Je - sus comes?

Divide the group into four sections. Each section sings the first phrase, sustaining the word "comes" until the four parts swell to a climax.

78 Jesus Is Coming

JOHN R. RICE

JOHN R. RICE

1. Come, dear Lord Je - sus, for long we've been watch-ing; God's chil - dren are
2. Mid - night ap-proach-es, wise vir - gins are read- y; With oil in our
3. Night when we sleep He may take one and leave one, Or day those we
4. Glad re-sur - rec -tion, O hap - py re - un -ion When we shall be

home-sick for Heav-en our Home. Come, then, Lord Je - sus, come quick - ly and
lamp, may our wicks be trimmed, too. "Ho! comes the Bride-groom, go ye out to
work with be left when we're gone. Wit - ness to - day then, and turn men to
changed in a mo-ment of time; Meet all our loved ones, re-deemed of all

take us; The wed-ding feast waits when the Bride-groom shall come.
meet Him!" O glad blest an-nounce-ment we hope to hear soon.
Je - sus, Soon pass-es the sea -son for win-ning our own.
a - ges, And O what glad greet-ings for mine and for thine!

Je - sus is

com - ing, is com - ing, is com - ing! It may be to - mor-row, It

may be to-day. May be the trum-pet sound, may be the an - gel shout,

When Jesus Comes to Reign   79

JOHN R. RICE

JOHN R. RICE

80   Coming Today?

JOHN R. RICE   JOHN R. RICE

1. Com-ing to-day? To-day? Yes, Je-sus may come to-day.
2. Saints from the North, South, East, West Come to the wed-ding grand;
3. Then will the King come lead-ing Ar-mies of Heav-en strong,
4. Then will our wrongs be right-ed; Then will be dried our tears!

Watch for the Lord's re-turn-ing, Watch as we work and pray. O what a
There with the shin-ing Bride-groom Saved ones from ev-'ry land. How we'll re-
On a white horse re-turn-ing To sit on Da-vid's throne. Bring-ing His
Then all our sins be con-quered; Still will be all our fears. Eyes of the

grand a-wak-'ning When shall a-rise the dead, And what a blest re-
joice and sing then And our re-wards re-ceive, And ev-er be with
saints to serve Him And to en-joy His peace; O-ver the whole world
blind be o-pened, Ears of the deaf shall hear, Sor-row and sigh-ing

(Unison)

un - ion | When He comes, as | He | said!
Je - sus | Him on whom we | be - | lieve.
reign - ing, | Mak - ing all wars | to | cease.
end - ed | Through-out the end - less | | years.

When He comes, we will hail Him! And it may be to - day. Then what a shout of tri - umph, Up and with Him a - way. There'll be a glad re - un - ion, All the re-deemed we'll see, And we will go to Heav - en, Ev - er with Christ to be!

81 When We See Christ

ESTHER KERR RUSTHOI   ESTHER KERR RUSTHOI

1. Oft - times the day seems long, our tri - als hard to bear, We're
2. Some-times the sky looks dark with not a ray of light, We're
3. Life's day will soon be o'er, all storms for-ev - er past, We'll

tempt-ed to com-plain, to mur-mur and de-spair; But Christ will soon ap-
tossed and driv-en on, no hu-man help in sight; But there is one in
cross the great di - vide to Glo -ry, safe at last; We'll share the joys of

pear to catch His Bride a-way, All tears for -ev - er o - ver in
Heav'n who knows our deep - est care, Let Je - sus solve your prob-lem— just
Heav'n— a harp, a Home, a crown, The tempt-er will be ban-ished, we'll

God's e - ter -nal day.
go to Him in pray'r. It will be worth it all when we see
lay our bur - den down.

Je - sus, Life's trials will seem so small when we see Christ;

Favorite song of Bill Gothard.

One glimpse of His dear face all sor-row will e-rase,

So brave-ly run the race till we see Christ.

When He Cometh 82

WILLIAM O. CUSHING

GEORGE F. ROOT

1. When He com-eth, when He com-eth To make up His jew-els,
2. He will gath-er, He will gath-er The gems for His king-dom,
3. Lit-tle chil-dren, lit-tle chil-dren Who love their Re-deem-er

All His jew-els, pre-cious jew-els, His loved and His own:
All the pure ones, all the bright ones, His loved and His own:
Are the jew-els, pre-cious jew-els, His loved and His own:

Like the stars of the morn-ing, His bright crown a-dorn-ing,

They shall shine in their beau-ty—Bright gems for His crown.

83 I'm Going Higher

HERBERT BUFFUM   HERBERT BUFFUM

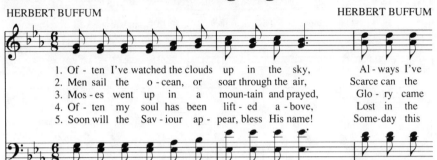

1. Of - ten I've watched the clouds up in the sky,   Al - ways I've
2. Men sail the o - cean, or soar through the air,   Scarce can the
3. Mos - es went up in a moun-tain and prayed,   Glo - ry came
4. Of - ten my soul has been lift - ed a - bove,   Lost in the
5. Soon will the Sav - iour ap - pear, bless His name!   Some-day this

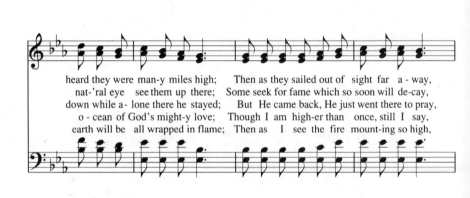

heard they were man-y miles high;   Then as they sailed out of sight far a - way,
nat-'ral eye see them up there;   Some seek for fame which so soon will de-cay,
down while a- lone there he stayed; But He came back, He just went there to pray,
o - cean of God's might-y love;   Though I am high-er than once, still I say,
earth will be all wrapped in flame; Then as I see the fire mount-ing so high,

I said, "I'm go-ing far   high-er some-day."
I'm go-ing high-er, yes,   high-er some-day.
I'm go-ing high-er, yes,   high-er some-day.   I'm go-ing high-er, yes,
"I'm go-ing high-er, yes,   high-er some-day."
I'm go-ing high-er, be - yond the blue sky.

high-er some-day, I'm go-ing high-er to stay; O - ver the clouds and be -

yond the blue sky, Go - ing where none ev - er sick - en or die,

Loved ones to meet in the "Sweet by and by";

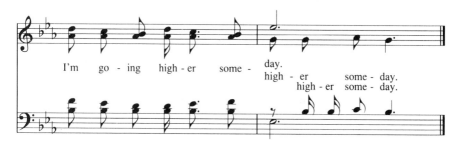

I'm go-ing high - er some - day.
high - er some - day.
high - er some - day.

84   Jesus Is Coming Again

JOHN W. PETERSON   JOHN W. PETERSON

1. Mar-vel-ous mes-sage we bring,   Glo-ri-ous car-ol we sing,
2. For-est and flow-er ex-claim,   Moun-tain and mead-ow the same,
3. Stand-ing be-fore Him at last,   Tri-al and trou-ble all past,

Won-der-ful word of the King—   Je-sus is com-ing a-gain! (a-gain!)
All earth and Heav-en pro-claim—   Je-sus is com-ing a-gain! (a-gain!)
Crowns at His feet we will cast—   Je-sus is com-ing a-gain! (a-gain!)

Unison

Com - ing a - gain,   Com - ing a -

gain;   May be morn - ing, may be noon,

May be eve - ning and may be soon!   Com - ing a -

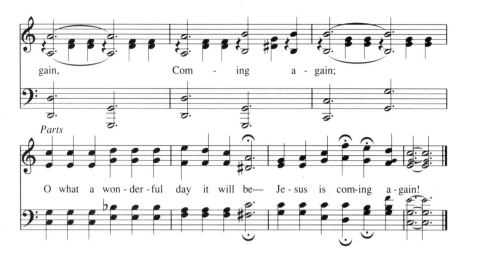

gain, Com - ing a - gain;

Parts

O what a won - der - ful day it will be— Je - sus is com - ing a - gain!

Jesus! Jesus! Jesus! 85

Llanthony Abbey Hymns

Anonymous

1. Je - sus! Je - sus! Je - sus! Sing a - loud the Name;
2. Je - sus! Name of cleans - ing, Wash - ing all our stains;
3. Je - sus! Name of bold - ness — Mak - ing cow - ards brave;
4. Je - sus! Name of vic - t'ry, Stretch - ing far a - way,
5. Je - sus! be our joy - note In this vale of tears;

Till it soft - ly, slow - ly, Sets all hearts a - flame.
Je - sus! Name of heal - ing, Balm for all our pains.
Name! that in the bat - tle, Cer - tain - ly must save.
Right a - cross earth's war - fields, To the plains of day.
Till we reach the home - land, And th'e - ter - nal years.

86 In the Garden

C. AUSTIN MILES

C. AUSTIN MILES

1. I come to the gar-den a-lone, While the dew is still on the ros - es, And the voice I hear, Fall-ing on my ear, The Son of God dis-clos - es.

2. He speaks, and the sound of His voice Is so sweet the birds hush their sing - ing, And the mel - o-dy That He gave to me, With-in my heart is ring - ing. And He walks with me, and He

3. I'd stay in the gar-den with Him Though the night a-round me be fall - ing, But He bids me go; Through the voice of woe His voice to me is call - ing.

talks with me, And He tells me I am His own; And the joy we share as we tar - ry there, None oth - er has ev - er known.

Just When I Need Him Most

87

WILLIAM POOLE

CHARLES H. GABRIEL

1. Just when I need Him, Je-sus is near, Just when I fal-ter, just when I fear; Read-y to help me, read-y to cheer, Just when I need Him most.
2. Just when I need Him, Je-sus is true, Nev-er for-sak-ing all the way through; Giv-ing for bur-dens pleas-ures a-new, Just when I need Him most.
3. Just when I need Him, Je-sus is strong, Bear-ing my bur-dens all the day long; For all my sor-row giv-ing a song, Just when I need Him most.
4. Just when I need Him, He is my all, An-swer-ing when up-on Him I call; Ten-der-ly watch-ing lest I should fall, Just when I need Him most.

Just when I need Him most, Just when I need Him most; Je-sus is near to com-fort and cheer, Just when I need Him most.

Favorite song of Dr. Lee Roberson.

88 Some Time We'll Understand

MAXWELL N. CORNELIUS

JAMES McGRANAHAN

1. Not now, but in the com-ing years, It may be in the bet-ter
2. We'll catch the bro-ken thread a - gain, And fin - ish what we here be-
3. We'll know why clouds in-stead of sun Were o - ver man - y cher-ished
4. God knows the way, He holds the key, He guides us with un - err-ing

Land, We'll read the mean-ing of our tears, And there, some time, we'll un-der-
gan; Heav'n will the mys-ter-ies ex- plain, And then, ah, then, we'll un-der-
plans; Why song has ceased when scarce be-gun; 'Tis there, some time, we'll un-der-
hand; Some time with tear-less eyes we'll see; Yes, there, up there, we'll un-der-

a little faster

stand. Then trust in God through all the days; Fear not, for

a tempo

He doth hold thy hand; Though dark thy way, still sing and
doth hold thy hand;

cresc. *ad lib.*

praise, Some time, some time, we'll un - der -stand.

Does Jesus Care? 89

FRANK E. GRAEFF

J. LINCOLN HALL

1. Does Je - sus care when my heart is pained Too deep - ly for
2. Does Je - sus care when my way is dark With a name - less
3. Does Je - sus care when I've tried, and failed To re - sist some temp-
4. Does Je - sus care when I've said "good-bye" To the dear - est on

mirth and song; As the bur - dens press, and the cares dis-tress, And the
dread and fear? As the day -light fades in-to deep night shades, Does He
ta - tion strong; When for my deep grief I find no re-lief, Though my
earth to me, And my sad heart aches till it near - ly breaks—Is it

way grows wea - ry and long?
care e-nough to be near?
tears flow all the night long?
aught to Him? Does He see?

O yes, He cares; I know He cares, His

heart is touched with my grief;

ad lib.

When the days are wea - ry, the

rit.

long nights drear - y, I know my Sav - iour cares.

cares, He cares.

90 Jesus, Lover of My Soul

CHARLES WESLEY   SIMEON B. MARSH

1. Je - sus, Lov - er of my soul, Let me to Thy bos-om fly,
2. Oth - er ref -uge have I none, Hangs my help - less soul on Thee;
3. Thou, O Christ, art all I want; More than all in Thee I find;
4. Plen -teous grace with Thee is found, Grace to cov - er all my sin;

While the near - er wa - ters roll, While the tem - pest still is high;
Leave, ah, leave me not a -lone, Still sup-port and com - fort me.
Raise the fall - en, cheer the faint, Heal the sick and lead the blind.
Let the heal- ing streams a-bound; Make and keep me pure with - in.

Hide me, O my Sav-iour, hide, Till the storm of life is past;
All my trust on Thee is stayed, All my help from Thee I bring;
Just and Ho - ly is Thy name, I am all un-right-eous -ness;
Thou of life the foun-tain art, Free-ly let me take of Thee;

Safe in -to the hav-en guide, O re-ceive my soul at last.
Cov-er my de - fense-less head With the shad-ow of Thy wing.
Vile and full of sin I am, Thou art full of truth and grace.
Spring Thou up with -in my heart, Rise to all e - ter - ni - ty. A-men.

Hiding in Thee

WILLIAM O. CUSHING

IRA D. SANKEY

1. O safe to the Rock that is high - er than I, My soul in its
con - flicts and sor - rows would fly; So sin - ful, so wea - ry, Thine,
Thine would I be; Thou blest "Rock of A - ges," I'm hid - ing in
Thee.

2. In the calm of the noon-tide, in sor - row's lone hour, In times when temp-
ta - tion casts o'er me its pow'r; In the tem - pests of life, on its
wide, heav-ing sea, Thou blest "Rock of A - ges," I'm hid - ing in
Thee.

3. How oft in the con - flict, when pressed by the foe, I have fled to my
Ref - uge and breathed out my woe; How oft - en, when tri - als like
sea bil-lows roll, Have I hid - den in Thee, O Thou Rock of my
soul.

Hid - ing in Thee, Hid - ing in Thee, Thou blest "Rock of A - ges," I'm hid - ing in Thee.

92 How Can I Be Lonely?

HALDOR LILLENAS   HALDOR LILLENAS

1. One is walk-ing with me o-ver life's un-e-ven way,
2. Days may bring their bur-dens and their tri-als as I go,
3. In the hour of sad be-reave-ment or of bit-ter loss,
4. In life's ros-y morn-ing when the skies a-bove are clear,

Con-stant-ly sup-port-ing me each mo-ment of the day;
But my Lord is near and helps to make them light-er grow.
I can find sup-port and con-so-la-tion at the cross;
In its noon-tide hours with man-y cares and prob-lems near,

How can I be lone-ly when such fel-low-ship is mine,
Life may have its cross-es, or its loss-es, or in-crease,
Want or woe or suf-f'ring all seem glo-ri-fied when He
Or when ev-'ning shad-ows fall at clos-ing of my day

With my bless-ed Lord di-vine!
Je-sus meets them all with peace.
Dai-ly walks and talks with me.
Je-sus will be there al-way.

How can I be lone-ly

When I've Je-sus on-ly To be my com-pan-ion and un-fail-ing guide;

Why should I be wea-ry, Or my path seem

drea-ry, When He's walk-ing by my side?

Art Thou Weary, Art Thou Languid? 93

JOHN M. NEALE
Based on an early Greek hymn

HENRY W. BAKER

1. Art thou wea-ry, art thou lan-guid, Art thou sore dis-tressed?
2. Hath He marks to lead me to Him, If He be my guide?
3. Is there di-a-dem, as Mon-arch, That His brow a-dorns?
4. If I ask Him to re-ceive me, Will He say me nay?
5. Find-ing, fol-l'wing, keep-ing, strug-gling, Is He sure to bless?

"Come to Me," saith One, "and com-ing, Be at rest."
In His feet and hands are wound-prints, And His side.
Yea, a crown, in ver-y sure-ty, But of thorns.
Not till earth and not till Heav-en Pass a-way.
Saints, a-pos-tles, proph-ets, mar-tyrs, An-swer, "Yes." A-men.

94   Stand by Me

C. A. TINDLEY

C. A. TINDLEY
Arranged by F. A. Clark

1. When the storms of life are rag-ing, Stand by me; (stand by me;) When the
2. In the midst of trib - u -la-tion, Stand by me; In the
3. In the midst of faults and failures, Stand by me; In the
4. When I'm grow-ing old and fee-ble, Stand by me; (by me;) When I'm

storms of life are rag-ing, Stand by me; (stand by me;) When the
midst of trib - u - la-tion, Stand by me; When the
midst of faults and fail-ures, Stand by me; When I
grow ing old and fee-ble, Stand by me; When my

world is toss - ing me Like a ship up-on the sea; Thou who
hosts of Hell as-sail, And my strength be-gins to fail, Thou who
do the best I can, And my friends mis-un - der-stand, Thou who
life be-comes a bur-den, And I'm near - ing chill - y Jor-dan, O Thou

rul - est wind and wa - ter, Stand by me. (stand by me.)
nev - er lost a bat - tle, Stand by me.
know - est all a - bout me, Stand by me.
"Lil - ly of the Val -ley," Stand by me. (by me.)

The Lord Is My Shepherd

JAMES MONTGOMERY

THOMAS KOSCHAT

1. The Lord is my shep-herd, no want shall I know; I
2. Thro' the val - ley and shad - ow of death though I stray, Since
3. In the midst of af - flic-tion my ta - ble is spread; With
4. Let good-ness and mer - cy, my boun - ti - ful God, Still

feed in green pas-tures, safe-fold - ed I rest; He lead-eth my
Thou art my Guard-ian, no e - vil I fear; Thy rod shall de -
bless - ings un - meas-ured my cup run - neth o'er; With per-fume and
fol - low my steps till I meet Thee a - bove; I seek by the

soul where the still wa - ters flow, Re - stores me when wand'ring, re -
fend me, Thy staff be my stay; No harm can be - fall, with my
oil Thou a - noint-est my head; O what shall I ask of Thy
path which my fore - fa - thers trod, Through the land of their so - journ, Thy

deems when op-pressed; Re - stores me when wand'ring, re-deems when op-pressed.
Com-fort - er near; No harm can be - fall, with my Com - fort - er near.
prov - i - dence more? O what shall I ask of Thy prov - i - dence more?
king-dom of love; Through the land of their so - journ, Thy king-dom of love.

God Leads Us Along

G. A. YOUNG

G. A. YOUNG

1. In shad-y, green pas-tures, so rich and so sweet, God leads His dear
2. Some-times on the mount where the sun shines so bright, God leads His dear
3. Though sor-rows be-fall us, and Sa-tan op-pose, God leads His dear
4. A - way from the mire, and a - way from the clay, God leads His dear

chil-dren a - long; Where the wa-ter's cold flow bathes the wea - ry one's feet,
chil-dren a - long; Some - times in the val - ley, in dark-est of night,
chil-dren a - long; Through grace we can con-quer, de - feat all our foes,
chil-dren a - long; A - way up in Glo - ry, e - ter - ni-ty's day,

God leads His dear chil-dren a - long. Some through the wa-ters,

Some through the flood, Some through the fire, but all through the blood;

Some through great sor - row, but God gives a song,

In the night sea-son and all the day long.

I Need Thee Every Hour 97

ANNIE S. HAWKS

ROBERT LOWRY

1. I need Thee ev - 'ry hour, Most gra - cious Lord; No
2. I need Thee ev - 'ry hour, Stay Thou near - by; Temp-
3. I need Thee ev - 'ry hour, In joy or pain; Come
4. I need Thee ev - 'ry hour, Most Ho - ly One; O

ten - der voice like Thine Can peace af - ford.
ta - tions lose their pow'r When Thou art nigh.
quick - ly and a - bide, Or life is vain.
make me Thine in - deed, Thou bless - ed Son!

I

need Thee, O I need Thee; Ev - 'ry hour I need Thee! O

bless me now, my Sav - iour, I come to Thee!

98 The Name of Jesus

W. C. MARTIN   EDMUND S. LORENZ

1. The name of Je - sus is so sweet, I love its music to re - peat; It makes my joys full and com-plete, The precious name of Je - sus.

2. I love the name of Him whose heart Knows all my griefs and bears a part; Who bids all anx - ious fears de-part — I love the precious name

3. That name I fond - ly love to hear, It nev - er fails my heart to cheer, Its mu - sic dries the fall - ing tear; Ex - alt the

4. No word of man can ev - er tell How sweet the name I love so well; O let its prais - es ev - er swell, O praise the The

"Je - sus," O how sweet the name! "Je - sus," ev - 'ry day the same; "Je - sus," let all saints pro - claim Its wor - thy praise for - ev - er.

Its wor - thy praise

Come, Ye Disconsolate

99

THOMAS MOORE
Altered by Thomas Hastings

SAMUEL WEBBE

1. Come, ye dis - con - so - late, wher - e'er ye lan - guish;
2. Joy of the des - o - late, Light of the stray - ing,
3. Here see the Bread of life, see wa - ters flow - ing

Come to the mer - cy seat, fer - vent - ly kneel; Here bring your
Hope of the pen - i - tent, fade - less and pure, Here speaks the
Forth from the throne of God, pure from a - bove; Come to the

wound-ed hearts, here tell your an - guish; Earth has no
Com - fort - er, ten - der - ly say - ing, "Earth has no
feast of love; come, ev - er know - ing Earth has no

sor - row that Heav'n can - not heal.
sor - row that Heav'n can - not cure."
sor - row but Heav'n can re - move. A - men.

Favorite song of Dr. Bob Jones, Jr.

100

Day by Day

LINA SANDELL BERG
Translated by Andrew L. Skoog

OSCAR AHNFELT

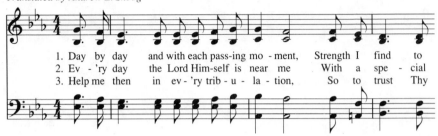

1. Day by day and with each pass-ing mo - ment, Strength I find to
2. Ev - 'ry day the Lord Him-self is near me With a spe - cial
3. Help me then in ev - 'ry trib - u - la - tion, So to trust Thy

meet my tri - als here; Trust-ing in my Fa-ther's wise be - stow -ment,
mer - cy for each hour; All my cares He fain would bear, and cheer me,
prom-is - es, O Lord, That I lose not faith's sweet con-so - la - tion

I've no cause for wor-ry or for fear. He whose heart is kind be-
He whose name is Coun-sel-lor and Pow'r. The pro - tec - tion of His
Of - fered me with - in Thy ho - ly Word. Help me, Lord, when toil and

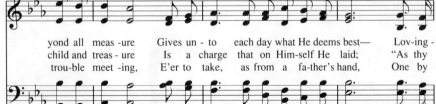

yond all meas -ure Gives un - to each day what He deems best— Lov-ing-
child and treas - ure Is a charge that on Him-self He laid; "As thy
trou-ble meet -ing, E'er to take, as from a fa-ther's hand, One by

ly,   its part of pain and pleas-ure, Min-gling toil with peace and   rest.
days, thy strength shall be in meas-ure," This the pledge to me   He   made.
one, the days, the mo-ments fleet-ing, Till I reach the Prom - ised   Land.

Jesus Never Fails

101

A. A. LUTHER

A. A. LUTHER

1. Earth - ly friends   may   prove un-true,   Doubts and fears as - sail;
2. Though the sky   be   dark and drear,   Fierce and strong the   gale,
3. In   life's dark   and   bit - ter hour,   Love will still   pre - vail;

One still loves and   cares for you: One who will not   fail.
Just re - mem - ber   He is near,   And He will not   fail.
Trust His ev - er - last-ing pow'r,   Je - sus will not   fail.

Je - sus nev - er   fails,   Je - sus nev - er   fails,

Heav'n and earth may pass   a - way, But   Je - sus nev - er   fails.

102   He Hideth My Soul

FANNY J. CROSBY   WILLIAM J. KIRKPATRICK

1. A won-der-ful Sav-iour is Je-sus my Lord, A won-der-ful
2. A won-der-ful Sav-iour is Je-sus my Lord, He tak-eth my
3. With num-ber-less bless-ings each mo-ment He crowns, And filled with His
4. When clothed in His bright-ness, trans-port-ed, I rise To meet Him in

Sav-iour to me, He hid-eth my soul in the cleft of the rock, Where
bur-den a-way, He hold-eth me up, and I shall not be moved, He
full-ness di-vine, I sing in my rap-ture, O glo-ry to God For
clouds of the sky, His per-fect sal-va-tion, His won-der-ful love, I'll

riv-ers of pleas-ure I see.
giv-eth me strength as my day.
such a Re-deem-er as mine!
shout with the mil-lions on high.

He hid-eth my soul in the cleft of the rock

That shad-ows a dry, thirst-y land; He hid-eth my life in the depths of His love,

And cov-ers me there with His hand, And cov-ers me there with His hand.

Under His Wings

103

WILLIAM O. CUSHING

IRA D. SANKEY

1. Un-der His wings I am safe-ly a-bid-ing; Though the night deep-ens and tem-pests are wild, Still I can trust Him; I know He will keep me; He has re-deemed me, and I am His child.

2. Un-der His wings, what a ref-uge in sor-row! How the heart yearn-ing-ly turns to His rest! Oft-en when earth has no balm for my heal-ing, There I find com-fort, and there I am blest.

3. Un-der His wings, O what pre-cious en-joy-ment! There will I hide till life's tri-als are o'er; Shel-tered, pro-tect-ed, no e-vil can harm me; Rest-ing in Je-sus I'm safe ev-er-more.

Un-der His wings, un-der His wings, Who from His love can sev-er? Un-der His wings my soul shall a-bide, Safe-ly a-bide for-ev-er.

104 Lean on His Arms

EDGAR LEWIS

L. E. JONES

1. Just lean up-on the arms of Je - sus, He'll help you a - long,
2. Just lean up-on the arms of Je - sus, He'll bright-en the way,
3. Just lean up-on the arms of Je - sus, O bring ev - 'ry care,
4. Just lean up-on the arms of Je - sus, Then leave all to Him,

help you a - long; If you will trust His love un - fail - ing, He'll
bright-en the way; Just fol - low glad - ly where He lead - eth, His
bring ev - 'ry care! The bur - den that has seemed so heav - y, Take
leave all to Him; His heart is full of love and mer - cy, His

fill your heart with song.   Lean on   His arms,   trust-ing in His love;
gen - tle voice o - bey.   Lean up - on His arms, ful-ly
to the Lord in pray'r.
eyes are nev - er dim.

Lean on   His arms,   all His mer-cies prove: Lean on   His
Lean up - on His arms, and   Lean up - on His

arms,   look-ing Home a-bove, Just lean on the Sav - iour's arms!
arms, ev - er

All That Thrills My Soul

105

THORO HARRIS

THORO HARRIS

1. Who can cheer the heart like Je - sus, By His pres-ence all di - vine?
2. Love of Christ so free-ly giv - en, Grace of God be-yond de-gree,
3. What a won-der-ful re-demp-tion! Nev - er can a mor-tal know
4. Ev - 'ry need His hand sup-ply - ing, Ev - 'ry good in Him I see;
5. By the crys-tal flow-ing riv - er, With the ran-somed I will sing,

True and ten-der, pure and pre - cious, O how blest to call Him mine!
Mer - cy, high-er than the heav - ens, Deep - er than the deep-est sea.
How my sin, though red like crim-son, Can be whit-er than the snow.
On His strength di-vine re - ly - ing, He is all in all to me.
And for - ev - er and for - ev - er Praise and glo - ri - fy the King.

All that thrills my soul is Je - sus, He is more than life to me (to me);

And the fair-est of ten thou - sand In my bless-ed Lord I see.

© Copyright 1931. Renewed 1959 by Mrs. Thoro Harris, Nazarene Publishing House, owner.
Used by Permission.

106 Abide With Me

HENRY F. LYTE

WILLIAM H. MONK

1. A - bide with me: fast falls the e - ven - tide; The dark-ness
2. Swift to its close ebbs out life's lit - tle day; Earth's joys grow
3. I need Thy pres - ence ev - 'ry pass-ing hour: What but Thy
4. Hold Thou Thy cross be - fore my clos-ing eyes; Shine through the

deep-ens; Lord, with me a - bide: When oth-er help - ers fail, and
dim, its glo-ries pass a - way; Change and de - cay in all a -
grace can foil the temp-ter's pow'r? Who like Thy - self my guide, and
gloom, and point me to the skies: Heav'n's morn-ing breaks, and earth's vain

com-forts flee, Help of the help-less, O a - bide with me!
round I see; O Thou who chang-est not, a - bide with me!
stay can be? Through cloud and sun-shine, O a - bide with me!
shad-ows flee: In life, in death, O Lord, a - bide with me! A-men.

107 Praise the Saviour

THOMAS KELLY

From the German

1. Praise the Sav-iour, ye who know Him! Who can tell how much we owe Him?
2. Je - sus is the name that charms us; He for con-flict fits and arms us;
3. Trust in Him, ye saints, for-ev - er; He is faith-ful, chang - ing nev - er;
4. Then we shall be where we would be, Then we shall be what we should be;

Glad - ly let us ren - der to Him All we are and have.
Noth -ing moves and noth -ing harms us While we trust in Him.
Nei - ther force nor guile can sev - er Those He loves from Him.
Things that are not now, nor could be, Soon shall be our own.

Sun of My Soul 108

JOHN KEBLE

Adapted from
Katholisches Gesangbuch

1. Sun of my soul! Thou Sav - iour dear, It is not night if
2. When the soft dews of kind - ly sleep My wea -ry eye - lids
3. A - bide with me from morn till eve, For with-out Thee I
4. Be near to bless us when we wake, Ere through the world our

Thou be near; O may no earth - born cloud a - rise
gen - tly steep, Be my last thought, how sweet to rest
can - not live; A - bide with me when night is nigh,
way we take; Till, in the o - cean of Thy love,

To hide Thee from Thy ser - vant's eyes.
For - ev - er on my Sav - iour's breast.
For with - out Thee I dare not die.
We lose our - selves in Heav'n a - bove. A - men.

109 Saviour, Like a Shepherd Lead Us

DOROTHY A. THRUPP

WILLIAM B. BRADBURY

1. Sav-iour, like a shep-herd lead us, Much we need Thy ten-der care;
2. We are Thine; do Thou be-friend us, Be the Guard-ian of our way;
3. Thou hast prom-ised to re-ceive us, Poor and sin-ful though we be;
4. Ear-ly let us seek Thy fa-vor; Ear-ly let us do Thy will;

In Thy pleas-ant pas-tures feed us, For our use Thy folds pre-pare:
Keep Thy flock, from sin de-fend us, Seek us when we go a-stray:
Thou hast mer-cy to re-lieve us, Grace to cleanse, and pow'r to free:
Bless-ed Lord and on-ly Sav-iour, With Thy love our bos-oms fill:

Bless-ed Je-sus, Bless-ed Je-sus, Thou hast bought us, Thine we are;
Bless-ed Je-sus, Bless-ed Je-sus, Hear, O hear us when we pray;
Bless-ed Je-sus, Bless-ed Je-sus, Ear-ly let us turn to Thee;
Bless-ed Je-sus, Bless-ed Je-sus, Thou hast loved us, love us still;

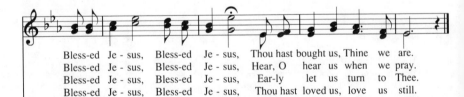

Bless-ed Je-sus, Bless-ed Je-sus, Thou hast bought us, Thine we are.
Bless-ed Je-sus, Bless-ed Je-sus, Hear, O hear us when we pray.
Bless-ed Je-sus, Bless-ed Je-sus, Ear-ly let us turn to Thee.
Bless-ed Je-sus, Bless-ed Je-sus, Thou hast loved us, love us still.

All the Way My Saviour Leads Me 110

FANNY J. CROSBY

ROBERT LOWRY

1. All the way my Sav-iour leads me; What have I to ask be-side?
2. All the way my Sav-iour leads me, Cheers each wind-ing path I tread,
3. All the way my Sav-iour leads me; O the full - ness of His love!

Can I doubt His ten-der mer - cy, Who through life has been my Guide?
Gives me grace for ev - 'ry tri - al, Feeds me with the liv - ing bread.
Per-fect rest to me is prom-ised In my Fa - ther's House a - bove.

Heav'n-ly peace, di - vin-est com - fort, Here by faith in Him to dwell!
Though my wea - ry steps may fal - ter, And my soul a -thirst may be,
When my spir - it, clothed im-mor - tal, Wings its flight to realms of day,

For I know, what-e'er be-fall me, Je - sus do - eth all things well;
Gush-ing from the Rock be - fore me, Lo! a spring of joy I see;
This my song through end-less a - ges: Je - sus led me all the way;

For I know, what-e'er be-fall me, Je - sus do - eth all things well.
Gush-ing from the Rock be - fore me, Lo! a spring of joy I see.
This my song through end-less a - ges: Je - sus led me all the way.

111 Sweet Peace, the Gift of God's Love

P. P. BILHORN

P. P. BILHORN

1. There comes to my heart one sweet strain, (sweet strain,) A glad and a joy-ous re-frain; (re-frain;) I sing it a-gain and a - gain, Sweet peace, the gift of God's love.

2. Through Christ on the cross peace was made, (was made,) My debt by His death was all paid; (all paid;) No oth - er foun-da-tion is laid For peace, the gift of God's love.

3. When Je - sus as Lord I had crowned, (had crowned,) My heart with this peace did a-bound; (a - bound;) In Him the rich bless-ing I found, Sweet peace, the gift of God's love.

4. In Je - sus for peace I a - bide, (a - bide,) And as I keep close to His side; (His side;) There's noth - ing but peace doth be - tide, Sweet peace, the gift of God's love.

Peace, peace, sweet peace! Won - der-ful gift from a - bove! (a-bove!) O

cresc.

won - der-ful, won - der - ful peace! Sweet peace, the gift of God's love!

Be Still, My Soul

112

Adapted from Psalm 46 by
KATHARINA von SCHLEGEL
Translated by Jane L. Borthwick

JEAN SIBELIUS

1. Be still, my soul: the Lord is on thy side; Bear patient-
2. Be still, my soul: thy God doth un-der-take To guide the
3. Be still, my soul: the hour is hast-'ning on When we shall

ly the cross of grief or pain; Leave to thy God to
fu-ture as He has the past. Thy hope, thy con-fi-
be for-ev-er with the Lord, When dis-ap-point-ment,

or-der and pro-vide; In ev-'ry change He faith-ful will re-
dence let noth-ing shake; All now mys-te-rious shall be bright at
grief, and fear are gone, Sor-row for-got, love's pur-est joys re-

main. Be still, my soul: thy best, thy heav'n-ly Friend
last. Be still, my soul: the waves and winds still know
stored. Be still, my soul: when change and tears are past,

Through thorn-y ways leads to a joy-ful end.
His voice who ruled them while He dwelt be-low.
All safe and bless-ed we shall meet at last. A-men.

113 Wonderful Peace

W. D. CORNELL, *altered*

W. G. COOPER

1. Far a-way in the depths of my spir-it to-night Rolls a
2. What a treas-ure I have in this won-der-ful peace, Bur-ied
3. I am rest-ing to-night in this won-der-ful peace, Rest-ing
4. And me-thinks when I rise to that Cit-y of peace, Where the
5. Ah! soul, are you here with-out com-fort or rest, March-ing

mel-o-dy sweet-er than psalm; In ce-les-tial-like strains it un-
deep in the heart of my soul; So se-cure that no pow-er can
sweet-ly in Je-sus' con-trol; For I'm kept from all dan-ger by
Au-thor of peace I shall see, That one strain of the song which the
down the rough path-way of time? Make Je-sus your Friend ere the

ceas-ing-ly falls O'er my soul like an in-fi-nite calm.
mine it a-way, While the years of e-ter-ni-ty roll.
night and by day, And His glo-ry is flood-ing my soul.
ran-somed will sing, In that heav-en-ly king-dom shall be:
shad-ows grow dark; O ac-cept this sweet peace so sub-lime.

Peace! peace! won-der-ful peace, Com-ing down from the Fa-ther a-bove; Sweep

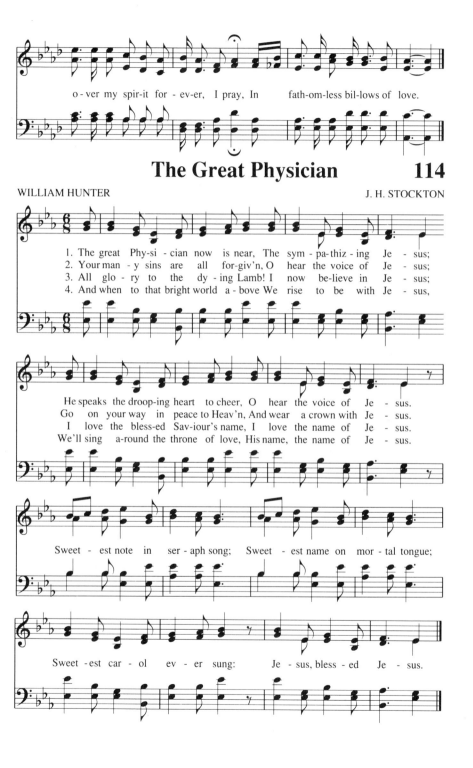

o - ver my spir-it for - ev-er, I pray, In fath-om-less bil-lows of love.

The Great Physician 114

WILLIAM HUNTER

J. H. STOCKTON

1. The great Phy-si - cian now is near, The sym - pa-thiz - ing Je - sus;
2. Your man - y sins are all for-giv'n, O hear the voice of Je - sus;
3. All glo - ry to the dy - ing Lamb! I now be-lieve in Je - sus;
4. And when to that bright world a - bove We rise to be with Je - sus,

He speaks the droop-ing heart to cheer, O hear the voice of Je - sus.
Go on your way in peace to Heav'n, And wear a crown with Je - sus.
I love the bless-ed Sav-iour's name, I love the name of Je - sus.
We'll sing a-round the throne of love, His name, the name of Je - sus.

Sweet - est note in ser - aph song; Sweet - est name on mor - tal tongue;

Sweet - est car - ol ev - er sung: Je - sus, bless - ed Je - sus.

115 No One Ever Cared for Me Like Jesus

CHARLES F. WEIGLE   CHARLES F. WEIGLE

1. I would love to tell you what I think of Je - sus, Since I
found in Him a Friend so strong and true; I would tell you how He
changed my life com-plete-ly, He did some-thing that no oth - er friend could
do.
No one ev - er cared for me like Je - sus, There's no
oth-er friend so kind as He; No one else could take the sin and dark-ness

2. All my life was full of sin when Je - sus found me, All my
heart was full of mis - er - y and woe; Je - sus placed His strong and
lov - ing arms a - bout me, And He led me in the way I ought to
go.

3. Ev - 'ry day He comes to me with new as - sur - ance, More and
more I un - der-stand His words of love; But I'll nev - er know just
why He came to save me, Till some - day I see His bless-ed face a -
bove.

from me, O how much He cared for me!

He Leadeth Me 116

JOSEPH H. GILMORE

WILLIAM B. BRADBURY

1. He lead-eth me, O bless-ed tho't! O words with heav'n-ly com-fort fraught!
2. Some-times mid scenes of deep-est gloom, Some-times where E-den's bow-ers bloom,
3. Lord, I would clasp Thy hand in mine, Nor ev-er mur-mur nor re-pine,
4. And when my task on earth is done, When by Thy grace, the vic-t'ry's won,

What-e'er I do, wher-e'er I be, Still 'tis God's hand that lead-eth me.
By wa-ters still, o'er trou-bled sea, Still 'tis His hand that lead-eth me!
Con-tent what-ev-er lot I see, Since 'tis my God that lead-eth me!
E'en death's cold wave I will not flee, Since God through Jor-dan lead-eth me.

He lead-eth me, He lead-eth me! By His own hand He lead-eth me!

His faith-ful fol-l'wer I would be, For by His hand He lead-eth me.

117 Safe in the Arms of Jesus

FANNY J. CROSBY

WILLIAM H. DOANE

1. Safe in the arms of Je - sus, Safe on His gen - tle breast,
2. Safe in the arms of Je - sus, Safe from cor-rod- ing care,
3. Je - sus, my heart's dear Ref - uge, Je - sus has died for me;

There by His love o'er-shad - ed, Sweet - ly my soul shall rest.
Safe from the world's temp-ta - tions, Sin can-not harm me there.
Firm on the Rock of A - ges, Ev - er my trust shall be.

Hark! 'tis the voice of an - gels, Borne in a song to me,
Free from the blight of sor - row, Free from my doubts and fears;
Here let me wait with pa - tience, Wait till the night is o'er;

O - ver the fields of Glo - ry, O - ver the jas - per sea.
On - ly a few more tri - als, On - ly a few more tears!
Wait till I see the morn - ing Break on the gold -en shore.

Safe in the arms of Je - sus, Safe on His gen - tle breast,

There by His love o'er -shad - ed, Sweet - ly my soul shall rest.

Near to the Heart of God 118

CLELAND B. McAFEE

CLELAND B. McAFEE

1. There is a place of qui - et rest, Near to the heart of God,
2. There is a place of com - fort sweet, Near to the heart of God,
3. There is a place of full re-lease, Near to the heart of God,

A place where sin can - not mo-lest, Near to the heart of God.
A place where we our Sav - iour meet, Near to the heart of God.
A place where all is joy and peace, Near to the heart of God.

O Je - sus, blest Re - deem - er, Sent from the heart of God,

Hold us who wait be - fore Thee, Near to the heart of God.

119   Till the Storm Passes By

MOSIE LISTER

MOSIE LISTER

1. In the dark of the mid-night have I oft hid my face, while the
2. Man-y times Sa-tan whis-pered, "There is no need to try, for there's
3. When the long night has end-ed and the storms come no more, let me

storm howls a-bove me, and there's no hid-ing place; 'Mid the crash of the
no end of sor-row, there's no hope by and by"; But I know Thou art
stand in Thy pres-ence, on that bright, peace-ful shore; In that Land where the

thun-der, Pre-cious Lord, hear my cry, keep me safe till the storm pass-es
with me, and to-mor-row I'll rise where the storms nev-er dark-en the
tem-pest nev-er comes, Lord, may I dwell with Thee when the storm pass-es

by.
skies.   Till the storm pass-es o-ver, Till the thun-der sounds no
by.

more, Till the clouds roll for-ev-er from the sky; Hold me

© Copyright 1958 by Lillenas Publishing Co. All rights reserved. Used by permission.

Favorite song of Dr. David Cavin and Dr. John Rawlings.

fast, let me stand in the hol-low of Thy hand, Keep me

safe Till the storm pass - es by.

Jesus, Saviour, Pilot Me 120

EDWARD HOPPER

JOHN E. GOULD

1. Je - sus, Sav - iour, pi - lot me O - ver life's tem-pes-tuous sea;
2. As a moth - er stills her child, Thou canst hush the o-cean wild;
3. When at last I near the shore, And the fear - ful break-ers roar

Un-known waves be- fore me roll, Hid-ing rock and treach-'rous shoal;
Boist-'rous waves o- bey Thy will When Thou say'st to them, "Be still!"
'Twixt me and the peace-ful rest, Then, while lean -ing on Thy breast,

Chart and com - pass come from Thee: Je - sus, Sav - iour, pi - lot me.
Won-drous Sov - 'reign of the sea, Je - sus, Sav - iour, pi - lot me.
May I hear Thee say to me, "Fear not, I will pi - lot thee."

121 Like a River Glorious

FRANCES R. HAVERGAL

JAMES MOUNTAIN

1. Like a riv-er glo-rious Is God's per-fect peace, O-ver all vic-to-rious
2. Hid-den in the hol-low Of His bless-ed hand, Nev-er foe can fol-low,
3. Ev-'ry joy or tri-al Fall-eth from a-bove, Traced up-on our di-al

In its bright in-crease; Per-fect, yet it flow-eth Full-er ev-'ry day,
Nev-er trai-tor stand; Not a surge of wor-ry, Not a shade of care,
By the Son of Love. We may trust Him ful-ly All for us to do;

Per-fect, yet it grow-eth Deep-er all the way.
Not a blast of hur-ry Touch the spir-it there. Stayed up-on Je-ho-vah,
They who trust Him whol-ly Find Him whol-ly true.

Hearts are ful-ly blest; Find-ing, as He prom-ised, Per-fect peace and rest.

122 O God, Our Help

ISAAC WATTS

WILLIAM CROFT

1. O God, our Help in a-ges past, Our Hope for years to come,
2. Un-der the shad-ow of Thy throne Thy saints have dwelt se-cure;
3. Be-fore the hills in or-der stood, Or earth re-ceived her frame,
4. A thou-sand a-ges in Thy sight Are like an ev-'ning gone,
5. O God, our Help in a-ges past, Our Hope for years to come,

Our shel-ter from the storm-y blast, And our e-ter-nal Home!
Suf-fi-cient is Thine arm a-lone, And our de-fense is sure.
From ev-er-last-ing Thou art God, To end-less years the same.
Short as the watch that ends the night Be-fore the ris-ing sun.
Be Thou our Guide while life shall last, And our e-ter-nal Home.

The Christian's Good-Night   123

SARAH DOUDNEY

IRA D. SANKEY

1. Sleep on, be-lov-ed, sleep, and take thy rest; Lay down thy
2. Calm is thy slum-ber as an in-fant's sleep; But thou shalt
3. Un-til e-ter-nal glo-ry lights the skies, Un-til the
4. On-ly "Good-night," be-lov-ed— not "Fare-well!" A lit-tle
5. Un-til we meet a-gain be-fore His throne, Clothed in the

head up-on thy Sav-iour's breast; We love thee well, but
wake no more to toil and weep: Thine is a per-fect
dead in Je-sus shall a-rise, And He shall come, but
while, and all His saints shall dwell In hal-lowed un-ion
spot-less robe He gives His own, Un-til we know e-

Je-sus loves thee best— Good-night! Good-night! Good-night!
rest, se-cure and deep— Good-night! Good-night! Good-night!
not in low-ly guise— Good-night! Good-night! Good-night!
in-di-vis-i-ble— Good-night! Good-night! Good-night!
ven as we are known— Good-night! Good-night! Good-night!

124   God Will Take Care of You

CIVILLA D. MARTIN

W. STILLMAN MARTIN

1. Be not dis-mayed what-e'er be-tide, God will take care of you;
2. Through days of toil when heart doth fail, God will take care of you;
3. All you may need He will pro-vide, God will take care of you;
4. No mat - ter what may be the test, God will take care of you;

Be-neath His wings of love a-bide, God will take care of you;
When dan - gers fierce your path as - sail, God will take care of you;
Noth-ing you ask will be de-nied, God will take care of you;
Lean, wea - ry one, up - on His breast, God will take care of you;

God will take care of you, Through ev - 'ry day, O'er all the way;

He will take care of you, God will take care of you.
take care of you.

The Solid Rock

125

EDWARD MOTE

WILLIAM B. BRADBURY

1. My hope is built on noth-ing less than Je - sus' blood and right-eous-ness;
2. When dark-ness veils His love-ly face, I rest on His un - chang-ing grace;
3. His oath, His cov - e - nant, His blood, Sup - port me in the whelm-ing flood;
4. When He shall come with trum-pet sound, O may I then in Him be found;

I dare not trust the sweet-est frame, But whol - ly lean on Je - sus' name.
In ev - 'ry high and storm - y gale, My an - chor holds with - in the veil.
When all a-round my soul gives way, He then is all my hope and stay.
Dressed in His right - eous - ness a - lone, Fault - less to stand be - fore the throne.

On Christ, the sol - id Rock I stand; All oth - er ground

is sink - ing sand, All oth - er ground is sink - ing sand.

Favorite song of Dr. Curtis Hutson.

126 Anywhere With Jesus

JESSIE H. BROWN
Mrs. C. M. ALEXANDER

DANIEL B. TOWNER

1. An - y - where with Je - sus I can safe - ly go; An - y - where He
2. An - y - where with Je - sus I am not a - lone; Oth - er friends may
3. An - y - where with Je - sus o - ver land and sea, Tell - ing souls in
4. An - y - where with Je - sus I can go to sleep, When the dark - 'ning

leads me in this world be - low; An - y - where with - out Him dear - est
fail me, He is still my own; Though His hand may lead me o - ver
dark - ness of sal - va - tion free; Read - y as He sum - mons me to
shad - ows round a - bout me creep; Know - ing I shall wak - en nev - er

joys would fade; An - y - where with Je - sus I am not a -
drear - y ways, An - y - where with Je - sus is a house of
go or stay, An - y - where with Je - sus when He points the
more to roam, An - y - where with Je - sus will be Home, sweet

fraid.
praise.   An - y - where, an - y - where! Fear I can - not know;
way.
Home.

An - y - where with Je - sus I can safe - ly go.

'Tis So Sweet to Trust in Jesus   127

LOUISA M. R. STEAD   WILLIAM J. KIRKPATRICK

1. 'Tis so sweet to trust in Je - sus, Just to take Him at His Word;
2. O how sweet to trust in Je - sus, Just to trust His cleans-ing blood;
3. Yes, 'tis sweet to trust in Je - sus, Just from sin and self to cease;
4. I'm so glad I learned to trust Thee, Pre-cious Je - sus, Sav - iour, Friend;

Just to rest up - on His prom-ise; Just to know, "Thus saith the Lord."
Just in sim - ple faith to plunge me 'Neath the heal - ing, cleans-ing flood!
Just from Je - sus sim-ply tak - ing Life and rest, and joy and peace.
And I know that Thou art with me, Wilt be with me to the end.

Je - sus, Je - sus, how I trust Him! How I've proved Him o'er and o'er!

Je - sus, Je - sus, pre - cious Je - sus! O for grace to trust Him more!

128
Each Step I Take

W. ELMO MERCER

W. ELMO MERCER

1. Each step I take my Sav-iour goes be - fore me, And with His
2. At times I feel my faith be-gin to wav - er, When up a -
3. I trust in God, no mat-ter come what may, For life e -

lov-ing hand He leads the way. And with each breath I whis-per, "I a -
head I see a chasm wide. It's then I turn and look up to my
ter - nal is in His hand. He holds the key that o-pens up the

dore Thee"; O what joy to walk with Him each day!
Sav-iour, I am strong when He is by my side. Each step I
way That will lead me to the Prom-ised Land.

take I know that He will guide me; To high - er ground He ev - er leads me

on. Un-til some-day the last step will be tak - en. Each step I

take just leads me clos - er Home.

Rock of Ages

129

AUGUSTUS M. TOPLADY

THOMAS HASTINGS

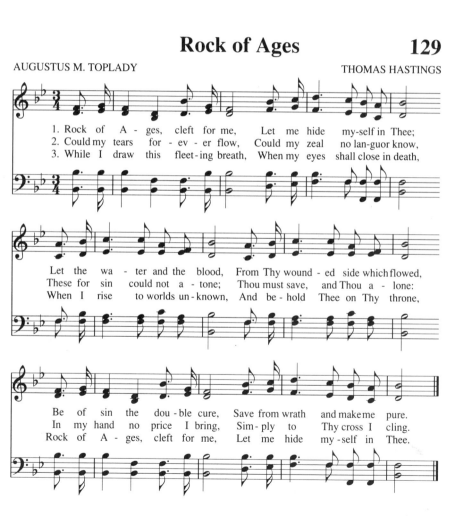

1. Rock of A - ges, cleft for me, Let me hide my-self in Thee;
2. Could my tears for - ev - er flow, Could my zeal no lan-guor know,
3. While I draw this fleet-ing breath, When my eyes shall close in death,

Let the wa - ter and the blood, From Thy wound - ed side which flowed,
These for sin could not a - tone; Thou must save, and Thou a - lone:
When I rise to worlds un - known, And be - hold Thee on Thy throne,

Be of sin the dou - ble cure, Save from wrath and make me pure.
In my hand no price I bring, Sim - ply to Thy cross I cling.
Rock of A - ges, cleft for me, Let me hide my - self in Thee.

130 Yesterday, Today, Forever

A. B. SIMPSON

J. H. BURKE

1. O how sweet the glo-rious mes-sage, Sim-ple faith may claim,
2. He who par-doned err-ing Pe-ter, Nev-er need'st thou fear;
3. He who 'mid the rag-ing bil-lows, Walked up-on the sea;
4. As of old He walked to Em-maus, With them to a-bide;

Yes-ter-day, to-day, for-ev-er, Je-sus is the same.
He that came to faith-less Tho-mas, All thy doubt will clear.
Still can hush our wild-est tem-pest, As on Gal-i-lee.
So through all life's way He walk-eth, Ev-er near our side.

Still He loves to save the sin-ful, Heal the sick and lame;
He who let the loved dis-ci-ple On His bos-om rest,
He who wept and prayed in an-guish, In Geth-sem-a-ne,
Soon a-gain shall we be-hold Him, Has-ten, Lord, the day!

Cheer the mourn-er, still the tem-pest, Glo-ry to His name!
Bids thee still, with love as ten-der, Lean up-on His breast.
Drinks with us each cup of trem-bling, In our ag-o-ny.
But 'twill still be "this same Je-sus," As He went a-way.

Yes-ter-day, to-day, for-ev-er, Je-sus is the same,

All may change, but Je - sus nev - er! Glo - ry to His name,

Glo - ry to His name, Glo - ry to His name,

All may change, but Je - sus nev - er! Glo - ry to His name.

Christ Is All I Need 131

Unknown

1. Christ is all I need, Christ is all I need, All, all I need.
2. He was cru - ci - fied, For me He died, On Cal - va - ry.

Christ is all I need, Christ is all I need, All, all I need.
That's why I know He loves me so, He's all I need.

132   Never Alone!

Anonymous
Arranged by B. B. McKinney

1. I've seen the light-ning flash - ing, And heard the thun - der roll,
2. The world's fierce winds are blow - ing, Temp-ta-tions are sharp and keen;
3. When in af - flic - tion's val - ley, I'm tread-ing the road of care,
4. He died for me on the moun - tain, For me they pierced His side,

I've felt sin's break - ers dash - ing, Try-ing to con-quer my soul;
I feel a peace in know - ing, My Sav - iour stands be-tween;
My Sav - iour helps me to car - ry My cross when heav-y to bear,
For me He o-pened that foun - tain, The crim - son, cleans-ing tide;

I've heard the voice of Je - sus, Tell-ing me still to fight on,
He stands to shield me from dan - ger, When earth-ly friends are gone,
My feet en-tan-gled with bri - ars, Read-y to cast me down;
For me He wait-eth in Glo - ry, Seat-ed up - on His throne;

He prom-ised nev-er to leave me, Nev - er to leave me a - lone.
He prom-ised nev-er to leave me, Nev - er to leave me a - lone.
My Sav - iour whis-pered His prom - ise, Nev - er to leave me a - lone.
He prom-ised nev-er to leave me, Nev - er to leave me a - lone.

Favorite song of Evangelist Hyman J. Appelman.

No, never alone,
No, never alone,
He promised never to leave me,
Never to leave me alone;
No, never alone,
No, never alone,
He promised never to leave me,
Never to leave me alone.

Safe Wherever I Go 133

JOHN R. RICE

JOHN R. RICE

Safe wherever I go, Peace the world cannot know;
Sins all forgiven, and Heaven my Home, I'm safe wherever I go.

134 My Anchor Holds

W. C. MARTIN, *altered*

DANIEL B. TOWNER

1. Though the an - gry sur - ges roll On my tem - pest-driv - en soul,
2. Might - y tides a - bout me sweep, Per - ils lurk with - in the deep,
3. I can feel the an - chor fast As I meet each sud - den blast,
4. Trou - bles al - most 'whelm the soul; Griefs like bil - lows o'er me roll;

I am peace - ful, for I know, Wild - ly though the winds may blow,
An - gry clouds o'er-shade the sky, And the tem - pest ris - es high;
And the ca - ble, though un - seen, Bears the heav - y strain be - tween;
Temp-ters seek to lure a - stray; Storms ob - scure the light of day:

I've an an - chor safe and sure, That can ev - er - more en - dure.
Still I stand the tem-pest's shock, For my an - chor grips the Rock.
Through the storm I safe - ly ride, Till the turn - ing of the tide.
But in Christ I can be bold, I've an an - chor that shall hold.

And it holds, my an - chor holds; Blow your wild - est, then, O
holds, my an - chor holds; wild - est,

gale, On my bark so small and frail: By His grace I shall not
then, O gale,

fail, For my an - chor holds, my an - chor holds.
an - chor holds, it firm - ly holds,

I Know I Am Saved 135

BUD LYLES

BUD LYLES

I know I am saved, For Christ set me free, He ran-somed my poor

soul on the cross of Cal - va - ry. And now I can sing, For

Christ is my King, I'll see His face in Glo - ry by and by.

136 Master, the Tempest Is Raging

MARY A. BAKER   H. R. PALMER

1. Mas - ter, the tem-pest is rag - ing! The bil-lows are toss - ing high!
2. Mas - ter, with an-guish of spir - it I bow in my grief to - day;
3. Mas - ter, the ter - ror is o - ver, The el - e - ments sweet - ly rest;

The sky is o'er-shad-owed with black- ness, No shel-ter or help is nigh:
The depths of my sad heart are trou - bled; O wak-en and save, I pray!
Earth's sun in the calm lake is mir - rored, And Heav-en's with-in my breast.

"Car - est Thou not that we per - ish?" How canst Thou lie a - sleep,
Tor-rents of sin and of an - guish Sweep o'er my sink - ing soul!
Lin - ger, O bless - ed Re - deem - er, Leave me a - lone no more;

When each mo-ment so mad - ly is threat -'ning A grave in the an - gry deep?
And I per - ish! I per - ish, dear Mas - ter; O has - ten, and take con - trol!
And with joy I shall make the blest har - bor, And rest on the bliss - ful shore.

137 In Times Like These

RUTH CAYE JONES   RUTH CAYE JONES

1. In times like these you need a Sav-iour, In times like
2. In times like these you need the Bi - ble, In times like
3. In times like these I have a Sav-iour, In times like

these you need an an-chor; Be ver - y sure (Be ver - y sure),
these, O be not i - dle; Be ver - y sure (Be ver - y sure),
these, I have an an-chor; I'm ver - y sure (I'm ver - y sure),

Be ver - y sure (Be ver - y sure), Your an - chor holds
Be ver - y sure (Be ver - y sure), Your an - chor holds
I'm ver - y sure (I'm ver - y sure), My an - chor holds

Fine

and grips the Sol - id Rock! This Rock is Je - sus,

D.S. al Fine

Yes, He's the One, This Rock is Je - sus— The on - ly One;

The Haven of Rest

138

HENRY L. GILMOUR

GEORGE D. MOORE

1. My soul in sad ex - ile was out on life's sea, So
2. I yield - ed my - self to His ten - der em - brace, And
3. The song of my soul, since the Lord made me whole, Has
4. O come to the Sav - iour, He pa - tient - ly waits To

bur-dened with sin and dis - tressed, Till I heard a sweet voice say-ing,
faith tak-ing hold of the Word, My fet-ters fell off, and I
been the old sto - ry so blessed, Of Je - sus who'll save who-so -
save by His pow - er di - vine; Come, an-chor your soul in the

D.S.: The tem-pest may sweep o'er the

Fine

"Make Me your choice"; And I en-tered the "Ha - ven of Rest"!
an - chored my soul; The "Ha-ven of Rest" is my Lord.
ev - er will have A home in the "Ha - ven of Rest"!
"Ha - ven of Rest," And say, "My Be - lov - ed is mine."

wild, storm-y deep, In Je - sus I'm safe ev - er - more.

I've an - chored my soul in the "Ha - ven of Rest,"

D.S. al Fine

I'll sail the wide seas no more;

Favorite song of singer Ray Hart.

139   I Know Whom I Have Believed

DANIEL W. WHITTLE

JAMES McGRANAHAN

1. I know not why God's won-drous grace To me He hath made known,
2. I know not how this sav-ing faith To me He did im-part,
3. I know not how the Spir-it moves, Con-vinc-ing men of sin,
4. I know not what of good or ill May be re-served for me,
5. I know not when my Lord may come, At night or noon-day fair,

Nor why un-wor-thy— Christ in love Re-deemed me for His own.
Nor how be-liev-ing in His Word Wrought peace with-in my heart.
Re-veal-ing Je-sus through the Word, Cre-at-ing faith in Him.
Of wea-ry ways or gold-en days, Be-fore His face I see.
Nor if I walk the vale with Him, Or "meet Him in the air."

But "I know whom I have be-liev-ed, and am per-suad-ed that He is

a-ble To keep that which I've com-mit-ted Un-to Him a-gainst that day."

Favorite song of Dr. Dwight Gustafson.

We Have an Anchor

140

PRISCILLA J. OWENS

WILLIAM J. KIRKPATRICK

1. Will your an - chor hold in the storms of life, When the clouds un - fold their wings of strife? When the strong tides lift and the ca - bles strain, Will your an - chor drift, or firm re - main?

2. It is safe - ly moored, 'twill the storm with - stand. For 'tis well se - cured by the Sav - iour's hand; Though the tem - pest rage and the wild winds blow, Not an an - gry wave shall our bark o'er - flow.

3. When our eyes be - hold through the gath - 'ring night The cit - y of gold, our har - bor bright, We shall an - chor fast by the heav'n - ly shore, With the storms all past for - ev - er - more.

We have an an-chor that keeps the soul Stead-fast and sure while the bil-lows roll,

Fast-ened to the Rock which can-not move, Ground-ed firm and deep in the Sav-iour's love.

141   What Will You Say Then?

JOHN R. RICE   JOHN R. RICE

1. What will you say to Jesus then, When you face all you might have been, And the Redeem-er long re-ject-ed through the years? How will you an-swer in that hour, When to the Judge in all His pow'r, You face your rec-ord and must an-swer thro' your tears?

2. What will you say; de-ny your sin? What poor ex-cuse can hope to win? Af-ter your hard-ened heart for years turned Him a-way? Look-ing in-to His pierc-ing eyes, Hid-den sin judged to your sur-prise, What can you say to Je-sus on that aw-ful day?

3. How will you an-swer calls de-ferred? Why did God's Spir-it plead un-heard? Why were the Gos-pel, love and mer-cy long so scorned? Now you must face the ris-en Christ, Pay for your sins an aw-ful price, If you have heed-ed not the judg-ment long fore-warned.

Slowly, earnestly

What will you say? What can you say? If un-for-
sin - ner, to Him

giv - en you face Christ that day. What will you say?

What can you say? Fac - ing the Lord you have scorned on that day.

The Old-Time Religion 142

Anonymous

Anonymous

Chorus: 'Tis the old - time re - lig - ion, 'Tis the old - time re - lig - ion,
1. It was good for our moth-ers, It was good for our moth-ers,
2. It has saved our fa-thers, It has saved our fa-thers,
3. Makes me love ev - 'ry-bod - y, Makes me love ev - 'ry - bod - y,
4. It will do when I'm dy - ing, It will do when I'm dy - ing,
5. It will take us to Heav-en, It will take us to Heav-en,

'Tis the old - time re - lig - ion, And it's good e-nough for me.
It was good for our moth-ers, And it's good e-nough for me.
It has saved our fa-thers, And it's good e-nough for me.
Makes me love ev - 'ry - bod - y, And it's good e-nough for me.
It will do when I'm dy - ing, And it's good e-nough for me.
It will take us to Heav-en, And it's good e-nough for me.

143 Blessed Assurance

FANNY J. CROSBY

PHOEBE P. KNAPP

1. Bless-ed as - sur - ance, Je- sus is mine, O what a fore - taste of glo - ry di - vine! Heir of sal - va - tion, pur-chase of God, Born of His Spir - it, washed in His blood.
2. Per - fect sub - mis - sion, per-fect de - light, Vi- sions of rap - ture now burst on my sight; An-gels de -scend - ing, bring from a - bove Ech-oes of mer - cy, whis-pers of love.
3. Per - fect sub - mis - sion, all is at rest, I in my Sav - iour am hap - py and blest; Watch-ing and wait - ing, look-ing a - bove, Filled with His good - ness, lost in His love.

This is my sto - ry, this is my song, Prais-ing my Sav - iour all the day long; This is my sto - ry, this is my song, Prais-ing my Sav - iour all the day long.

Favorite song of Dr. Jack Hyles, singer Jerome Hines, Dr. Clarence Sexton and Dr. Bruce Cummons.

A Mighty Fortress Is Our God   144

MARTIN LUTHER

Translated by Frederick H. Hedge

MARTIN LUTHER

1. A might-y For-tress is our God, A Bul-wark nev-er fail - ing;
2. Did we in our own strength con-fide, Our striv-ing would be los - ing;
3. And though this world, with dev - ils filled, Should threat-en to un - do us;
4. That Word a -bove all earth - ly pow'rs—No thanks to them—a-bid - eth;

Our Help-er He a - mid the flood Of mor-tal ills pre - vail - ing.
Were not the right Man on our side, The Man of God's own choos - ing.
We will not fear, for God hath willed His Truth to tri-umph through us.
The Spir - it and the gifts are ours Thro' Him who with us sid - eth.

For still our an - cient foe Doth seek to work us woe; His craft and pow'r are
Dost ask who that may be? Christ Je-sus, it is He; Lord Sab - a - oth His
The prince of dark - ness grim—We trem-ble not for him; His rage we can en -
Let goods and kin - dred go, This mor-tal life al - so; The bod - y they may

great, And, armed with cru - el hate, On earth is not his e - qual.
name, From age to age the same, And He must win the bat - tle.
dure, For lo! his doom is sure, One lit - tle word shall fell him.
kill: God's truth a - bid - eth still, His king - dom is for - ev - er.

145 It Is Well With My Soul

H. G. SPAFFORD

PHILIP P. BLISS

1. When peace, like a river, at-tend-eth my way, When sor-rows like sea-bil-lows roll; What-ev-er my lot, Thou hast taught me to say, It is well, it is well with my soul.

2. Though Sa-tan should buf-fet, tho' tri-als should come, Let this blest as-sur-ance con-trol, That Christ has re-gard-ed my help-less es-tate, And hath shed His own blood for my soul. It is well

3. My sin— O the bliss of this glo-ri-ous thought—My sin— not in part, but the whole— Is nailed to the cross and I bear it no more, Praise the Lord, praise the Lord, O my soul! It is

4. And, Lord, haste the day when my faith shall be sight, The clouds be rolled back as a scroll, The trump shall re-sound and the Lord shall de-scend, "E-ven so"— it is well with my soul.

with my soul, It is well, it is well with my soul.

well with my soul,

A Shelter in the Time of Storm 146

IRA D. SANKEY, *altered*

IRA D. SANKEY

1. The Lord's our Rock, in Him we hide, A Shel-ter in the time of storm;
2. A Shade by day, De-fense by night, A Shel-ter in the time of storm;
3. The rag-ing storms may round us beat, A Shel-ter in the time of storm;
4. O Rock di-vine, O Ref-uge dear, A Shel-ter in the time of storm;

Se - cure what-ev - er ill be-tide, A Shel-ter in the time of storm.
No fears a-larm, no foes af-fright, A Shel-ter in the time of storm.
We'll nev - er leave our safe re-treat, A Shel-ter in the time of storm.
Be Thou our Help-er ev - er near, A Shel-ter in the time of storm.

O Je-sus is a Rock in a wea-ry land, a wea-ry land, a wea-ry land;

O Je-sus is a Rock in a wea-ry land, A Shel-ter in the time of storm.

147　Leaning on the Everlasting Arms

ELISHA A. HOFFMAN　　　　　　　　　　　　　ANTHONY J. SHOWALTER

1. What a fel-low-ship, what a joy di-vine, Lean-ing on the ev - er -last-ing arms;
2. O　how sweet to walk in this pil-grim way, Lean-ing on the ev - er - last-ing arms;
3. What have I to dread, what have I to fear, Lean-ing on the ev - er -last-ing arms?

What a bless-ed-ness, what a peace is mine, Lean-ing on the ev - er -last-ing arms.
O how bright the path grows from day to day, Lean-ing on the ev - er -last-ing arms.
I have bless-ed peace with my Lord so near, Lean-ing on the ev - er -last-ing arms.

Lean　-　ing,　lean　-　ing,　Safe and se-cure from all a - larms;
Lean-ing on Je-sus,　lean-ing on Je - sus,

Lean　-　ing,　lean　-　ing,　Lean-ing on the ev - er -last-ing arms.
Lean-ing on Je - sus,　lean-ing on Je - sus,

Jesus, Only Jesus

148

JOHN R. RICE

JOHN R. RICE

1. I walked the path of pleas - ure, I toiled for earth - ly treas - ure,
2. My boast - ed good-ness failed me, No cure for sin that ailed me,
3. God's Word I long re - sist - ed, His Spir - it called, in - sist - ed,
4. O Christ, for love un - ceas - ing, For bless - ings e'er in - creas - ing,

But peace be - yond all meas - ure, I found in on - ly Je - sus.
God's Spir - it then pre - vailed me, To leave my sins on Je - sus.
Re - pent - ing I en - list - ed, With Je - sus, on - ly Je - sus.
For all my fears, re - leas - ing, I praise and love my Je - sus.

My sins are all for - giv - en, The chains of sin are riv - en,

And all my heart is giv - en, To Je - sus, on - ly Je - sus.

149 Trusting Jesus

EDGAR P. STITES

IRA D. SANKEY

1. Sim - ply trust -ing ev - 'ry day, Trust -ing through a storm - y way;
2. Bright-ly doth His Spir - it shine In - to this poor heart of mine;
3. Sing -ing if my way is clear; Pray - ing if the path be drear;
4. Trust - ing Him while life shall last, Trust -ing Him till earth be past;

E - ven when my faith is small, Trust - ing Je - sus, that is all.
While He leads I can - not fall; Trust - ing Je - sus, that is all.
If in dan - ger, for Him call; Trust - ing Je - sus, that is all.
Till with - in the jas - per wall: Trust - ing Je - sus, that is all.

Trust - ing as the mo - ments fly, Trust - ing as the days go by;

Trust - ing Him what - e'er be - fall, Trust - ing Je - sus, that is all.

My Faith Has Found a Resting Place 150

LIDIE H. EDMUNDS

Anonymous
Arranged by William J. Kirkpatrick

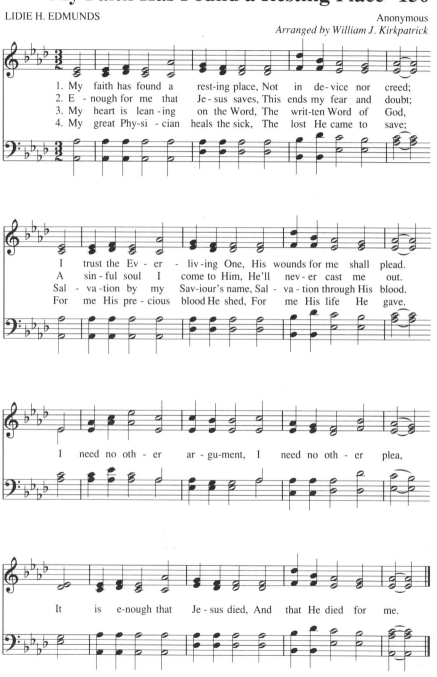

1. My faith has found a resting place, Not in device nor creed;
2. E-nough for me that Je-sus saves, This ends my fear and doubt;
3. My heart is lean-ing on the Word, The writ-ten Word of God,
4. My great Phy-si-cian heals the sick, The lost He came to save;

I trust the Ev-er-liv-ing One, His wounds for me shall plead.
A sin-ful soul I come to Him, He'll nev-er cast me out.
Sal-va-tion by my Sav-iour's name, Sal-va-tion through His blood.
For me His pre-cious blood He shed, For me His life He gave.

I need no oth-er ar-gu-ment, I need no oth-er plea,

It is e-nough that Je-sus died, And that He died for me.

151   I Do Believe

CHARLES WESLEY   Unknown

1. Fa - ther, I stretch my   hands to Thee, No   oth - er help   I   know;
2. What did Thine on - ly   Son en-dure, Be - fore I drew my   breath;
3. O   Je - sus, could I   this be-lieve, I   now should feel Thy   pow'r;
4. Au - thor of faith, to   Thee I lift My   wea - ry, long -ing   eyes;

Chorus: I   do be-lieve,   I   now be-lieve That   Je - sus died   for   me;

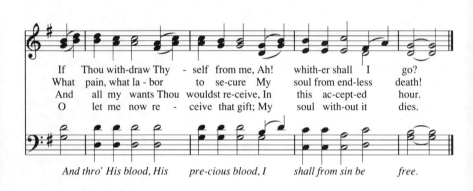

If   Thou with-draw Thy - self from me, Ah!   whith-er shall   I   go?
What   pain, what la - bor   to se-cure My   soul from end-less   death!
And   all my wants Thou wouldst re-ceive, In   this ac-cept-ed   hour.
O   let me now re - ceive that gift; My   soul with-out it   dies.

And thro' His blood, His   pre-cious blood, I   shall from sin be   free.

152   Security

LINA SANDELL   Swedish Folk Tune
Translated by various writers

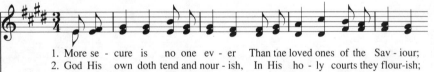

1. More se - cure is   no one ev - er   Than the loved ones of the   Sav - iour;
2. God His   own doth tend and nour - ish, In His   ho - ly courts they flour-ish;
3. Nei - ther   life nor death can ev - er   From the Lord His chil-dren sev - er;
4. Lit - tle   flock, to   joy then yield thee! Ja-cob's God will   ev - er shield thee;
5. What He   takes or   what He gives us   Shows the Fa - ther's love so pre - cious;

Not yon star on high a-bid-ing, Nor the bird in home-nest hid-ing.
Like a Fa-ther kind He spares them, In His lov-ing arms He bears them.
For His love and deep com-pas-sion Com-fort them in trib-u-la-tion.
Rest se-cure with this De-fend-er, At His will all foes sur-ren-der.
We may trust His pur-pose whol-ly—'Tis His chil-dren's wel-fare sole-ly.

How Firm a Foundation 153

GEORGE KEITH

ANNE STEELE

1. How firm a foun-da-tion, ye saints of the Lord, Is laid for your
2. "In ev-'ry con-di-tion, in sick-ness, in health, In pov-er-ty's
3. "When through fi-ery tri-als thy path-way shall lie, My grace, all suf-
4. "E'en down to old age, all My peo-ple shall prove My sov-'reign, e-
5. "The soul that on Je-sus hath leaned for re-pose, I will not, I

faith in His ex-cel-lent Word! What more can He say than to
vale, or a-bound-ing in wealth; At home and a-broad, on the
fi-cient, shall be thy sup-ply; The flame shall not hurt thee—I
ter-nal, un-chang-a-ble love; And when hoar-y hairs shall their
will not de-sert to its foes; That soul, though all Hell should en-

you He hath said, To you who for ref-uge to Je-sus have fled?
land, on the sea, As your days may de-mand, shall your strength ev-er be.
on-ly de-sign Thy dross to con-sume, and thy gold to re-fine.
tem-ples a-dorn, Like lambs they shall still in My bos-om be borne.
deav-or to shake, I'll nev-er, no, nev-er, no, nev-er for-sake!"

Favorite song of Dr. G. Archer Weniger and Dr. Noel Smith.

154   Blest Be the Tie That Binds

JOHN FAWCETT

HANS G. NÄGELI
Arranged by Lowell Mason

1. Blest be the tie that binds Our hearts in Chris - tian love; The fel - low-
2. Be - fore our Fa - ther's throne, We pour our ar - dent prayers; Our fears, our
3. We share our mu - tual woes, Our mu - tual bur - dens bear; And oft - en
4. When we a - sun - der part, It gives us in - ward pain; But we shall

ship of kin - dred minds Is like to that a - bove.
hopes, our aims are one, Our com - forts and our cares.
for each oth - er flows The sym - pa - thiz - ing tear.
still be joined in heart, And hope to meet a - gain. A - men.

155   Doxology

THOMAS KEN

LOUIS BOURGEOIS

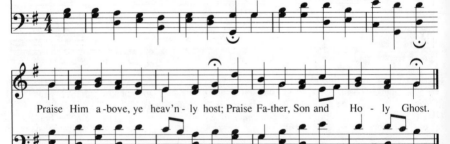

Praise God from whom all bless-ings flow; Praise Him, all crea-tures here be - low;

Praise Him a-bove, ye heav'n - ly host; Praise Fa-ther, Son and Ho - ly Ghost.

Jesus Is the Sweetest Name I Know   156

LELA LONG   LELA LONG

1. There have been names that I have loved to hear, But nev-er has there
2. There is no name in earth or Heav'n a-bove, That we should give such
3. And some-day I shall see Him face to face To thank and praise Him

been a name so dear   To this heart of mine,   as the name di-vine, The
hon-or and such love   As the bless-ed name,   let us all ac-claim That
for His won-drous grace,   Which He gave to me,   when He made me free, The

pre-cious, pre-cious name of   Je-sus.
won-drous, glo-rious name of   Je-sus.   Je-sus is the sweet-est name I
bless-ed Son of God called   Je-sus.

know,   And He's just the same   as His love-ly name, And that's the rea-son

rall.

why I love Him so;   O Je-sus is the sweet-est name I know.

157   Come, Thou Almighty King

Anonymous   FELICE de GIARDINI

1. Come, Thou Al-might-y King, Help us Thy name to sing,
2. Come, Thou In-car-nate Word, Gird on Thy might-y sword,
3. Come, Ho-ly Com-fort-er, Thy sa-cred wit-ness bear
4. To the great One in Three E-ter-nal prais-es be

Help us to praise: Fa-ther, all-glo-ri-ous, O'er all vic-
Our prayer at-tend: Come, and Thy peo-ple bless, And give Thy
In this glad hour: Thou who al-might-y art, Now rule in
Hence ev-er-more. His sov-'reign maj-es-ty May we in

to-ri-ous, Come, and reign o-ver us, An-cient of days.
Word suc-cess: Spir-it of ho-li-ness, On us de-scend.
ev-'ry heart, And ne'er from us de-part, Spir-it of pow'r.
Glo-ry see, And to e-ter-ni-ty Love and a-dore.

158   O for a Thousand Tongues to Sing

CHARLES WESLEY   CARL G. GLASER
Arranged by Lowell Mason

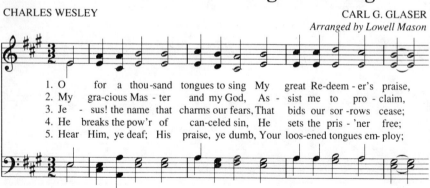

1. O for a thou-sand tongues to sing My great Re-deem-er's praise,
2. My gra-cious Mas-ter and my God, As-sist me to pro-claim,
3. Je-sus! the name that charms our fears, That bids our sor-rows cease;
4. He breaks the pow'r of can-celed sin, He sets the pris-'ner free;
5. Hear Him, ye deaf; His praise, ye dumb, Your loos-ened tongues em-ploy;

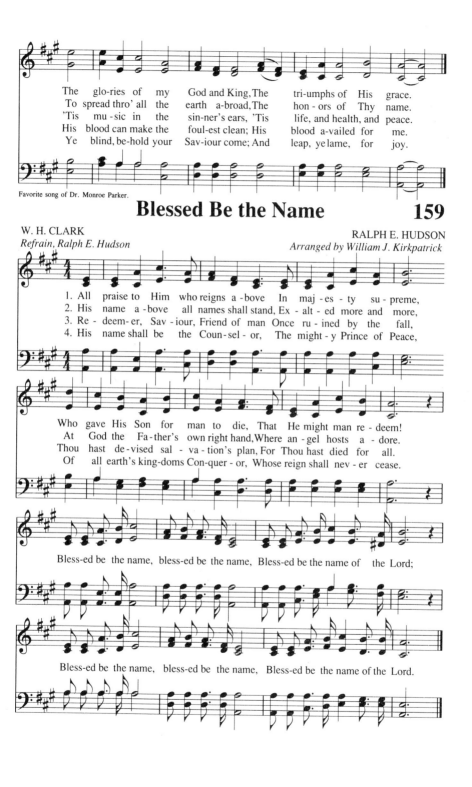

The glo-ries of my God and King, The tri-umphs of His grace.
To spread thro' all the earth a-broad, The hon-ors of Thy name.
'Tis mu-sic in the sin-ner's ears, 'Tis life, and health, and peace.
His blood can make the foul-est clean; His blood a-vailed for me.
Ye blind, be-hold your Sav-iour come; And leap, ye lame, for joy.

Favorite song of Dr. Monroe Parker.

Blessed Be the Name 159

W. H. CLARK
Refrain, Ralph E. Hudson

RALPH E. HUDSON
Arranged by William J. Kirkpatrick

1. All praise to Him who reigns a-bove In maj-es-ty su-preme,
2. His name a-bove all names shall stand, Ex-alt-ed more and more,
3. Re-deem-er, Sav-iour, Friend of man Once ru-ined by the fall,
4. His name shall be the Coun-sel-or, The might-y Prince of Peace,

Who gave His Son for man to die, That He might man re-deem!
At God the Fa-ther's own right hand, Where an-gel hosts a-dore.
Thou hast de-vised sal-va-tion's plan, For Thou hast died for all.
Of all earth's king-doms Con-quer-or, Whose reign shall nev-er cease.

Bless-ed be the name, bless-ed be the name, Bless-ed be the name of the Lord;

Bless-ed be the name, bless-ed be the name, Bless-ed be the name of the Lord.

160 Crown Him With Many Crowns

MATTHEW BRIDGES
and GODFREY THRING

GEORGE J. ELVEY

1. Crown Him with man - y crowns, The Lamb up - on His throne;
2. Crown Him the Lord of love! Be - hold His hands and side,
3. Crown Him the Lord of life! Who tri - umphed o'er the grave;
4. Crown Him the Lord of Heav'n! One with the Fa - ther known,

Hark! how the heav'n-ly an-them drowns All mu - sic but its own!
Rich wounds, yet vis - i - ble a - bove, In beau -ty glo - ri - fied:
Who rose vic - to - rious to the strife For those He came to save:
One with the Spir - it through Him giv'n From yon - der glo - rious throne!

A - wake, my soul, and sing Of Him who died for thee;
No an - gel in the sky Can ful - ly bear that sight,
His glo - ries now we sing, Who died and rose on high;
To Thee be end - less praise, For Thou for us hast died;

And hail Him as thy match-less King Thro' all e - ter - ni - ty.
But down - ward bends his won-d'ring eye At mys -ter - ies so bright.
Who died e - ter -nal life to bring, And lives that death may die.
Be Thou, O Lord, thro' end-less days A - dored and mag - ni - fied.

Our Great Saviour

161

J. WILBUR CHAPMAN

ROWLAND W. PRICHARD
Arranged by Robert Harkness

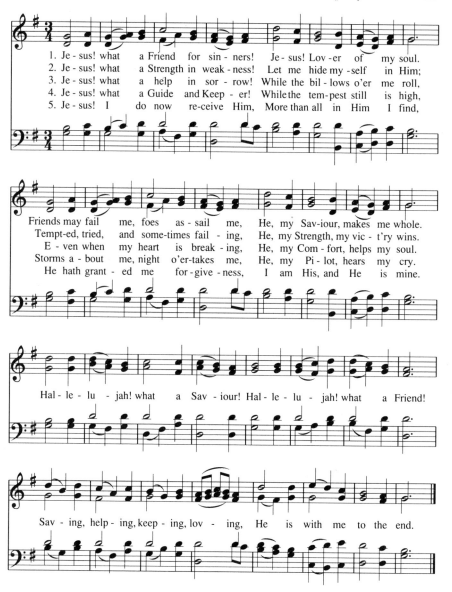

1. Je - sus! what a Friend for sin - ners! Je - sus! Lov - er of my soul.
2. Je - sus! what a Strength in weak - ness! Let me hide my - self in Him;
3. Je - sus! what a help in sor - row! While the bil - lows o'er me roll,
4. Je - sus! what a Guide and Keep - er! While the tem - pest still is high,
5. Je - sus! I do now re - ceive Him, More than all in Him I find,

Friends may fail me, foes as - sail me, He, my Sav - iour, makes me whole.
Tempt-ed, tried, and some-times fail - ing, He, my Strength, my vic - t'ry wins.
E - ven when my heart is break - ing, He, my Com - fort, helps my soul.
Storms a - bout me, night o'er-takes me, He, my Pi - lot, hears my cry.
He hath grant - ed me for - give - ness, I am His, and He is mine.

Hal - le - lu - jah! what a Sav - iour! Hal - le - lu - jah! what a Friend!

Sav - ing, help - ing, keep - ing, lov - ing, He is with me to the end.

Favorite song of Dr. J. R. Faulkner and Dr. Bob Gray.

162 To God Be the Glory

FANNY J. CROSBY

WILLIAM H. DOANE

1. To God be the glo - ry—great things He hath done, So loved He the
2. O per - fect re - demp-tion, the pur-chase of blood! To ev - 'ry be -
3. Great things He hath taught us, great things He hath done, And great our re -

world that He gave us His Son, Who yield - ed His life an a -
liev - er the prom - ise of God; The vil - est of - fend - er who
joic - ing through Je - sus the Son; But pur - er and high - er and

tone-ment for sin And o - pened the Life-gate that all may go in.
tru - ly be - lieves, That mo-ment from Je - sus a par - don re - ceives.
great - er will be Our won-der, our trans-port, when Je - sus we see.

Praise the Lord, praise the Lord, Let the earth hear His voice! Praise the Lord, praise the

Lord, Let the peo - ple re - joice! O come to the Fa - ther through

Je - sus the Son, And give Him the glo - ry—great things He hath done.

When Morning Gilds the Skies 163

From the German

Translated by Edward Caswall

JOSEPH BARNBY

1. When morn-ing gilds the skies, My heart a - wak-ing cries:
2. When sleep her balm de - nies, My si - lent spir - it sighs:
3. Does sad - ness fill my mind, A sol - ace here I find:
4. In Heav'n's e - ter - nal bliss, The love-liest strain is this:
5. Be this, while life is mine, My can - ti - cle di - vine,

May Je - sus Christ be praised; A - like at work and prayer
May Je - sus Christ be praised; When e - vil thoughts mo - lest,
May Je - sus Christ be praised; Or fades my earth - ly bliss,
May Je - sus Christ be praised; The pow'rs of dark - ness fear,
May Je - sus Christ be praised; Be this th'e - ter - nal song,

To Je - sus I re - pair: May Je - sus Christ be praised.
With this I shield my breast: May Je - sus Christ be praised.
My com-fort still is this: May Je - sus Christ be praised.
When this sweet chant they hear: May Je - sus Christ be praised.
Through all the a - ges on: May Je - sus Christ be praised.

164 Praise Him! Praise Him!

FANNY J. CROSBY

CHESTER G. ALLEN

1. Praise Him! praise Him! Je-sus, our bless-ed Re-deem-er! Sing, O Earth, His won-der-ful love pro-claim! Hail Him! hail Him! high-est arch-an-gels in Glo-ry; Strength and hon-or give to His ho-ly name! Like a shep-herd, Je-sus will guard His chil-dren, In His arms He car-ries them all day long:

2. Praise Him! praise Him! Je-sus, our bless-ed Re-deem-er! For our sins He suf-fered, and bled, and died; He our Rock, our hope of e-ter-nal sal-va-tion, Hail Him! hail Him! Je-sus the Cru-ci-fied. Sound His prais-es! Je-sus who bore our sor-rows, Love un-bound-ed, won-der-ful, deep and strong:

3. Praise Him! praise Him! Je-sus, our bless-ed Re-deem-er! Heav'n-ly por-tals loud with ho-san-nas ring! Je-sus, Sav-iour, reign-eth for-ev-er and ev-er; Crown Him! crown Him! Proph-et, and Priest, and King! Christ is com-ing! o-ver the world vic-to-rious, Pow'r and glo-ry un-to the Lord be-long:

Praise Him! praise Him! tell of His ex - cel - lent great - ness;

Praise Him! praise Him! ev - er in joy - ful song!

O Worship the King 165

ROBERT GRANT

Adapted from J. Michael Haydn

1. O wor-ship the King, all - glo-rious a - bove, And grate-ful-ly
2. O tell of His might, and sing of His grace, Whose robe is the
3. Thy boun - ti - ful care what tongue can re - cite? It breathes in the
4. Frail chil-dren of dust, and fee - ble as frail, In Thee do we

sing His won - der - ful love; Our Shield and De - fend-er, the An-cient of
light, whose can - o - py space; His char-iots of wrath the deep thun-der-clouds
air, it shines in the light; It streams from the hills, it de-scends to the
trust, nor find Thee to fail; Thy mer-cies how ten-der! how firm to the

Days, Pa - vil-ioned in splen-dor, and gird - ed with praise.
form, And dark is His path on the wings of the storm.
plain, And sweet-ly dis - tills in the dew and the rain.
end! Our Mak-er, De - fend - er, Re - deem - er and Friend. A - men.

166   I Will Praise Him

Mrs. M. J. HARRIS   Mrs. M. J. HARRIS

1. When I saw the cleans-ing foun-tain O - pen wide for all my
2. Though the way seems straight and nar-row, All I claimed was swept a-
3. Then God's fire up - on the al - tar Of my heart was set a -
4. Bless - ed be the name of Je - sus! I'm so glad He took me
5. Glo - ry, glo - ry to the Fa - ther! Glo - ry, glo - ry to the

sin, I o-beyed the Spir-it's woo-ing, When He said, "Wilt thou be
way; My am-bi-tions, plans, and wish-es, At my feet in ash - es
flame; I shall nev-er cease to praise Him Glo-ry, glo-ry to His
in; He's for-giv-en my trans-gres-sions, He has cleansed my heart from
Son! Glo - ry, glo - ry to the Spir-it! Glo-ry to the Three in

clean?"
lay.   I will praise Him!   I will praise Him!   Praise the Lamb for sin-ners
name!
sin.
One!

slain;   Give Him glo-ry, all ye peo - ple,
for sin - ners slain;

For His blood can wash a - way each stain.

All Hail the Power of Jesus' Name 167

EDWARD PERRONET

OLIVER HOLDEN

1. All hail the pow'r of Je - sus' name! Let an - gels pros-trate fall:
2. Ye cho - sen seed of Is - rael's race, Ye ran-somed from the fall,
3. Let ev - 'ry kin - dred, ev - 'ry tribe, On this ter - res-trial ball,
4. O that with yon - der sa - cred throng We at His feet may fall!

Bring forth the roy - al di - a - dem, And crown Him Lord of all,
Hail Him who saves you by His grace, And crown Him Lord of all,
To Him all maj - es - ty as - cribe, And crown Him Lord of all,
We'll join the ev - er - last - ing song, And crown Him Lord of all,

Bring forth the roy - al di - a - dem, And crown Him Lord of all!
Hail Him who saves you by His grace, And crown Him Lord of all!
To Him all maj - es - ty as - cribe, And crown Him Lord of all!
We'll join the ev - er - last - ing song, And crown Him Lord of all!

168 All Hail the Power of Jesus' Name

(Diadem)

EDWARD PERRONET
Altered by John Rippon

JAMES ELLOR

1. All hail the pow'r of Je - sus' name! Let an - gels pros-trate
2. Ye cho - sen seed of Is - rael's race, Ye ran-somed from the
3. Let ev - 'ry kin - dred, ev - 'ry tribe, On this ter - res-trial
4. O that with yon - der sa - cred throng We at His feet may

fall, Let an - gels pros - trate fall; Bring forth the
fall, Ye ran - somed from the fall, Hail Him who
ball, On this ter - res - trial ball, To Him all
fall, We at His feet may fall! We'll join the

And crown

roy - al di - a - dem,
saves you by His grace,
maj - es - ty as - cribe,
ev - er - last - ing song,

And crown Him,

And crown

And crown Him,
Him,
Crown Him,

crown Him, crown Him, crown Him, And crown Him Lord of
Him, Crown Him,

crown Him, crown Him, Crown

crown Him,

all, crown Him; And crown Him Lord of all!

Crown _____ Him;

_____ Him; And crown Him Lord of all!

Come, Thou Fount 169

ROBERT ROBINSON   JOHN WYETH

1. Come, Thou Fount of ev-'ry bless-ing, Tune my heart to sing Thy grace;
2. Here I raise mine Eb-en-e-zer; Hith-er by Thy help I'm come;
3. O to grace how great a debt-or Dai-ly I'm con-strained to be!

Streams of mer-cy, nev-er ceas-ing, Call for songs of loud-est praise.
And I know, by Thy good pleas-ure, Safe-ly I'll ar-rive at Home.
Let Thy good-ness, like a fet-ter, Bind my wan-d'ring heart to Thee:

Teach me some mel-o-dious son-net, Sung by flam-ing tongues a-bove;
Je-sus sought me when a stran-ger, Wan-d'ring from the fold of God;
Prone to wan-der, Lord, I feel it, Prone to leave the God I love;

Praise the mount—I'm fixed up-on it—Mount of Thy re-deem-ing love.
He, to res-cue me from dan-ger, In-ter-posed His pre-cious blood.
Here's my heart, O take and seal it; Seal it for Thy courts a-bove.

170 Hallelujah, What a Saviour!

PHILIP P. BLISS   PHILIP P. BLISS

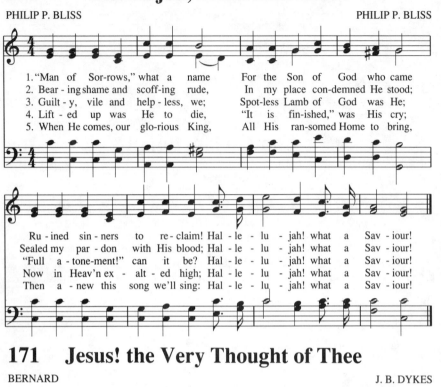

1. "Man of Sor-rows," what a name For the Son of God who came
2. Bear-ing shame and scoff-ing rude, In my place con-demned He stood;
3. Guilt-y, vile and help-less, we; Spot-less Lamb of God was He;
4. Lift-ed up was He to die, "It is fin-ished," was His cry;
5. When He comes, our glo-rious King, All His ran-somed Home to bring,

Ru-ined sin-ners to re-claim! Hal-le-lu-jah! what a Sav-iour!
Sealed my par-don with His blood; Hal-le-lu-jah! what a Sav-iour!
"Full a-tone-ment!" can it be? Hal-le-lu-jah! what a Sav-iour!
Now in Heav'n ex-alt-ed high; Hal-le-lu-jah! what a Sav-iour!
Then a-new this song we'll sing: Hal-le-lu-jah! what a Sav-iour!

171 Jesus! the Very Thought of Thee

BERNARD   J. B. DYKES

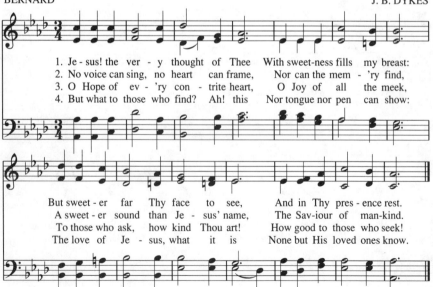

1. Je-sus! the ver-y thought of Thee With sweet-ness fills my breast:
2. No voice can sing, no heart can frame, Nor can the mem-'ry find,
3. O Hope of ev-'ry con-trite heart, O Joy of all the meek,
4. But what to those who find? Ah! this Nor tongue nor pen can show:

But sweet-er far Thy face to see, And in Thy pres-ence rest.
A sweet-er sound than Je-sus' name, The Sav-iour of man-kind.
To those who ask, how kind Thou art! How good to those who seek!
The love of Je-sus, what it is None but His loved ones know.

Love Divine, All Loves Excelling 172

CHARLES WESLEY

JOHN ZUNDEL

1. Love di- vine, all loves ex - cel - ling, Joy of Heav'n, to earth come down;
2. Breathe, O breathe Thy lov -ing Spir - it In - to ev - 'ry trou - bled breast!
3. Come, Al - might-y to de - liv - er, Let us all Thy life re - ceive;
4. Fin - ish then Thy new cre - a -tion; Pure and spot-less let us be;

Fix in us Thy hum - ble dwell-ing; All Thy faith - ful mer-cies crown.
Let us all in Thee in - her - it, Let us find that sec - ond rest.
Sud-den - ly re - turn, and nev - er, Nev - er-more Thy tem - ples leave:
Let us see Thy great sal - va - tion Per - fect - ly re - stored in Thee:

Je - sus, Thou art all com - pas-sion, Pure un-bound-ed love Thou art;
Take a -way our bent to sin-ning, Al - pha and O - meg - a be;
Thee we would be al - ways bless-ing, Serve Thee as Thy hosts a - bove,
Changed from glo - ry in - to glo - ry, Till in Heav'n we take our place,

Vis - it us with Thy sal - va - tion; En - ter ev - 'ry trem-bling heart.
End of faith, as its be - gin-ning, Set our hearts at lib - er - ty.
Pray, and praise Thee with - out ceas-ing, Glo - ry in Thy per - fect love.
Till we cast our crowns be - fore Thee, Lost in won - der, love, and praise.

173 Love Lifted Me

JAMES ROWE

HOWARD E. SMITH

1. I was sink-ing deep in sin, Far from the peace-ful shore,
2. All my heart to Him I give, Ev-er to Him I'll cling,
3. Souls in dan-ger, look a-bove, Je-sus com-plete-ly saves;

Ver-y deep-ly stained with-in, Sink-ing to rise no more;
In His bless-ed pres-ence live, Ev-er His prais-es sing.
He will lift you by His love Out of the an-gry waves.

But the Mas-ter of the sea Heard my des-pair-ing cry,
Love so might-y and so true Mer-its my soul's best songs;
He's the Mas-ter of the sea, Bil-lows His will o-bey;

From the wa-ters lift-ed me, Now safe am I.
Faith-ful, lov-ing ser-vice, too, To Him be-longs.
He your Sav-iour wants to be— Be saved to-day.

Love lift-ed me! Love lift-ed me!
e-ven me! e-ven me!

When noth-ing else could help, Love lift-ed me. Love lift-ed me.

My Jesus, I Love Thee 174

WILLIAM R. FEATHERSTONE

ADONIRAM J. GORDON

1. My Je - sus, I love Thee, I know Thou art mine, For Thee all the
2. I love Thee, be - cause Thou hast first lov - ed me, And pur-chased my
3. I'll love Thee in life, I will love Thee in death, And praise Thee as
4. In man-sions of Glo - ry and end - less de - light, I'll ev - er a -

fol - lies of sin I re - sign; My gra - cious Re - deem - er, my
par - don on Cal - va - ry's tree; I love Thee for wear - ing the
long as Thou lend - est me breath; And say when the death - dew lies
dore Thee in Heav - en so bright; I'll sing with the glit - ter - ing

Sav - iour art Thou; If ev - er I loved Thee, my Je - sus, 'tis now.
thorns on Thy brow: If ev - er I loved Thee, my Je - sus, 'tis now.
cold on my brow, If ev - er I loved Thee, my Je - sus, 'tis now.
crown on my brow, If ev - er I loved Thee, my Je - sus, 'tis now.

Favorite song of Dr. Alfred B. Smith.

175 It's Just Like His Great Love

EDNA H. WORRELL

CLARENCE B. STROUSE

1. A Friend I have, called Je - sus, Whose love is strong and true, And
2. Some - times the clouds of trou-ble Be - dim the sky a - bove, I
3. When sor-row's clouds o'er-take me, And break up-on my head, When
4. O I could sing for - ev - er Of Je - sus' love di - vine, Of

nev - er fails how - e'er 'tis tried, No mat - ter what I do; I've
can - not see my Sav-iour's face, I doubt His won-drous love; But
life seems worse than use-less, And I were bet-ter dead; I
all His care and ten - der-ness For this poor life of mine; His

sinned a-gainst this love of His, But when I knelt to pray, Con -
He, from Heav-en's mer - cy seat, Be - hold - ing my des - pair, In
take my grief to Je - sus then, Nor do I go in vain, For
love is in and o - ver all, And wind and waves o - bey When

fess - ing all my guilt to Him, The sin-clouds rolled a - way.
pit - y bursts the clouds be-tween, And shows me He is there. It's
heav'n - ly hope He gives that cheers Like sun-shine af - ter rain.
Je - sus whis - pers "Peace, be still!" And rolls the clouds a - way.

just like Je - sus to roll the clouds a-way, It's just like

Je - sus to keep me day by day, It's just like Je - sus all a - long the way, It's just like His great love.

Jesus Loves the Little Children 176

Anonymous

GEORGE F. ROOT

Je - sus loves the lit - tle chil - dren, All the chil-dren of the world; Red and yel - low, black and white, They are pre - cious in His sight; Je - sus loves the lit - tle chil - dren of the world.

177 When Love Shines In

MRS. FRANK A. BRECK

WILLIAM J. KIRKPATRICK

1. Je - sus comes with pow'r to glad-den, When love shines in,
2. How the world will glow with beau - ty, When love shines in,
3. Dark - est sor - row will grow bright-er, When love shines in,
4. We may have un - fad - ing splen-dor, When love shines in,

Ev - 'ry life that woe can sad-den, When love shines in.
And the heart re - joice in du - ty, When love shines in.
And the heav - iest bur - den light-er, When love shines in.
And a friend-ship true and ten - der, When love shines in.

Love will teach us how to pray, Love will drive the gloom a - way,
Tri - als may be sanc - ti - fied, And the soul in peace a - bide,
'Tis the glo - ry that will throw Light to show us where to go;
When earth vic - t'ries shall be won, And our life in Heav'n be - gun,

Turn our dark - ness in - to day, When love shines in.
Life will all be glo - ri - fied, When love shines in.
O, the heart shall bless - ing know, When love shines in.
There will be no need of sun, When love shines in.

When love shines in, When love shines in,

When love shines in,

When love shines in, When love shines in, When love shines in,

How the heart is tuned to sing-ing When love shines in;

When love shines in;

When love shines in, When love shines in,

When love shines in,

When love shines in, When love shines in, When love shines in,

Joy and peace to oth - ers bring-ing, When love shines in.

When love, when love shines in.

178 Jesus Loves Even Me

PHILIP P. BLISS

PHILIP P. BLISS

1. I am so glad that our Fa-ther in Heav'n Tells of His love in the Book He has giv'n; Won-der-ful things in the Bi-ble I see— This is the dear-est, that Je-sus loves me.

2. Though I for-get Him and wan-der a-way, Still He doth love me wher-ev-er I stray; Back to His dear lov-ing arms would I flee When I re-mem-ber that Je-sus loves me.

3. O if there's on-ly one song I can sing When in His beau-ty I see the great King, This shall my song in e-ter-ni-ty be: "O what a won-der that Je-sus loves me!"

I am so glad that Je-sus loves me, Je-sus loves me, Je-sus loves me, I am so glad that Je-sus loves me, Je-sus loves e-ven me.

Such Love

179

C. BISHOP

ROBERT HARKNESS

1. That God should love a sinner such as I, Should yearn to change my
2. That Christ should join so free-ly in the scheme, Al-though it meant His
3. That for a wil - ful out-cast such as I, The Fa - ther planned, the
4. And now He takes me to His heart—a son, He asks me not to

sor-row in - to bliss, Nor rest till He had planned to bring me nigh,
death on Cal-va-ry, Did ev - er hu - man tongue find no-bler theme
Sav-iour bled and died; Re - demp-tion for a worth-less slave to buy,
fill a ser-vant's place; The "Far - off coun - try" wan-d'rings all are done,

How won - der - ful is love like this!
Than love di - vine that ran - somed me?
Who long had law and grace de - fied.
Wide o - pen are His arms of grace.

Such love, such
Such love,

won-drous love, Such love, such won-drous love, That God should
Such love,

love a sin-ner such as I, How won - der-ful is love like this!

Isn't the Love of Jesus Something Wonderful

180

JOHN W. PETERSON   JOHN W. PETERSON

1. There will nev-er be a sweet-er sto-ry, Sto-ry of the
2. Bound-less as the u-ni-verse a-round me, Reach-ing to the
3. Love be-yond our hu-man com-pre-hend-ing, Love of God in

Sav-iour's love di-vine— Love that brought Him from the realms of
far-thest soul a-way— Sav-ing, keep-ing love it was that
Christ—how can it be! This will be my theme and nev-er

Glo-ry, Just to save a sin-ful soul like mine.
found me, That is why my heart can tru-ly say:
end-ing, Great re-deem-ing love of Cal-va-ry.

Is-n't the love of Je-sus some-thing won-der-ful, won-der-ful,
it is
won-der-ful, O is-n't the love of Je-sus some-thing won-der-

ful,   Won - der - ful   it   is   to   me.   to   me.

I Love Him   181

From the *English Hymn Book*

S. C. FOSTER

1. Gone from my heart the world and all its charm; Gone are my sins and
2. Once   I was lost   up - on the plains of sin; Once was a slave to
3. Once   I was bound, but now I am set free; Once   I   was blind, but

all that would a - larm;   Gone ev - er-more, and by His grace I know   The
doubts and fears with-in;   Once was   a-fraid   to   trust a lov-ing God,   But
now the light I see;   Once   I   was dead, but now in Christ I live,   To

pre-cious blood of Je-sus cleans-es white as snow.
now my guilt is washed a-way in Je - sus' blood.   I love Him,   I love Him, Be-
tell the world the peace that He a- lone can give.

cause He first loved me,   And pur-chased my sal - va - tion on Cal-v'ry's tree.

182 Wonderful Story of Love

J. M. DRIVER

J. M. DRIVER

1. Won - der - ful sto - ry of love; Tell it to me a - gain;
2. Won - der - ful sto - ry of love; Though you are far a - way;
3. Won - der - ful sto - ry of love; Je - sus pro - vides a rest;

Won - der - ful sto - ry of love; Wake the im - mor - tal strain!
Won - der - ful sto - ry of love; Still He doth call to - day;
Won - der - ful sto - ry of love; For all the pure and blest,

An - gels with rap - ture an - nounce it, Shep - herds with won - der re - ceive it;
Call - ing from Cal - va - ry's moun - tain, Down from the crys - tal bright foun - tain,
Rest in those man - sions a - bove us, With those who've gone on be - fore us,

Sin - ner, O won't you be - lieve it?
E'en from the dawn of cre - a - tion, Won - der - ful sto - ry of love.
Sing - ing the rap - tur - ous cho - rus,

Won - der - ful! Won - der - ful!
Won - der - ful sto - ry of love; Won - der - ful sto - ry of love;

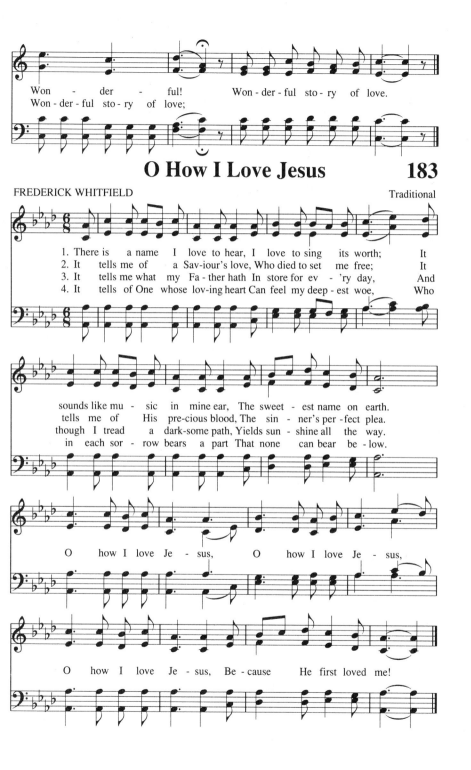

Won - der - ful! Won - der - ful sto - ry of love.
Won - der - ful sto - ry of love;

O How I Love Jesus

183

FREDERICK WHITFIELD

Traditional

1. There is a name I love to hear, I love to sing its worth; It
2. It tells me of a Sav-iour's love, Who died to set me free; It
3. It tells me what my Fa - ther hath In store for ev - 'ry day, And
4. It tells of One whose lov-ing heart Can feel my deep - est woe, Who

sounds like mu - sic in mine ear, The sweet - est name on earth.
tells me of His pre-cious blood, The sin - ner's per -fect plea.
though I tread a dark-some path, Yields sun - shine all the way.
in each sor - row bears a part That none can bear be - low.

O how I love Je - sus, O how I love Je - sus,

O how I love Je - sus, Be - cause He first loved me!

184   I Love Thee, My Jesus

JOHN R. RICE

JOHN R. RICE

1. What words can I find to tell Jesus I love Him, Be - cause He
2. O come, let us mag - ni - fy Jesus to - geth - er, For praise be -
3. May nev - er my prais - es be slow or be si - lent, Nor e'er my
4. O how can I love Thee e - nough, dear Re - deem - er, How e'er re -

first loved me;   Be - cause of my ran - som He paid with such
com - eth Thee;   And bless - ings a - bout me I owe to my
love grow dumb.   This sin - ner is saved and my sins all for -
pay my Friend?   I'll spread the glad sound of my praise and my

suf - f'ring, Up - on the curs - ed tree.
Sav - iour, Who all things bought for me.
giv - en, The Sav - iour's work is done.   In the morn - ing, at the
heart love On ev - 'ry joy - ful wind.

noon-time, And when come e - v'ning shad - ows, I love Thee, my Je - sus, I

love Thee, my King. In re - joic - ing and in sor - row, To - day and to -

mor - row I love Thee, my Sav - iour and Lord.

My Saviour's Love   185

CHARLES H. GABRIEL   CHARLES H. GABRIEL

1. I   stand a-mazed in the   pres - ence of   Je - sus the Naz - a - rene,   And
2. For me it was in the gar - den He prayed: "Not My will, but Thine"; He
3. He   took my sins and my sor - rows, He made them His ver - y own;   He
4. When with the ran-somed in Glo - ry His face I at last shall see, 'Twill

won - der how He could love me, A   sin - ner, con-demned, un - clean.
had   no tears for His own griefs, But sweat-drops of blood for   mine.
bore the bur - den to Cal - v'ry, And suf-fered, and died a - lone.
be   my joy through the a - ges To sing of His love for   me.

How   mar-vel-ous! How   won - der-ful! And my song shall ev - er be;
O   how mar-vel-ous!   O   how won - der-ful!

How   mar-vel-ous! How   won-der-ful! Is my   Sav-iour's love for me!
O how mar-vel-ous!   O   how won-der-ful!

186 Jesus Loves Me

JOHN R. RICE

JOHN R. RICE

1. Je - sus is such a Sav - iour, Je - sus is such a Friend.
2. Now in His love I glo - ry, Rest and re - joice in Him.
3. Why should you slight the Sav - iour? Why from Him turn a - way?
4. What can I do for Je - sus? How may I Him re - pay?

Nev - er for-sakes nor leaves me, Nor fails my needs to send.
Blood-bought and dear to Je - sus, My joy is full with - in.
Where will you find for - give - ness, Lov - ing care, night and day?
O to tell all the sto - ry Of His sal - va - tion's way.

Je - sus who died to save me, Je - sus who sought for me,
Noth-ing then, I'm per - suad - ed, Can take me from His hand,
No - bod - y else could save you, No - bod - y else could pay
Nev - er a theme for sing - ing, Nev - er a truth for praise

Now with His love sur-rounds me, O what a Friend is He!
Nor height nor depth, nor pow - ers, Sa - tan, nor self, nor man.
Sin's debt for poor, lost sin - ners, He would be yours to - day.
As Je - sus' love for sin - ners, I'll sing it all my days.

Je - sus loves me, Yes, Je - sus loves me; For me He died, and the crim - son

tide proves that He loves me, that Je - sus loves me; So

sing it a - gain, that Je - sus loves me.

Jesus Loves Me

187

ANNA B. WARNER

WILLIAM B. BRADBURY

1. Je - sus loves me! this I know, For the Bi - ble tells me so;
2. Je - sus loves me! He who died, Heav-en's gate to o - pen wide;
3. Je - sus loves me! He will stay Close be - side me all the way;

Lit - tle ones to Him be - long, They are weak but He is strong.
He will wash a - way my sin, Let His lit - tle child come in.
Thou hast bled and died for me, I will hence-forth live for Thee.

Yes, Je - sus loves me! Yes, Je - sus loves me!

Yes, Je - sus loves me! The Bi - ble tells me so.

188 The Love of God

FREDERICK M. LEHMAN

FREDERICK M. LEHMAN
Arranged by Claudia L. Mays

1. The love of God is great-er far Than tongue or pen can ev-er tell;
2. When hoar-y time shall pass a-way, And earth-ly thrones and king-doms fall;
3. Could we with ink the o-cean fill, And were the skies of parch-ment made,

It goes be-yond the high-est star, And reach-es to the low-est Hell;
When men who here re-fuse to pray, On rocks and hills and moun-tains call;
Were ev-'ry stalk on earth a quill, And ev-'ry man a scribe by trade;

The guilt-y pair, bowed down with care, God gave His Son to win;
God's love, so sure, shall still en-dure, All meas-ure-less and strong;
To write the love of God a-bove Would drain the o-cean dry;

His err-ing child He rec-on-ciled, And par-doned from his sin.
Re-deem-ing grace to Ad-am's race— The saints' and an-gels' song.
Nor could the scroll con-tain the whole, Tho' stretched from sky to sky.

O love of God, how rich and pure! How meas-ure-less and strong!

It shall for-ev-er-more en-dure, The saints' and an-gels' song.

I Never Will Cease to Love Him 189

CHARLES H. GABRIEL

CHARLES H. GABRIEL

1. For all the Lord has done for me, I nev-er will cease to love Him;
2. He gives me strength for ev-'ry day, I nev-er will cease to love Him;
3. Though all the world His love ne-glect, I nev-er will cease to love Him;
4. While on my jour-ney here be-low, I nev-er will cease to love Him;

And for His grace so rich and free, I nev-er will cease to love Him.
He leads and guides me all the way, I nev-er will cease to love Him.
I could not such a Friend re-ject, I nev-er will cease to love Him.
And when to that bright world I go, I nev-er will cease to love Him.

I nev-er will cease to love Him; my Sav-iour, my Sav-iour;
I nev-er will cease to love Him, He's my Sav-iour, He's my Sav-iour;

I nev-er will cease to love Him, He's done so much for me.
For

190 Wonderful, Wonderful Jesus

ANNA B. RUSSELL

ERNEST O. SELLERS

1. There is nev - er a day so drear - y, There is nev - er a
2. There is nev - er a cross so heav - y, There is nev - er a
3. There is nev - er a care or bur - den, There is nev - er a
4. There is nev - er a guilt - y sin - ner, There is nev - er a

night so long, (so long,) But the soul that is trust - ing Je - sus Will
weight of woe, (of woe,) But that Je - sus will help to car - ry Be-
grief or loss, (or loss,) But that Je - sus in love will light - en When
wan - d'ring one, (not one,) But that God can in mer - cy par - don Through

some - where find a song. (a song.)
cause He lov - eth so. (loves so.) Won-der-ful, won-der-ful Je - sus,
car - ried to the cross. (the cross.)
Je - sus Christ, His Son. (His Son.)

In the heart He im-plant-eth a song: A song of de-liv-'rance, of
He plant-eth a song:

cour - age, of strength, In the heart He im-plant-eth a song. (a song.)

In My Heart There Rings a Melody 191

ELTON M. ROTH

ELTON M. ROTH

1. I have a song that Je - sus gave me, It was sent from
2. I love the Christ who died on Cal - v'ry, For He washed my
3. 'Twill be my end - less theme in Glo - ry, With the an - gels

Heav'n a - bove; There nev - er was a sweet - er mel - o - dy, 'Tis a
sins a - way; He put with - in my heart a mel - o - dy, And I
I will sing; 'Twill be a song with glo - rious har - mo - ny, When the

mel - o - dy of love.
know it's there to stay. In my heart there rings a mel - o - dy, There
courts of Heav - en ring.

rings a mel - o - dy with Heav-en's har - mo - ny. In my heart there

rings a mel - o - dy; There rings a mel - o - dy of love.

192 Ring the Bells of Heaven

WILLIAM O. CUSHING

GEORGE F. ROOT

1. Ring the bells of Heav-en! there is joy to-day, For a soul re-turning from the wild;
2. Ring the bells of Heav-en! there is joy to-day, For the wan-d'rer now is rec-on-ciled;
3. Ring the bells of Heav-en! spread the feast to-day, An-gels swell the glad tri-um-phant strain!

See! the Fa-ther meets him out up-on the way, Wel-com-ing His wea-ry, wan-d'ring child.
Yes, a soul is res-cued from his sin-ful way, And is born a-new a ran-somed child.
Tell the joy-ful tid-ings, bear it far a-way! For a pre-cious soul is born a-gain.

Glo-ry! glo-ry! how the an-gels sing; Glo-ry! glo-ry! how the loud harps ring! 'Tis the ran-somed ar-my, like a might-y sea, Peal-ing forth the an-them of the free.

You May Have the Joy-bells   193

J. EDWARD RUARK

WILLIAM J. KIRKPATRICK

1. You may have the joy - bells ring - ing in your heart, And a peace that
2. Love of Je - sus in its full - ness you may know, And this love to
3. You will meet with tri - als as you jour - ney home; Grace suf - fi - cient
4. Let your life speak well of Je - sus ev - 'ry day; Own His right to

from you nev - er will de - part; Walk the straight and nar - row way,
those a-round you sweet - ly show; Words of kind-ness al - ways say,
He will give to o - ver - come; Though un-seen by mor - tal eye,
ev - 'ry ser - vice you can pay; Sin - ners you can help to win

Live for Je - sus ev - 'ry day, He will keep the joy-bells ring-ing in your heart.
Deeds of mer - cy do each day, Then He'll keep the joy-bells ring-ing in your heart.
He is with you ev - er nigh, And He'll keep the joy-bells ring-ing in your heart.
If your life is pure and clean, And you keep the joy-bells ring-ing in your heart.

Joy - bells ring-ing in your heart, Joy - bells
Ring-ing in your heart, You may have the joy - bells

ring-ing in your heart; Take the Sav-iour here be-low With you ev-'ry where you go;

194 Since Jesus Came Into My Heart

RUFUS H. McDANIEL

CHARLES H. GABRIEL

1. What a won-der-ful change in my life has been wrought Since Je-sus came
2. I have ceased from my wan-d'ring and go-ing a-stray, Since Je-sus came
3. I'm pos-sessed of a hope that is stead-fast and sure, Since Je-sus came
4. There's a light in the val-ley of death now for me, Since Je-sus came
5. I shall go there to dwell in that Cit-y, I know, Since Je-sus came

in-to my heart! I have light in my soul for which long I had sought,
in-to my heart! And my sins, which were man-y, are all washed a-way,
in-to my heart! And no dark clouds of doubt now my path-way ob-scure,
in-to my heart! And the gates of the Cit-y be-yond I can see,
in-to my heart! And I'm hap-py, so hap-py, as on-ward I go,

Since Jesus came in-to my heart! Since Jesus came in-to my
Since Jesus came in, came

heart, Since Jesus came in-to my heart, Floods of joy o'er my
in-to my heart, Since Jesus came in, came in-to my heart,

soul like the sea bil-lows roll, Since Jesus came in-to my heart.

I Will Sing of the Mercies 195

Psalm 89:1

Anonymous
Arranged by Frank P. Nickel

196   I Will Sing the Wondrous Story

FRANCIS H. ROWLEY

PETER P. BILHORN

1. I will sing the won-drous sto - ry Of the Christ who died for me,
2. I was lost, but Je - sus found me, Found the sheep that went a - stray,
3. I was bruised, but Je - sus healed me, Faint was I from many a fall;
4. Days of dark - ness still come o'er me, Sor-row's paths I of - ten tread,
5. He will keep me till the riv - er Rolls its wa - ters at my feet;

How He left His Home in Glo - ry For the cross of Cal - va - ry.
Threw His lov - ing arms a - round me, Drew me back in - to His way.
Sight was gone, and fears pos-sessed me, But He freed me from them all.
But the Sav - iour still is with me; By His hand I'm safe-ly led.
Then He'll bear me safe-ly o - ver, Where the loved ones I shall meet.

Yes, I'll sing the won-drous sto - ry Of the Christ
Yes, I'll sing the won-drous sto-ry Of the

who died for me, Sing it with the saints in
Christ who died for me, Sing it with

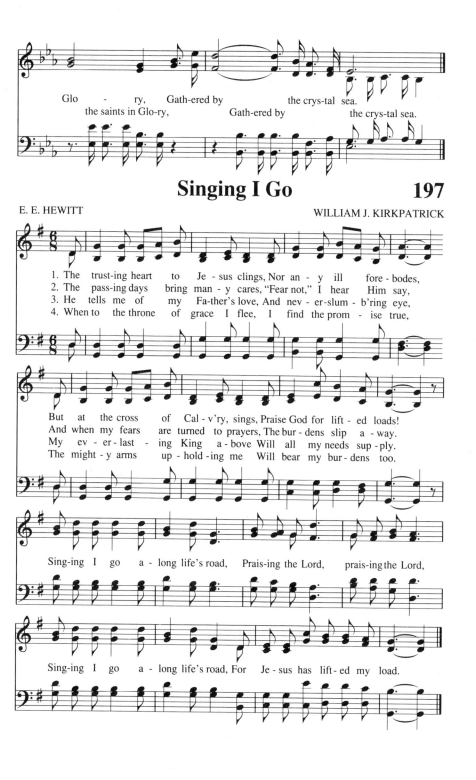

Glo - ry, Gath-ered by the crys-tal sea.
the saints in Glo-ry, Gath-ered by the crys-tal sea.

Singing I Go   197

E. E. HEWITT

WILLIAM J. KIRKPATRICK

1. The trust-ing heart to Je - sus clings, Nor an - y ill fore - bodes,
2. The pass-ing days bring man - y cares, "Fear not," I hear Him say,
3. He tells me of my Fa-ther's love, And nev - er-slum - b'ring eye,
4. When to the throne of grace I flee, I find the prom - ise true,

But at the cross of Cal - v'ry, sings, Praise God for lift - ed loads!
And when my fears are turned to prayers, The bur - dens slip a - way.
My ev - er-last - ing King a - bove Will all my needs sup - ply.
The might - y arms up - hold -ing me Will bear my bur - dens too.

Sing-ing I go a - long life's road, Prais-ing the Lord, prais-ing the Lord,

Sing-ing I go a - long life's road, For Je - sus has lift-ed my load.

198   **Joy Unspeakable**

B. E. WARREN   B. E. WARREN

1. I have found His grace is all com-plete, He sup-pli-eth ev-'ry need;
2. I have found the pleas-ure I once craved, It is joy and peace with-in;
3. I have found that hope so bright and clear, Liv-ing in the realm of grace;
4. I have found the joy no tongue can tell, How its waves of glo-ry roll!

While I sit and learn at Je-sus' feet, I am free, yes, free in-deed.
What a won-drous bless-ing! I am saved From the aw-ful gulf of sin.
O the Sav-iour's pres-ence is so near, I can see His smil-ing face.
It is like a great o'er-flow-ing well, Spring-ing up with-in my soul.

It is joy un-speak-a-ble and full of glo-ry, Full of glo-ry, full of glo-ry; It is joy un-speak-a-ble and full of glo-ry, O the half has nev-er yet been told.

Let the Joy Overflow

199

E. E. HEWITT

S. B. JACKSON

1. There's a clear foun-tain flow-ing From the bright throne a-bove, And its wa-ters are
2. Man - y hearts need the sto - ry—Are a-thirst for His grace; Go to them with His
3. Be our lives free - ly yield - ed to the Sav-iour's com-mand; By His care ev - er

glow-ing With the sun-shine of love; Take the blest con - so - la - tion, Which the
glo - ry Shin-ing out from your face; Tell of Je - sus your Sav-iour! If His
shield-ed And up-held by His hand; In the path-ways of sad-ness, Sweet-est

Lord will be-stow, Take the cup of sal - va-tion— Let the joy o - ver-flow.
mer-cies you know, Show the light of His fav - or— Let the joy o - ver-flow.
lil - ies may grow; Let us sow seeds of glad-ness—Let the joy o - ver-flow.

O the joy! With this won-drous sal-va-tion Be our hearts all a - glow;
O the joy!

O the joy! Let the bless-ing run o - ver, And joy o - ver - flow.
O the joy!

200 He's a Wonderful Saviour to Me

VIRGIL P. BROCK

BLANCHE KERR BROCK

1. I was lost in sin, but Je-sus res-cued me, He's a won-der-ful
2. He's a Friend so true, so pa-tient and so kind, He's a won-der-ful
3. He is al-ways near to com-fort and to cheer, He's a won-der-ful
4. Dear-er grows the love of Je-sus ev-'ry day, He's a won-der-ful

Sav-iour to me; (So won-der-ful!) I was bound by fear, but Je-sus set me free,
Sav-iour to me; (So won-der-ful!) Ev-'ry-thing I need in Him I al-ways find, He's a
Sav-iour to me; (So won-der-ful!) He for-gives my sins, He dries my ev'ry tear,
Sav-iour to me; (So won-der-ful!) Sweet-er is His grace while press-ing on my way,

won-der-ful Sav-iour to me. (So won-der-ful!) For He's a won-der-ful Sav-iour to

me, (won-der-ful!) He's a won-der-ful Sav-iour to me; (won-der-ful!) I was

lost in sin, but Je-sus took me in: He's a won-der-ful Sav-iour to me.

Jesus, I Am Resting

201

JEAN SOPHIE PIGOTT

J. MOUNTAIN

1. Je - sus, I am rest - ing, rest - ing In the joy of what Thou art;
2. Sim - ply trust-ing Thee, Lord Je - sus, I be-hold Thee as Thou art;
3. Ev - er lift Thy face up - on me, As I work and wait for Thee;

Chorus: Je - sus, I am rest - ing, rest - ing In the joy of what Thou art;

Fine

I am find - ing out the great - ness Of Thy lov - ing heart.
And Thy love, so pure, so change-less, Sat - is - fies my heart;
Rest - ing 'neath Thy smile, Lord Je - sus, Earth's dark shad - ows flee.

I am find - ing out the great - ness Of Thy lov - ing heart.

Thou hast bid me gaze up - on Thee, And Thy beau - ty fills my soul,
Sat - is - fies its deep - est long-ings, Meets, sup-plies its ev - 'ry need,
Bright-ness of my Fa-ther's glo - ry, Sun-shine of my Fa-ther's face,

D. C. Chorus

For by Thy trans - form - ing pow - er, Thou hast made me whole.
Com - pass-eth me round with bless-ings: Thine is love in - deed!
Keep me ev - er trust - ing, rest - ing, Fill me with Thy grace.

202 My Redeemer

PHILIP P. BLISS

JAMES McGRANAHAN

1. I will sing of my Re-deem-er, And His won - drous love to me;
2. I will tell the won - drous sto - ry, How my lost es-tate to save,
3. I will praise my dear Re-deem-er, His tri - um - phant pow'r I'll tell,
4. I will sing of my Re-deem-er, And His heav'n - ly love to me;

On the cru - el cross He suf-fered, From the curse to set me free.
In His bound-less love and mer - cy, He the ran - som free - ly gave.
How the vic - to - ry He giv - eth O - ver sin, and death and Hell.
He from death to life hath brought me, Son of God with Him to be.

Sing, O sing of my Re-deem - er,
of my Re-deem - er, Sing O sing of my Re-deem - er,

With His blood He pur - chased me,
He pur-chased me, With His blood He pur-chased me,

On the cross He sealed my par - don,
He sealed my par - don, On the cross He sealed my par - don,

Paid the debt and made me free.

and made me free, and made me free.

The Windows of Heaven 203

Anonymous
Arranged by John R. Rice

The win-dows of Heav-en are o-pen, The bless-ings are fall-ing to-night;

There's joy, joy, joy in my heart, since Je-sus made ev-'ry-thing right;

I gave Him my old tat-tered gar-ment, He gave me a robe of pure white;

I'm feast-ing on man-na from Heav-en and that's why I'm hap-py to-night.

204 Songs in the Mountains

JOHN R. RICE

JOHN R. RICE

1. There are songs in the moun-tains, There are songs in the vale;
2. There will come days of sad - ness, There may come times of need;
3. The light songs of the world-lings Do not last through the night,
4. I've a Spir - it to com - fort, And to teach and to guide,

Hearts may sing in the day - time, And when night-shades pre - vail. O then
But the Sav - iour is with me, He's my Shep - herd in - deed. For He
And the joy of the sin - ners Of - ten chang - es to fright. But the
I've a Fa - ther to hear me, Let what - ev - er be - tide. And my

sing when the birds sing or when storm - clouds are low, For the
bears all my bur - dens And He com - forts my heart, He is
heart ease of E - den, In the soul of God's own, Is the
High Priest for - ev - er Takes my part at the throne, So I

saints can re - joice while God His bless-ings be - stows.
here when I need Him, He will nev - er de - part. So I sing,
gift of our Sav-iour, With His Pres-ence made known. sing all the
sing on my jour-ney For I'm nev - er a - lone.

sing, sing, sing, sing,
day and I sing all the night, And I sing when it's cloud - y, I

© Copyright 1965 by John R. Rice in "Revival Specials No. 2."

sing,   For I'm hap-py in   Je-sus, There's a song in my soul!
sing when it's light.

He Keeps Me Singing   205

LUTHER B. BRIDGERS   **LUTHER B. BRIDGERS**

1. There's with-in my heart a   mel - o - dy,   Je - sus   whis-pers sweet and
2. All   my life was wrecked by   sin and strife,   Dis-cord   filled my heart with
3. Feast - ing on the rich - es   of His grace,   Rest-ing 'neath His shel-t'ring
4. Tho' some-times He leads through wa - ters deep,   Tri - als   fall a-cross the
5. Soon He's com-ing back to   wel-come me   Far be - yond the star - ry

low,   "Fear not, I am with thee, peace, be still," In all of life's ebb and
pain,   Je-sus swept a-cross the bro-ken strings, Stirred the slum-b'ring chords a-
wing,   Al-ways look-ing on His   smil-ing face,   That is   why I shout and
way,   Tho' some-times the path seems rough and steep, See His foot-prints all the
sky;   I shall wing my flight to   worlds un-known, I shall reign with Him on

flow.
gain.
sing.   Je - sus, Je - sus, Je - sus— Sweet-est name I
way.
high.

know,   Fills my ev - 'ry long - ing, Keeps me sing-ing as I   go.

206 O! Say, But I'm Glad

JAMES P. SULLIVAN

MILDRED ELLEN SULLIVAN

1. There is a song in my heart to-day, Some-thing I nev - er had;
2. Won - der-ful, mar-vel-ous love He brings, In - to a heart that's sad;
3. We have a fel-low-ship rich and sweet, Tongues can nev-er re - late;
4. Won't you come to Him with all your care, Wea-ry and worn and sad?

Je - sus has tak-en my sins a - way, O! say, but I'm glad.
Thro' dark-est tun-nels the soul just sings, O! say, but I'm glad.
A - bid-ing in Him: the soul's re-treat, O! say, but I'm glad.
You, too, will sing as His love you share, O! say, but I'm glad.

O! say, but I'm glad, I'm glad, O! say, but I'm glad;

Je - sus has come and my cup's o-ver-run; O! say, but I'm glad.

Only a Sinner

207

JAMES M. GRAY

DANIEL B. TOWNER

1. Naught have I got-ten but what I re-ceived; Grace hath be-stowed it since
2. Once I was fool-ish, and sin ruled my heart, Caus-ing my foot-steps from
3. Tears un-a-vail-ing, no mer-it had I; Mer-cy had saved me, or
4. Suf-fer a sin-ner whose heart o-ver-flows, Lov-ing his Sav-iour to

I have be-lieved; Boast-ing ex-clud-ed, pride I a-base; I'm on-ly a
God to de-part; Je-sus hath found me, hap-py my case; I now am a
else I must die; Sin had a-larmed me fear-ing God's face; But now I'm a
tell what he knows; Once more to tell it would I em-brace—I'm on-ly a

sin-ner saved by grace! On-ly a sin-ner saved by grace!

On-ly a sin-ner saved by grace! This is my sto-ry, to

God be the glo-ry— I'm on-ly a sin-ner saved by grace!

Favorite song of Dr. Ed Nelson and Dr. G. B. Vick.

208 Grace Greater Than Our Sin

JULIA H. JOHNSTON

DANIEL B. TOWNER

1. Mar - vel-ous grace of our lov - ing Lord, Grace that ex - ceeds our
2. Sin and de - spair like the sea waves cold, Threat-en the soul with
3. Dark is the stain that we can - not hide, What can a - vail to
4. Mar - vel-ous, in - fi - nite, match-less grace, Free - ly be - stowed on

sin and our guilt, Yon - der on Cal - va - ry's mount out - poured,
in - fi - nite loss; Grace that is great - er, yes, grace un - told,
wash it a - way? Look! there is flow - ing a crim - son tide;
all who be - lieve; You that are long - ing to see His face,

There where the blood of the Lamb was spilt.
Points to the Ref - uge, the Might - y Cross. Grace, grace,
Whit - er than snow you may be to - day. Mar - vel - ous grace,
Will you this mo - ment His grace re - ceive?

God's grace, Grace that will par - don and cleanse with - in; Grace,
In - fi - nite grace, Mar-vel-ous

grace, God's grace, Grace that is great-er than all our sin.
grace. In - fi-nite grace,

Sunshine in the Soul

ELIZA E. HEWITT

JOHN R. SWENEY

1. There's sunshine in my soul to-day, More glo - ri - ous and bright
2. There's mu - sic in my soul to-day, A car - ol to the King,
3. There's spring-time in my soul to-day, For, when the Lord is near,
4. There's glad - ness in my soul to-day, And hope and praise and love,

Than glows in an - y earth-ly skies, For Je - sus is my Light.
And Je - sus, lis - ten-ing, can hear The songs I can - not sing.
The dove of peace sings in my heart, The flow'rs of grace ap - pear.
For bless-ings which He gives me now, For joys laid up a - bove.

O there's sun - shine, bless - ed sun - shine,
O there's sun-shine in the soul, bless - ed sun-shine in the soul,

When the peace - ful, hap - py mo-ments roll; When

hap - py mo-ments roll;

Je - sus shows His smil - ing face, There is sun-shine in the soul.

210 Wonderful Grace of Jesus

HALDOR LILLENAS   HALDOR LILLENAS

1. Won - der-ful grace of Je - sus, Great-er than all my sin;
2. Won - der-ful grace of Je - sus, Reach-ing to all the lost,
3. Won - der-ful grace of Je - sus, Reach-ing the most de - filed,

How shall my tongue de- scribe it, Where shall its praise be - gin?
By it I have been par - doned, Saved to the ut - ter- most,
By its trans-form-ing pow - er, Mak - ing him God's dear child,

Tak - ing a - way my bur - den, Set - ting my spir - it free;
Chains have been torn a - sun - der, Giv - ing me lib - er - ty;
Pur - chas-ing peace and Heav - en, For all e - ter - ni - ty;

For the won - der-ful grace of Je - sus reach - es me.
For the won - der-ful grace of Je - sus reach - es me.
And the won - der-ful grace of Je - sus reach - es me.

211   "Whosoever" Meaneth Me

J. EDWIN McCONNELL   J. EDWIN McCONNELL

1. I am hap-py to-day and the sun shines bright, The clouds have been rolled a-way; For the Sav-iour said Who-so-ev-er will, May come with Him to stay. (to stay.)

2. All my hopes have been raised, O His name be praised, His glo-ry has filled my soul; I've been lift-ed up and from sin set free, His blood hath made me whole.(me whole.)

3. O what won-der-ful love, O what grace di-vine, That Je-sus should die for me! I was lost in sin, for the world I pined, But now I am set free. (set free.)

"Who-so-ev-er" sure-ly mean-eth me, Sure-ly mean-eth me, O sure-ly mean-eth me; "Who-so-ev-er" sure-ly mean-eth me, "Who-so-ev-er" mean-eth me.

mean-eth me.

O Happy Day

212

PHILIP DODDRIDGE

EDWARD F. RIMBAULT

1. O hap-py day that fixed my choice On Thee, my Sav - iour and my God!
2. O hap-py bond, that seals my vows To Him who mer - its all my love!
3. 'Tis done: the great trans-ac-tion's done; I am my Lord's, and He is mine;
4. Now rest, my long di - vid - ed heart; Fixed on this bliss - ful cen-ter, rest;

Well may this glow - ing heart re - joice, And tell its rap - tures all a - broad.
Let cheer-ful an - thems fill His house, While to that sa - cred shrine I move.
He drew me and I fol-lowed on, Charmed to con - fess the voice di - vine.
Nor ev - er from my Lord de - part, With Him of ev - 'ry good pos - sessed.

Hap - py day, hap - py day, When Je - sus washed my sins a - way!

He taught me how to watch and pray, And live re - joic - ing ev - 'ry day;

Hap - py day, hap - py day, When Je - sus washed my sins a - way!

213 There Is Glory in My Soul

GRACE WELSER DAVIS   CHARLES H. GABRIEL

1. Since I lost my sins and I found my Sav-iour, There is glo-ry
2. Since He cleansed my heart, gave me sight for blind-ness,There is glo-ry
3. Since with God I've walked, hav-ing sweet com-mun-ion, There is glo-ry
4. Since I en-tered Ca-naan on my way to Heav-en, There is glo-ry

in my soul! Since by faith I sought and ob-tained God's fa-vor,There is
in my soul! Since He touched and healed me in lov-ing-kind-ness,There is
in my soul! Bright-er grows each day in this heav'n-ly un-ion, There is
in my soul! Since the day my life to the Lord was giv-en, There is

glo-ry in my soul! There is glo-ry, glo-ry, there is glo-ry in my soul!

glo-ry,

Ev-'ry day bright-er grows, And I con-quer all my foes; There is glo-ry,

glo-ry,

glo-ry, there is glo-ry in my soul! There is glo-ry in my soul!

glo-ry in my

Builded on the Rock

214

Mrs. C. RICE

Mrs. C. RICE

1. I build-ed on the Rock, on the Rock of God, Build - ed on the
2. Why should I fear when the winds sweep by? Build - ed on the
3. Hush, rag - ing bil - lows at His com - mand, Build - ed on the
4. Praise God for our foun - da - tion sure! Build - ed on the

Rock, Christ Je - sus; I dug down deep and build-ed on the Rock,
Rock, Christ Je - sus; Or shak - en be when the waves roll high?
Rock, Christ Je - sus; O peace be still 'neath His lov - ing hand!
Rock, Christ Je - sus; No storms can harm our house se - cure,

Build-ed on the Rock of God. I hold not the Rock, but the

Rock holds me, The Rock holds me, the Rock holds me; I rest on the

Rock and the Rock holds me, Rest -ing on the Rock of God.

Heaven Came Down and Glory Filled My Soul

215

JOHN W. PETERSON

JOHN W. PETERSON

1. O what a won-der-ful, won-der-ful day— Day I will nev-er for-get;
2. Born of the Spir-it with life from a-bove In-to God's fam-'ly di-vine,
3. Now I've a hope that will sure-ly en-dure Af-ter the pass-ing of time;

Af-ter I'd wan-dered in dark-ness a-way, Je-sus my Sav-iour I met.
Just-i-fied ful-ly through Cal-va-ry's love, O what a stand-ing is mine!
I have a fu-ture in Heav-en for sure, There in those man-sions sub-lime.

O what a ten-der, com-pas-sion-ate Friend— He met the need of my heart;
And the trans-ac-tion so quick-ly was made When as a sin-ner I came,
And it's be-cause of that won-der-ful day When at the cross I be-lieved;

Shad-ows dis-pel-ling, With joy I am tell-ing, He made all the dark-ness de-part!
Took of the of-fer Of grace He did prof-fer—He saved me, O praise His dear name!
Rich-es e-ter-nal and bless-ings su-per-nal From His pre-cious hand I re-ceived.

Heav-en came down and glo-ry filled my soul, filled my soul,

When at the cross the Sav-iour made me whole; made me whole; My

sins were washed a-way And my night was turned to day—

Heav-en came down and glo-ry filled my soul! filled my soul!

CODA *(after the last chorus only)*

Heav-en came down and glo-ry filled my soul!

216 Surely Goodness and Mercy

JOHN W. PETERSON
and ALFRED B. SMITH

JOHN W. PETERSON

1. A pil-grim was I and a-wand'ring, In the cold night of
2. He re-stor-eth my soul when I'm wea-ry, He giv-eth me
3. When I walk through the dark lone-some val-ley, My Sav-iour will

sin I did roam, When Je-sus the kind Shep-herd found me,
strength day by day; He leads me be-side the still wa-ters,
walk with me there; And safe-ly His great hand will lead me,

And now I am on my way Home.
He guards me each step of the way. Sure-ly good-ness and
To the man-sions He's gone to pre-pare.

mer-cy shall fol-low me All the days, all the days of my

217 He Included Me

JOHNSON OATMAN, JR.

HAMPTON H. SEWELL

1. I am so hap-py in Christ to-day, That I go sing-ing a-
2. Glad-ly I read, "Who-so - ev - er may Come to the foun-tain of
3. Ev - er God's Spir - it is say - ing, "Come!" Hear the Bride say - ing, "No
4. "Free - ly come drink," words the soul to thrill! O with what joy they my

long my way; Yes, I'm so hap-py to know and say,
life to - day"; But when I read it I al - ways say,
long - er roam"; But I am sure while they're call - ing Home,
heart do fill! For when He said, "Who-so - ev - er will,"

"Je-sus in-clud-ed me too," Je - sus in - clud-ed me,
"Je-sus in-clud-ed me too,"
Je -sus in-clud-ed me too,
Je -sus in-clud-ed me too,

Yes, He in-clud-ed me, When the Lord said, "Who-so-ev-er," He in-clud-ed

me; Je - sus in - clud-ed me, Yes, He in-clud-ed me,

When the Lord said, "Who - so - ev - er," He in - clud - ed me.

Hallelujah, 'Tis Done

218

PHILIP P. BLISS

PHILIP P. BLISS

1. 'Tis the prom - ise of God, full sal - va - tion to give
2. Though the path - way be lone - ly, and dan - ger - ous too,
3. Man - y loved ones have I in yon heav - en - ly throng,
4. There's a part in that cho - rus for you and for me,

Un - to him who on Je - sus, His Son, will be - lieve.
Sure - ly Je - sus is a - ble to car - ry me through.
They are safe now in Glo - ry, and this is their song:
And the theme of our prais - es for - ev - er will be:

Hal - le - lu - jah, 'tis done! I be - lieve on the Son; I am

1.
saved by the blood of the cru - ci - fied One;

2.
cru - ci - fied One.

219 My Burdens Rolled Away

MINNIE A. STEELE   MINNIE A. STEELE

1. I re-mem-ber when my bur-dens rolled a-way, I had car-ried them for years, night and day; When I sought the bless-ed Lord, and I took Him at His Word, Then at once all my bur-dens rolled a-way.

2. I re-mem-ber when my bur-dens rolled a-way, That I feared would nev-er leave night and day; Je-sus showed to me the loss, so I left them at the cross, I was glad when my bur-dens rolled a-way.

3. I re-mem-ber when my bur-dens rolled a-way, That had hin-dered me for years, night and day; As I sought the throne of grace, just a glimpse of Je-sus' face, And I knew that my bur-dens rolled a-way.

4. I am sing-ing since my bur-dens rolled a-way, There's a song with-in my heart night and day; I am liv-ing for my King, and with joy I shout and sing, Hal-le-lu-jah! all my bur-dens rolled a-way.

Rolled a-way, Rolled a-way, I am hap-py since my bur-dens rolled a-way; Rolled a-way, rolled a-way, I am hap-py since my bur-dens rolled a-way.

Jesus Is All the World to Me

WILL L. THOMPSON

WILL L. THOMPSON

1. Je-sus is all the world to me, My Life, my Joy, my All;
2. Je-sus is all the world to me, My Friend in tri-als sore;
3. Je-sus is all the world to me, And true to Him I'll be;
4. Je-sus is all the world to me, I want no bet-ter friend;

He is my strength from day to day, With-out Him I would fall.
I go to Him for bless-ings, and He gives them o'er and o'er.
O how could I this Friend de-ny, When He's so true to me?
I trust Him now, I'll trust Him when Life's fleet-ing days shall end.

When I am sad to Him I go, No oth-er one can
He sends the sun-shine and the rain, He sends the har-vest
Fol-low-ing Him I know I'm right, He watch-es o'er me
Beau-ti-ful life with such a Friend, Beau-ti-ful life that

cheer me so; When I am sad He makes me glad— He's my Friend.
gold-en grain; Sun-shine and rain, har-vest of grain— He's my Friend.
day and night; Fol-low-ing Him by day and night— He's my Friend.
has no end; E-ter-nal life, e-ter-nal joy— He's my Friend.

221 A Child of the King

HARRIET E. BUELL

JOHN B. SUMMERS

1. My Fa - ther is rich in hous - es and lands, He hold - eth the
2. My Fa - ther's own Son, the Sav - iour of men, Once wan - dered on
3. I once was an out - cast stran - ger on earth, A sin - ner by
4. A tent or a cot - tage, why should I care? They're build - ing a

wealth of the world in His hands! Of ru - bies and dia - monds, of
earth as the poor - est of them; But now He is plead - ing our
choice, and an a - lien by birth; But I've been a - dopt - ed, my
pal - ace for me o - ver there; Though ex - iled from Home, yet,

sil - ver and gold, His cof - fers are full, He has rich - es un - told.
par - don on high, That we may be His when He comes by and by.
name's writ - ten down, An heir to a man - sion, a robe and a crown.
still I may sing: All glo - ry to God, I'm a child of the King.

I'm a child of the King, A child of the King:

With Je - sus my Sav - iour I'm a child of the King.

Moment by Moment

222

DANIEL W. WHITTLE

MAY WHITTLE MOODY

1. Dy-ing with Je - sus by death reck-oned mine; Liv-ing with Je - sus, a
2. Nev-er a tri - al that He is not there, Nev - er a bur-den that
3. Nev-er a heart-ache and nev - er a groan; Nev - er a tear-drop and
4. Nev-er a weak-ness that He doth not feel, Nev - er a sick-ness that

new life di - vine; Look-ing to Je - sus till glo-ry doth shine, Mo-ment by
He doth not bear, Nev-er a sor-row that He doth not share, Mo-ment by
nev - er a moan; Nev-er a dan-ger but there on the throne, Mo-ment by
He can-not heal; Mo-ment by mo-ment, in woe or in weal, Je - sus my

mo-ment, O Lord, I am Thine.
mo-ment, I'm un-der His care. Mo-ment by mo-ment I'm kept in His love;
mo-ment, He thinks of His own.
Sav-iour a - bides with me still.

Mo-ment by mo-ment I've life from a - bove; Look-ing to Je - sus till

glo - ry doth shine; Mo-ment by mo-ment, O Lord, I am Thine.

223 Springs of Living Water

JOHN W. PETERSON   JOHN W. PETERSON

1. I thirst-ed in the bar-ren land of sin and shame, And
2. How sweet the liv-ing wat-er from the hills of God, It
3. O sin-ner, won't you come to-day to Cal-va-ry? A

noth-ing sat-is-fy-ing there I found; But to the bless-ed cross of Christ one
makes me glad and hap-py all the way; Now glo-ry, grace and bless-ing mark the
foun-tain there is flow-ing deep and wide; The Sav-iour now in-vites you to the

day I came, Where springs of liv-ing wa-ter did a-bound.
path I've trod, I'm shout-ing "Hal-le-lu-jah" ev-'ry day.
wa-ter free, Where thirst-ing spir-its can be sat-is-fied.

Drink-ing at the springs of liv-ing wa-ter, Hap-py now am
Hap-py

I, my soul they sat-is-fy; Drink-ing at the
now am I, My soul they sat-is-fy; I'm

springs of liv-ing wa-ter, O won-der-ful and boun-ti-ful sup-ply.

There Shall Be Showers of Blessing 224

DANIEL W. WHITTLE   JAMES McGRANAHAN

1. "There shall be show-ers of bless-ing";   This is the prom-ise of love;
2. "There shall be show-ers of bless-ing";   Pre-cious re-viv-ing a-gain;
3. "There shall be show-ers of bless-ing";   Send them up-on us, O Lord;
4. "There shall be show-ers of bless-ing";   O that to-day they might fall,

There shall be sea-sons re-fresh-ing,   Sent from the Sav-iour a-bove.
O - ver the hills and the val - leys,   Sound of a-bun-dance of rain.
Grant to us now a re-fresh-ing,   Come, and now hon-or Thy Word.
Now as to God we're con-fess-ing,   Now as on Je-sus we call!

Show   -   ers of bless-ing,   Show-ers of bless-ing we need:
Show - ers, show - ers

Mer-cy-drops round us are fall - ing,   But for the show-ers we plead.

225 Nor Silver Nor Gold

JAMES M. GRAY

DANIEL B. TOWNER

1. Nor sil-ver nor gold hath ob-tained my re-demp-tion, Nor rich-es of
2. Nor sil-ver nor gold hath ob-tained my re-demp-tion, The guilt on my
3. Nor sil-ver nor gold hath ob-tained my re-demp-tion, The ho-ly com-
4. Nor sil-ver nor gold hath ob-tained my re-demp-tion, The way in-to

earth could have saved my poor soul; The blood of the cross is my
con-science too heav-y had grown; The blood of the cross is my
mand-ment for-bade me draw near; The blood of the cross is my
Heav-en could not thus be bought; The blood of the cross is my

on-ly foun-da-tion, The death of my Sav-iour now mak-eth me whole.
on-ly foun-da-tion, The death of my Sav-iour could on-ly a-tone.
on-ly foun-da-tion, The death of my Sav-iour re-mov-eth my fear.
on-ly foun-da-tion, The death of my Sav-iour re-demp-tion hath wrought.

I am re-deemed, but not with sil-ver;
I am re-deemed, I am re-deemed, but not with sil-ver;

I am bought, but not with gold;
I am bought, I am bought, but not with gold;

Bought with a

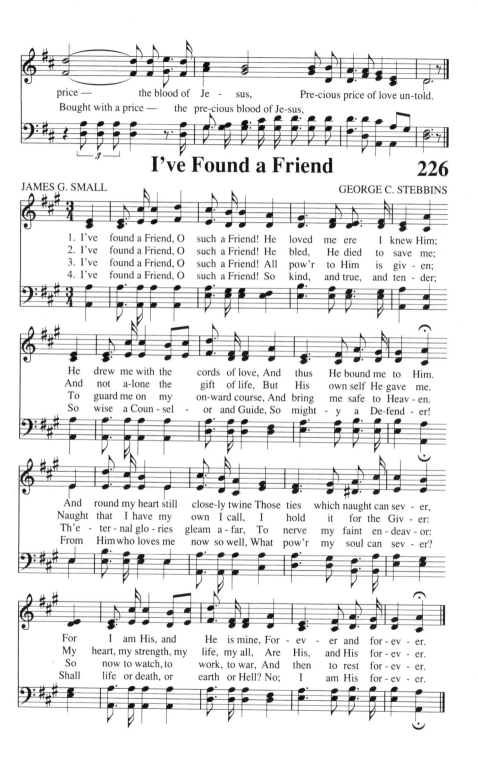

price — the blood of Je - sus, Pre-cious price of love un-told.
Bought with a price — the pre-cious blood of Je-sus,

I've Found a Friend   226

JAMES G. SMALL

GEORGE C. STEBBINS

1. I've found a Friend, O such a Friend! He loved me ere I knew Him;
2. I've found a Friend, O such a Friend! He bled, He died to save me;
3. I've found a Friend, O such a Friend! All pow'r to Him is giv - en;
4. I've found a Friend, O such a Friend! So kind, and true, and ten - der;

He drew me with the cords of love, And thus He bound me to Him.
And not a-lone the gift of life, But His own self He gave me.
To guard me on my on-ward course, And bring me safe to Heav - en.
So wise a Coun - sel - or and Guide, So might - y a De-fend - er!

And round my heart still close-ly twine Those ties which naught can sev - er,
Naught that I have my own I call, I hold it for the Giv - er:
Th'e - ter - nal glo - ries gleam a - far, To nerve my faint en - deav - or:
From Him who loves me now so well, What pow'r my soul can sev - er?

For I am His, and He is mine, For - ev - er and for - ev - er.
My heart, my strength, my life, my all, Are His, and His for - ev - er.
So now to watch, to work, to war, And then to rest for - ev - er.
Shall life or death, or earth or Hell? No; I am His for - ev - er.

227 Saved by the Blood

S. J. HENDERSON

DANIEL B. TOWNER

I Love to Tell the Story

A. CATHERINE HANKEY

WILLIAM G. FISCHER

228

1. I love to tell the sto - ry Of un-seen things a - bove, Of
2. I love to tell the sto - ry More won-der-ful it seems Than
3. I love to tell the sto - ry, 'Tis pleas-ant to re - peat What
4. I love to tell the sto - ry, For those who know it best Seem

Je - sus and His glo - ry, Of Je - sus and His love. I love to
all the gold - en fan-cies Of all our gold - en dreams. I love to
seems, each time I tell it, More won-der-ful - ly sweet. I love to
hun - ger-ing and thirst-ing To hear it like the rest. And when, in

tell the sto - ry, Be - cause I know 'tis true; It sat - is-fies my
tell the sto - ry, It did so much for me; And that is just the
tell the sto - ry, For some have nev - er heard The mes-sage of sal -
scenes of Glo - ry, I sing the new, new song, 'Twill be the old, old

long-ings As noth-ing else can do.
rea - son I tell it now to thee.
va - tion From God's own ho - ly Word. I love to tell the sto - ry, 'Twill
sto - ry That I have loved so long.

be my theme in Glo-ry To tell the old, old sto-ry Of Je-sus and His love.

229 Since I Have Been Redeemed

EDWIN O. EXCELL

EDWIN O. EXCELL

1. I have a song I love to sing, Since I have been re-deemed,
2. I have a Christ that sat-is-fies, Since I have been re-deemed,
3. I have a wit-ness bright and clear, Since I have been re-deemed,
4. I have a Home pre-pared for me, Since I have been re-deemed,

Of my Re-deem-er, Sav-iour, King, Since I have been re-deemed.
To do His will my high-est prize, Since I have been re-deemed.
Dis-pel-ling ev-'ry doubt and fear, Since I have been re-deemed.
Where I shall dwell e-ter-nal-ly, Since I have been re-deemed.

Since I have been re-deemed, Since I have been re-
Since I have been re-deemed, Since I have been re-deemed,

deemed, I will glo-ry in His name; Since I have been re-
Since I have been re-deemed, Since

deemed, I will glo-ry in my Sav-iour's name.
I have been re-deemed,

Heavenly Sunlight

230

H. J. ZELLEY

GEORGE H. COOK

1. Walk-ing in sun - light, all of my jour - ney; O-ver the moun - tains, through the deep vale; Je-sus has said, "I'll nev-er for - sake thee," Prom-ise di - vine that nev-er can fail.
2. Shad-ows a - round me, shad-ows a - bove me, Nev-er con - ceal my Sav-iour and Guide; He is the Light, in Him is no dark - ness; Ev - er I'm walk - ing close to His side.
3. In the bright sun - light, ev - er re - joic - ing, Press-ing my way to man-sions a - bove; Sing-ing His prais - es glad-ly I'm walk - ing, Walk-ing in sun - light, sun-light of love.

Heav-en - ly sun - light, heav-en - ly sun - light, Flood-ing my soul with glo - ry di - vine: Hal - le - lu - jah, I am re - joic - ing, Sing-ing His prais - es, Je - sus is mine.

231 Sunlight

JUDSON W. VAN DeVENTER

WINFIELD S. WEEDEN

1. I wan-dered in the shades of night, Till Je - sus came to me,
2. Though clouds may gath - er in the sky, And bil - lows round me roll,
3. While walk - ing in the light of God, I sweet com-mun - ion find;
4. I cross the wide ex-tend - ed fields, I jour - ney o'er the plain,
5. Soon I shall see Him as He is, The Light that came to me;

And with the sun - light of His love bid all my dark - ness flee.
How - ev - er dark the world may be I've sun - light in my soul.
I press with ho - ly vig - or on, And leave the world be-hind.
And in the sun - light of His love I reap the gold - en grain.
Be - hold the bright-ness of His face, Through-out e - ter - ni - ty.

Sun - light, sun - light in my soul to-day, Sun - light, sun - light
to-day, yes,

all a - long the way; Since the Sav - iour found me,
nar - row way;

Took a - way my sin, I have had the sun-light of His love with-in.
load of sin,

Tell Me the Story of Jesus

232

FANNY J. CROSBY

JOHN R. SWENEY

1. Tell me the sto-ry of Je-sus, Write on my heart ev-'ry word;
2. Fast-ing a-lone in the des-ert, Tell of the days that are past,
3. Tell of the cross where they nailed Him, Writh-ing in an-guish and pain;

Chorus: Tell me the sto-ry of Je-sus, Write on my heart ev-'ry word;

Fine

Tell me the sto-ry most pre-cious, Sweet-est that ev-er was heard.
How for our sins He was tempt-ed, Yet was tri-um-phant at last.
Tell of the grave where they laid Him, Tell how He liv-eth a-gain.

Tell me the sto-ry most pre-cious, Sweet-est that ev-er was heard.

Tell how the an-gels, in cho-rus, Sang as they wel-comed His birth,
Tell of the years of His la-bor, Tell of the sor-row He bore,
Love in that sto-ry so ten-der, Clear-er than ev-er I see:

D.C. al fine

"Glo-ry to God in the high-est! Peace and good tid-ings to earth."
He was de-spised and af-flict-ed, Home-less, re-ject-ed and poor.
Stay, let me weep while you whis-per, Love paid the ran-som for me.

233 Tell Me the Old, Old, Story

A. CATHERINE HANKEY

WILLIAM H. DOANE

1. Tell me the old, old sto - ry, Of un-seen things a - bove, Of Je - sus
2. Tell me the sto - ry slow - ly, That I may take it in— That won-der-
3. Tell me the sto - ry soft - ly, With ear-nest tones and grave; Re - mem-ber
4. Tell me the same old sto - ry, When you have cause to fear That this world's

and His glo - ry, Of Je - sus and His love; Tell me the sto - ry
ful re - demp-tion, God's rem - e - dy for sin; Tell me the sto - ry
I'm the sin - ner Whom Je - sus came to save; Tell me the sto - ry
emp - ty glo - ry Is cost-ing me too dear; Yes, and when that world's

sim - ply, As to a lit - tle child, For I am weak and wea - ry,
of - ten, For I for - get so soon, The "ear - ly dew" of morn - ing,
al - ways, If you would real - ly be, In an - y time of trou - ble,
glo - ry Is dawn - ing on my soul, Tell me the old, old sto - ry:

And help-less and de - filed.
Has passed a - way at noon.
A com-fort - er to me.
"Christ Je - sus makes thee whole."

Tell me the old, old sto - ry, Tell me the

old, old sto - ry, Tell me the old, old sto - ry Of Je - sus and His love.

He Is So Precious to Me

234

CHARLES H. GABRIEL

CHARLES H. GABRIEL

235 I Know I Love Thee Better, Lord

FRANCES R. HAVERGAL

RALPH E. HUDSON

1. I know I love Thee bet-ter, Lord, Than an - y earth - ly joy;
2. I know that Thou art near-er still Than an - y earth - ly throng;
3. Thou hast put glad-ness in my heart; Then may I well be glad!
4. O Sav - iour, pre-cious Sav-iour mine! What will Thy pres - ence be,

For Thou hast giv - en me the peace Which noth - ing can de - stroy.
And sweet - er is the thought of Thee Than an - y love - ly song.
With - out the se-cret of Thy love I could not be but sad.
If such a life of joy can crown Our walk on earth with Thee?

The half has nev-er yet been told, Of love so full and free!
yet been told,

The half has nev-er yet been told, The blood—it cleans-eth me!
yet been told, cleans-eth me!

No, Not One!

JOHNSON OATMAN, JR.

GEORGE C. HUGG

1. There's not a friend like the lowly Jesus, No, not one! no, not one!
2. No friend like Him is so high and ho-ly, No, not one! no, not one!
3. There's not an hour that He is not near us, No, not one! no, not one!
4. Did ev-er saint find this Friend for-sake him? No, not one! no, not one!
5. Was e'er a gift like the Sav-iour giv-en? No, not one! no, not one!

None else could heal all our soul's dis-eas-es, No, not one! no, not one!
And yet no friend is so meek and low-ly, No, not one! no, not one!
No night so dark but His love can cheer us, No, not one! no, not one!
Or sin-ner find that He would not take him? No, not one! no, not one!
Will He re-fuse us a home in Heav-en? No, not one! no, not one!

Je-sus knows all a-bout our strug-gles, He will guide till the day is done;

There's not a friend like the lowly Jesus, No, not one! no, not one!

237 The Cleansing Wave

PHOEBE PALMER

Mrs. JOSEPH F. KNAPP

1. O now I see the crim-son wave, The foun-tain deep and wide;
2. I see the new cre - a -tion rise, I hear the speak-ing blood;
3. I rise to walk in Heav'n's own light A - bove the world and sin,
4. A - maz-ing grace! 'tis Heav'n be - low To feel the blood ap - plied,

Je - sus, my Lord, might - y to save, Points to His wound-ed side.
It speaks! pol -lu - ted na - ture dies! Sinks 'neath the cleans-ing flood.
With heart made pure, and gar-ments white, And Christ en-throned with - in.
And Je - sus, on - ly Je - sus know, My Je - sus cru - ci - fied.

The cleans-ing stream, I see, I see! I plunge, and O it cleans-eth me!

O praise the Lord, it cleans-eth me, It cleans-eth me, yes, cleans-eth me!

Christ Liveth in Me

238

DANIEL W. WHITTLE

JAMES McGRANAHAN

1. Once far from God and dead in sin, No light my heart could see,
2. As rays of light from yon - der sun The flow'rs of earth set free,
3. As lives the flow'r with - in the seed, As in the cone the tree,
4. With long - ing all my heart is filled That like Him I may be,

But in God's Word the light I found—Now Christ liv - eth in me.
So life and light and love came forth From Christ liv - ing in me.
So, praise the God of truth and grace, His Spir - it dwell-eth in me.
As on the won - drous thought I dwell, That Christ liv - eth in me.

Christ liv - eth in me, Christ liv - eth in me;
Christ liv - eth in me, Christ liv - eth in

O what a sal - va - tion this—That Christ liv - eth in me.
me; O

239 Seeking for Me

A. N.   E. E. HASTY

1. Je - sus my Sav-iour to Beth - le-hem came, Born in a man-ger to
2. Je - sus my Sav-iour, on Cal - va-ry's tree, Paid the great debt and my
3. Je - sus my Sav-iour, the same as of old, While I was wan-d'ring a -
4. Je - sus my Sav-iour shall come from on high— Sweet is the prom-ise as

sor-row and shame; O it was won-der-ful—blest be His name! Seek-ing for me, for
soul He set free; O it was won-der-ful—how could it be? Dy-ing for me, for
far from the fold, Gen-tly and long did He plead with my soul, Call-ing for me, for
wea - ry years fly; O I shall see Him de-scend-ing the sky, Com-ing for me, for

For me!   For me!

me! Seek-ing for me! Seek-ing for me! Seek-ing for me! Seek-ing for me!
me! Dy-ing for me! Dy-ing for me! Dy-ing for me! Dy-ing for me!
me! Call-ing for me! Call-ing for me! Call-ing for me! Call-ing for me!
me! Com-ing for me! Com-ing for me! Com-ing for me! Com-ing for me!

O it was won - der-ful—blest be His name! Seek-ing for me, for me!
O it was won - der-ful—how could it be? Dy - ing for me, for me!
Gen -tly and long did He plead with my soul, Call-ing for me, for me!
O I shall see Him de-scend-ing the sky, Com-ing for me, for me!

The Lily of the Valley

240

CHARLES W. FRY

Arranged from William S. Hays

1. I have found a Friend in Je - sus, He's ev - 'ry-thing to me, He's the
2. He all my griefs has tak - en, and all my sor-rows borne; In temp-
3. He will nev - er, nev - er leave me, nor yet for - sake me here, While I

fair - est of ten thou-sand to my soul; The Lil - y of the Val - ley, in
ta - tion He's my strong and might-y tower; I have all for Him for - sak - en, and
live by faith and do His bless-ed will; A wall of fire a - bout me, I've

D.S.: Lil - y of the Val - ley, the

Fine

Him a - lone I see All I need to cleanse and make me ful - ly whole.
all my i - dols torn From my heart, and now He keeps me by His power.
noth-ing now to fear, With His man - na He my hun - gry soul shall fill.

Bright and Morn-ing Star, He's the fair - est of ten thou-sand to my soul.

In sor - row He's my Com - fort, in trou - ble He's my Stay,
Though all the world for - sake me, and Sa - tan tempt me sore,
Then sweep-ing up to Glo - ry to see His bless - ed face,

D.S.

He tells me ev - 'ry care on Him to roll: He's the
Through Je - sus I shall safe - ly reach the goal: He's the
Where riv - ers of de - light shall ev - er roll: He's the

241   O It Is Wonderful!

CHARLES H. GABRIEL   CHARLES H. GABRIEL

1. I stand all a-mazed at the love Je-sus of-fers me, Con-fused at the
2. I mar-vel that He would des-cend from His throne di-vine, To res-cue a
3. I think of His hands pierced and bleed-ing to pay the debt! Such mer-cy, such

grace that so free-ly He prof-fers me; I trem-ble to know that for
soul so re-bel-lious and proud as mine; That He should ex-tend His great
love and de-vo-tion can I for-get? No, no! I will praise and a-

me He was cru-ci-fied— That for me, a sin-ner, He suf-fered, He
love un-to such as I; Suf-fi-cient to own, to re-deem, and to
dore at the mer-cy seat, Un-til at the glo-ri-fied throne I kneel

bled, and died.
jus-ti-fy.   O it is won-der-ful that He should care for me, E-nough to
at His feet.

die for me! O it is won-der-ful, won-der-ful to me!
won-der-ful!

It Took a Miracle

242

JOHN W. PETERSON

JOHN W. PETERSON

1. My Fa - ther is om - nip - o - tent, And that you can't de - ny;
2. Though here His glo - ry has been shown, We still can't ful - ly see
3. The Bi - ble tells us of His pow'r And wis - dom all way through,

A God of might and mir - a - cles—'Tis writ - ten in the sky.
The won - der of His might, His pow'r—'Twill take e - ter - ni - ty.
And ev - 'ry lit - tle bird and flow'r Are tes - ti - mo - nies too.

It took a mir - a - cle to put the stars in place, It took a

mir - a - cle to hang the world in space; But when He saved my soul,

Cleansed and made me whole, It took a mir - a - cle of love and grace!

243   Victory in Jesus

E. M. BARTLETT   E. M. BARTLETT

1. I heard an old, old sto - ry, How a Sav-iour came from Glo - ry,
2. I heard a-bout His heal - ing, Of His cleans-ing pow'r re- veal - ing,
3. I heard a-bout a man-sion He has built for me in Glo - ry,

How He gave His life on Cal - va - ry To save a wretch like me;
How He made the lame to walk a - gain And caused the blind to see;
And I heard a-bout the streets of gold Be - yond the crys - tal sea;

I heard a-bout His groan-ing, Of His pre-cious blood's a - ton - ing,
And then I cried, "Dear Je - sus, Come and heal my bro - ken spir - it,"
A - bout the an - gels sing - ing, And the old re-demp - tion sto - ry,

Then I re - pent - ed of my sins And won the vic - to - ry.
And some-how Je - sus came and brought To me the vic - to - ry.
And some sweet day I'll sing up there The song of vic - to - ry.

O vic - to - ry in Je - sus, My Sav-iour, for - ev - er, He sought me and

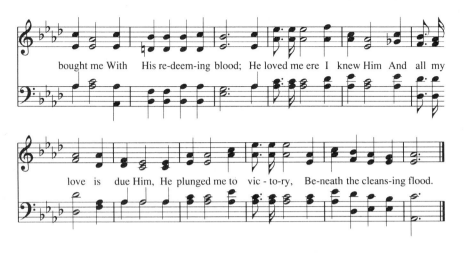

bought me With His re-deem-ing blood; He loved me ere I knew Him And all my

love is due Him, He plunged me to vic - to-ry, Be-neath the cleans-ing flood.

Amazing Grace 244

JOHN NEWTON

Arranged by Edwin O. Excell

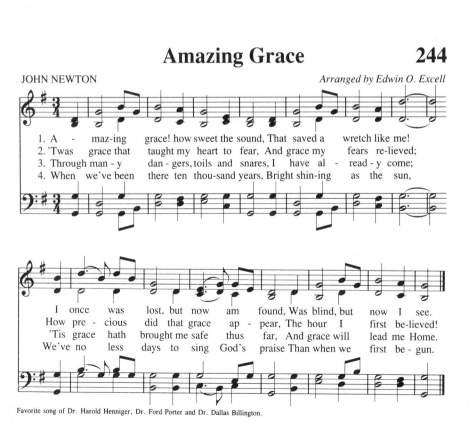

1. A - maz-ing grace! how sweet the sound, That saved a wretch like me!
2. 'Twas grace that taught my heart to fear, And grace my fears re-lieved;
3. Through man - y dan - gers, toils and snares, I have al - read - y come;
4. When we've been there ten thou-sand years, Bright shin-ing as the sun,

I once was lost, but now am found, Was blind, but now I see.
How pre - cious did that grace ap - pear, The hour I first be-lieved!
'Tis grace hath brought me safe thus far, And grace will lead me Home.
We've no less days to sing God's praise Than when we first be - gun.

Favorite song of Dr. Harold Henniger, Dr. Ford Porter and Dr. Dallas Billington.

245   The Old Account Was Settled

F. M. GRAHAM   F. M. GRAHAM

1. There was a time on earth, When in the book of Heav'n An old ac-count was standing For sins yet un-for-giv'n; My name was at the top, And man-y things be-low, I went un-to the Keep-er, And set-tled long a-go.

2. The old ac-count was large, And grow-ing ev-'ry day, For I was al-ways sin-ning, And nev-er tried to pay; But when I looked a-head, And saw such pain and woe, I said that I would set-tle, I set-tled long a-go.

3. When in that hap-py Home, My Sav-iour's Home a-bove, I'll sing re-demp-tion's sto-ry, And praise Him for His love; I'll not for-get that book, With pag-es white as snow, Be-cause I came and set-tled, And set-tled long a-go.

4. O sin-ner, trust the Lord, Be cleansed of all your sin, For thus He hath pro-vid-ed For you to en-ter in; And then if you should live A hun-dred years be-low, Up there you'll not re-gret it, You set-tled long a-go.

Long a-go, Long a-go, Yes, the
Down on my knees, I set-tled it all,

old ac-count was set-tled long a-go; And the rec-ord's clear to-day,
Hal-le-lu-jah!

For He washed my sins a-way, When the old ac-count was set-tled long a-go.

Redeemed

246

FANNY J. CROSBY

WILLIAM J. KIRKPATRICK

1. Re-deemed, how I love to pro - claim it! Re-deemed by the blood of the Lamb;
2. Re-deemed, and so hap-py in Je - sus, No lan-guage my rap-ture can tell;
3. I think of my bless-ed Re - deem-er, I think of Him all the day long;
4. I know I shall see in His beau - ty The King in whose law I de-light;

Re-deemed thro' His in - fi - nite mer - cy, His child, and for - ev - er I am.
I know that the light of His pres - ence With me doth con-tin - ual - ly dwell.
I sing, for I can-not be si - lent; His love is the theme of my song.
Who lov-ing - ly guard-eth my foot-steps, And giv-eth me songs in the night.

Re - deemed, re - deemed, Re-deemed by the blood of the Lamb;
re-deemed, re-deemed,

Re - deemed, re - deemed, His child, and for - ev - er I am.
re-deemed, re-deemed,

247 Saved, Saved!

JACK P. SCHOLFIELD

JACK P. SCHOLFIELD

1. I've found a Friend who is all to me, His
2. He saves me from ev-'ry sin and harm, Se-
3. When poor and need-y and all a-lone, In

love is ev-er true; I
cures my soul each day; I'm
love He said to me, "Come

love to tell how He lift-ed me And
lean-ing strong on His might-y arm; I
un-to Me and I'll lead you Home, To

what His grace can do for you.
know He'll guide me all the way.
live with Me e-ter-nal-ly."

Saved by His
Saved by His pow'r,

pow'r di-vine, Saved to new life sub-lime! Life now is
Saved to new life,

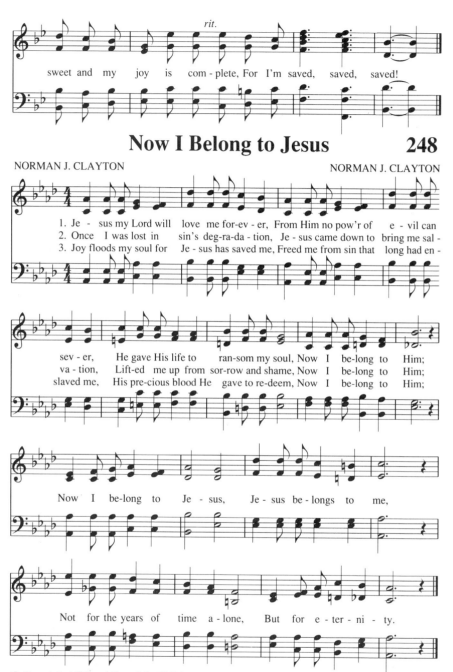

Now I Belong to Jesus 248

NORMAN J. CLAYTON

NORMAN J. CLAYTON

1. Je - sus my Lord will love me for-ev - er, From Him no pow'r of e - vil can
2. Once I was lost in sin's deg-ra-da - tion, Je - sus came down to bring me sal -
3. Joy floods my soul for Je - sus has saved me, Freed me from sin that long had en -

sev - er, He gave His life to ran-som my soul, Now I be-long to Him;
va - tion, Lift-ed me up from sor-row and shame, Now I be-long to Him;
slaved me, His pre-cious blood He gave to re-deem, Now I be-long to Him;

Now I be-long to Je - sus, Je - sus be - longs to me,

Not for the years of time a - lone, But for e - ter - ni - ty.

249 Saved!

OSWALD J. SMITH

ROGER M. HICKMAN

1. Saved! saved! saved! my sins are all for-giv'n; Christ is
2. Saved! saved! saved! by grace and grace a-lone; O what
3. Saved! saved! saved! O joy be-yond com-pare! Christ my

mine! I'm on my way to Heav'n; Once a guilt - y
won - drous love to me was shown; In my stead Christ
life, and I His con-stant care; Yield - ing all and

sin - ner, lost un-done, Now a child of God saved thro' His
Je - sus bled and died, Bore my sins, for me was cru - ci -
trust-ing Him a-lone, Liv - ing now each mo-ment as His

Son.
fied. Saved! I'm saved through Christ, my all in all;
own. all in all;

Saved! I'm saved, what - ev - er may be-fall; He

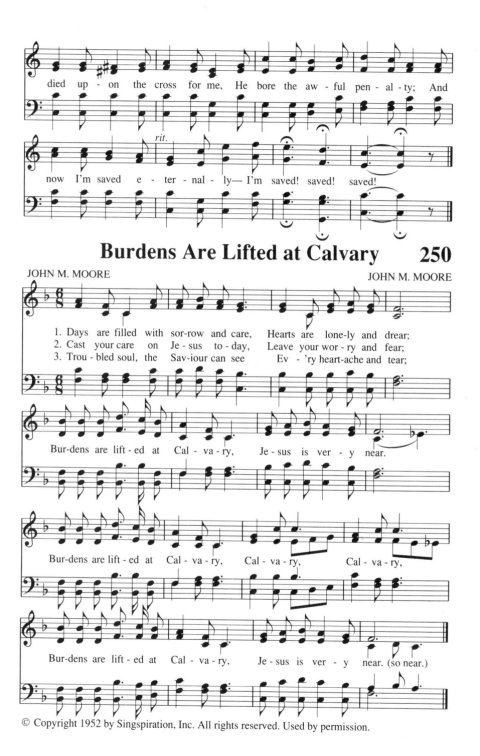

died up - on the cross for me, He bore the aw - ful pen - al - ty; And

now I'm saved e - ter - nal - ly— I'm saved! saved! saved!

Burdens Are Lifted at Calvary   250

JOHN M. MOORE

JOHN M. MOORE

1. Days are filled with sor-row and care, Hearts are lone-ly and drear;
2. Cast your care on Je - sus to - day, Leave your wor - ry and fear;
3. Trou - bled soul, the Sav-iour can see Ev - 'ry heart-ache and tear;

Bur-dens are lift - ed at Cal - va - ry, Je - sus is ver - y near.

Bur-dens are lift - ed at Cal - va - ry, Cal - va - ry, Cal - va - ry,

Bur-dens are lift - ed at Cal - va - ry, Je - sus is ver - y near. (so near.)

251 If I Gained the World

ANNA OLANDER
Translation composite

Swedish

1. If   I gained the world, but lost the Sav - iour, Were my life worth liv - ing for a
2. Had I wealth and love in full-est meas - ure, And a name re-vered both far and
3. O what emp-ti-ness!—with-out the Sav - iour, 'Mid the sins and sor-rows here be -
4. O the joy of hav-ing all in Je - sus! What a balm the bro-ken heart to

day?   Could my yearn-ing heart find rest and com - fort   In the
near,   Yet   no hope be-yond, no har - bor wait - ing, Where my
low!   And   e - ter - ni - ty, how dark with-out Him!— On - ly
heal!   Ne'er   a   sin so great, but He'll for - give it,   Nor a

things that soon must pass a - way?   If   I   gained the world, but lost the
storm-tossed ves - sel I could steer;   If   I   gained the world, but lost the
night and tears and end - less woe!   What, though I   might live with-out the
sor - row that He does not feel!   If   I   have but Je - sus, on - ly

Sav - iour Would my gain be worth the life - long strife?   Are all
Sav - iour, Who en-dured the cross and died for   me,   Could then
Sav - iour, When I come to die, how would it be?   O to
Je - sus —Noth - ing else in all the world be - side—   O then

earth-ly pleas-ures worth com-par - ing For a mo-ment with a Christ-filled life?
all the world af-ford a ref - uge, Whith-er, in my an-guish, I might flee?
face the val-ley's gloom with-out Him! And with-out Him all e - ter - ni - ty.
ev - 'ry-thing is mine in Je - sus; For my needs and more He will pro - vide.

Whiter Than Snow 252

JAMES NICHOLSON

WILLIAM G. FISCHER

1. Lord Je - sus, I long to be per-fect-ly whole; I want Thee for - ev - er to
2. Lord Je - sus, for this I most hum-bly en - treat, I wait, bless-ed Lord, at Thy
3. Lord Je - sus, Thou see - st I pa-tient-ly wait, Come now, and with - in me a

live in my soul, Break down ev - 'ry i - dol, cast out ev - 'ry foe;
cru - ci - fied feet; By faith, for my cleans - ing, I see Thy blood flow,
new heart cre - ate; To those who have sought Thee, Thou nev - er saidst, "No,"

Now wash me, and I shall be whit - er than snow. Whit - er than snow, yes,

whit - er than snow; Now wash me, and I shall be whit - er than snow.

253   "Ye Must Be Born Again"

WILLIAM T. SLEEPER

GEORGE C. STEBBINS

1. A ru-ler once came to Je-sus by night, To ask Him the way of sal-
2. Ye chil-dren of men, at-tend to the word So sol-emn-ly ut-tered by
3. O ye who would en-ter that glo-ri-ous rest, And sing with the ran-somed the
4. A dear one in Heav-en thy heart yearns to see, At the beau-ti-ful gate may be

va-tion and light; The Mas-ter made an-swer in words true and plain,
Je-sus the Lord; And let not the mes-sage to you be in vain,
song of the blest; The life ev-er-last-ing if ye would ob-tain,
watch-ing for thee; Then list to the note of this sol-emn re-frain,

"Ye must be born a-gain." a-gain. "Ye must be born a-

gain, Ye must be born a-gain; I ver-i-ly,
a-gain, a-gain;

ver-i-ly say un-to thee, Ye must be born a-gain."
a-gain.

"Whosoever Will"

PHILIP P. BLISS

PHILIP P. BLISS

1. Who - so-ev - er hear - eth, shout, shout the sound! Spread the bless-ed ti - dings
2. Who - so-ev - er com - eth need not de-lay, Now the door is o - pen,
3. "Who - so-ev - er will!" the prom-ise is se-cure; "Who - so-ev - er will," for -

all the world a-round; Tell the joy-ful news wher - ev - er man is found,
en - ter while you may; Je - sus is the true, the on - ly Liv - ing Way:
ev - er must en-dure; "Who - so-ev - er will!" 'tis life for-ev - er-more;

"Who - so - ev - er will may come." "Who - so - ev - er will, who - so - ev - er will!"

Send the proc - la - ma - tion o - ver vale and hill; 'Tis a lov - ing

Fa - ther calls the wan-derer home: "Who - so - ev - er will may come."

255 Come and Dine

Words and Melody
C. B. WIDMEYER

S. H. BOLTON

1. Je - sus has a ta - ble spread Where the saints of God are fed,
2. The dis - ci - ples came to land, Thus o - bey - ing Christ's com-mand,
3. Soon the Lamb will take His bride To be ev - er at His side,

He in - vites His cho - sen peo - ple, "Come and dine"; With His man - na He doth
For the Mas - ter called un - to them, "Come and dine"; There they found their hearts's de-
All the host of Heav-en will as - sem - bled be; O 'twill be a glo - rious

feed And sup-plies our ev - 'ry need: O 'tis sweet to sup with Je - sus all the time!
sire, Bread and fish up - on the fire; Thus He sat - is-fies the hun-gry ev - 'ry time.
sight, All the saints in spot-less white; And with Je - sus they will feast e - ter - nal - ly.

"Come and dine," the Mas - ter call - eth, "Come and dine; (O come and dine;)" You may

feast at Je - sus' ta - ble all the time; (O come and dine;) He who fed the mul - ti - tude,

Turned the wa - ter in - to wine, To the hun - gry call-eth now, "Come and dine."

Look to the Lamb of God 256

H. G. JACKSON   JAMES M. BLACK

1. If you from sin are long-ing to be free, Look to the Lamb of God;
2. When Sa-tan tempts, and doubts and fears as-sail, Look to the Lamb of God;
3. Are you a - wea - ry, does the way seem long? Look to the Lamb of God;
4. Fear not when shad-ows on your path-way fall, Look to the Lamb of God;

He, to re-deem you, died on Cal - va - ry, Look to the Lamb of God.
You in His strength shall o - ver all pre-vail, Look to the Lamb of God.
His love will cheer and fill your heart with song, Look to the Lamb of God.
In joy or sor - row Christ is all in all, Look to the Lamb of God.

Look to the Lamb of God,   Look to the Lamb of God,
the Lamb of God,   the Lamb of God,

For He a - lone is a - ble to save you Look to the Lamb of God.

257 Look and Live

WILLIAM A. OGDEN   WILLIAM A. OGDEN

1. I've a mes-sage from the Lord, hal - le - lu - jah! The mes-sage un - to
2. I've a mes-sage full of love, hal - le - lu - jah! A mes-sage, O my
3. Life is of-fered un - to you, hal - le - lu - jah! E - ter - nal life thy
4. I will tell you how I came, hal - le - lu - jah! To Je - sus when He

you I'll give; 'Tis re - cord-ed in His Word, hal - le - lu - jah!
friend, for you; 'Tis a mes-sage from a-bove, hal - le - lu - jah!
soul shall have, If you'll on - ly look to Him, hal - le - lu - jah!
made me whole: 'Twas be - liev-ing on His name, hal - le - lu - jah!

It is on - ly that you "look and live." Look and live,
Je - sus said it and I know 'tis true. Look and live,
Look to Je - sus who a - lone can save.
I trust-ed and He saved my soul.

my broth-er, live! Look to Je - sus now and live; 'Tis re-
live, look and live!

cord-ed in His Word, hal - le - lu - jah! It is on - ly that you "look and live."

Christ Receiveth Sinful Men

258

ERDMAN NEUMEISTER
Translated by Emma F. Bevan

JAMES McGRANAHAN

1. Sin - ners Je - sus will re - ceive; Sound this word of grace to all
2. Come, and He will give you rest; Trust Him, for His Word is plain;
3. Now my heart con-demns me not, Pure be - fore the law I stand;
4. Christ re - ceiv - eth sin - ful men, E - ven me with all my sin;

Who the heav'n - ly path-way leave, All who lin - ger, all who fall.
He will take the sin - ful - est; Christ re - ceiv - eth sin - ful men.
He who cleansed me from all spot, Sat - is - fied its last de - mand.
Purged from ev - 'ry spot and stain, Heav'n with Him I en - ter in.

Sing it o'er and o'er a - gain; Christ re-
Sing it o'er a-gain, Sing it o'er a - gain;

ceiv - eth sin - ful men; Make the mes - sage
ceiv-eth sin-ful men, Christ re - ceiv-eth sin-ful men; Make the mes-sage plain,

clear and plain: Christ re - ceiv - eth sin - ful men.
Make the mes-sage plain: re - ceiv - eth

259 Jesus Saves

PRISCILLA J. OWENS

WILLIAM J. KIRKPATRICK

1. We have heard the joy-ful sound: Je-sus saves! Je-sus saves!
2. Waft it on the roll-ing tide; Je-sus saves! Je-sus saves!
3. Sing a-bove the bat-tle strife, Je-sus saves! Je-sus saves!
4. Give the winds a might-y voice, Je-sus saves! Je-sus saves!

Spread the ti - dings all a-round: Je-sus saves! Je-sus saves!
Tell to sin - ners far and wide: Je-sus saves! Je-sus saves!
By His death and end-less life, Je-sus saves! Je-sus saves!
Let the na - tions now re-joice— Je-sus saves! Je-sus saves!

Bear the news to ev-'ry land, Climb the steeps and cross the waves;
Sing, ye is - lands of the sea; Ech-o back ye o-cean caves;
Sing it soft - ly thro' the gloom, When the heart for mer-cy craves;
Shout sal - va - tion full and free; High-est hills and deep-est caves;

On-ward!—'Tis our Lord's com-mand; Je-sus saves! Je-sus saves!
Earth shall keep her ju - bi - lee: Je-sus saves! Je-sus saves!
Sing in tri - umph o'er the tomb— Je-sus saves! Je-sus saves!
This our song of vic - to - ry— Je-sus saves! Je-sus saves!

He Is Able to Deliver Thee

260

WILLIAM A. OGDEN

WILLIAM A. OGDEN

1. 'Tis the grand-est theme thro' the a- ges rung: 'Tis the grand-est theme for a
2. 'Tis the grand-est theme in the earth or main; 'Tis the grand-est theme for a
3. 'Tis the grand-est theme, let the ti-dings roll, To the guilt-y heart, to the

mor-tal tongue; 'Tis the grand-est theme that the world e'er sung, "Our God is
mor-tal strain; 'Tis the grand-est theme, tell the world a-gain, "Our God is
sin-ful soul; Look to God in faith, He will make thee whole, "Our God is

a-ble to de-liv-er thee." He is a - ble to de-liv-er thee,
a-ble, He is a-ble

He is a - ble to de-liv-er thee; Though by sin op-pressed
a-ble, He is a-ble

Go to Him for rest; "Our God is a-ble to de-liv-er thee."

261   Turn Your Eyes Upon Jesus

HELEN HOWARTH LEMMEL   HELEN HOWARTH LEMMEL

1. O soul, are you wea-ry and trou - bled? No light in the
dark-ness you see? There's light for a look at the Sav - iour,
And life more a - bun-dant and free!

2. Through death in - to life ev - er - last - ing He passed, and we
fol - low Him there; O - ver us sin no more hath do - min - ion—
For more than con-qu'rors we are!

3. His Word shall not fail you— He prom - ised; Be - lieve Him, and
all will be well: Then go to a world that is dy - ing,
His per-fect sal - va-tion to tell!

Turn your eyes up-on Je - sus, Look full in His won - der - ful face; And the things of earth will grow strange-ly dim In the light of His glo - ry and grace.

The Light of the World Is Jesus 262

PHILIP P. BLISS

PHILIP P. BLISS

1. The whole world was lost in the dark-ness of sin; The light of the world is Je - sus; Like sun-shine at noon-day His glo - ry shone in, The light of the world is Je - sus.

2. No dark-ness have we who in Je - sus a - bide, The light of the world is Je - sus; We walk in the light when we fol - low our Guide, The light of the world is Je - sus.

3. Ye dwell - ers in dark-ness with sin-blind - ed eyes, The light of the world is Je - sus; Go, wash at His bid-ding, and light will a - rise, The light of the world is Je - sus.

4. No need of the sun-light in Heav-en, we're told, The light of the world is Je - sus; The Lamb is the Light in the Cit - y of Gold, The light of the world is Je - sus.

Come to the Light, 'tis shin-ing for thee; Sweet-ly the Light has dawned up-on me; Once I was blind, but now I can see; The Light of the world is Je - sus.

263 Verily, Verily

G. M. J.

JAMES McGRANAHAN

1. O what a Sav-iour, that He died for me! From con-dem-
na-tion He hath made me free; "He that be-liev-eth on the
Son," saith He, "Hath ev-er-last-ing life."

2. All my in-i-qui-ties on Him were laid, All my in-
debt-ed-ness by Him was paid; All who be-lieve on Him, the
Lord hath said, "Hath ev-er-last-ing life."

3. Though poor and need-y I can trust my Lord, Though weak and
sin-ful I be-lieve His Word; O glad mes-sage! ev-'ry
child of God "Hath ev-er-last-ing life."

4. Though all un-wor-thy, yet I will not doubt, For him that
com-eth, He will not cast out; "He that be-liev-eth," O the
good news shout, "Hath ev-er-last-ing life."

"Ver-i-ly, ver-i-ly, I say un-to you," "Ver-i-ly, ver-i-ly," mes-sage ev-er new; "He that be-liev-eth on the Son," 'tis true, "Hath ev-er-last-ing life."

Once for All

264

PHILIP P. BLISS

PHILIP P. BLISS

1. Free from the law, O happy con-di-tion, Je-sus hath
2. Now are we free— there's no con-dem-na-tion, Je-sus pro-
3. "Chil-dren of God," O glo-ri-ous call-ing, Sure-ly His

bled, and there is re-mis-sion; Cursed by the law and bruised by the
vides a per-fect sal-va-tion; "Come un-to Me," O hear His sweet
grace will keep us from fall-ing; Pass-ing from death to life at His

fall, Grace hath re-deemed us once for all.
call, Come, and He saves us once for all. Once for all, O sin-ner, re-
call, Bless-ed sal-va-tion once for all.

ceive it, Once for all, O broth-er, be-lieve it; Cling to the

cross, the bur-den will fall, Christ hath re-deemed us once for all.

Favorite song of Dr. Hugh Pyle.

265 Someone's Last Call

EDNA R. WORRWELL

CLARENCE B. STROUSE, arranged

1. Come, O come to the bless-ed Sav - iour, List, O list to His
2. Deep, deep, deep in the heart there whis - pers God's own voice to each
3. Long, long, long have you tried to sti - fle Yearn-ings sweet to a
4. Now, now NOW as the Spir-it stirs you, Hard - en not your fast

lov - ing call, Of - fer - ing par - don, Par-don from sin to
way-ward child; Heed it! O heed it! Be no more sin - be -
life more pure; Quench them no long - er But in God rest se -
melt - ing heart; Take, take sal - va - tion Else shall your chance de -

all; O come, He gives par-don from sin to all, to all.
guiled, O heed His voice, be now no more be-guiled, be- guiled.
cure; O strive no more, but in God rest se - cure, se - cure.
part; O take it *now,* else shall your chance de-part, de-part.

Parts

Come, come to Je - sus, Come ere this mo-ment takes flight; It

may be now some-one's last call, last call to - night.

Honey in the Rock

266

F. A. GRAVES

F. A. GRAVES

1. O my broth-er, do you know the Sav - iour, Who is won-drous
2. Have you "tast-ed that the Lord is gra - cious"? Do you walk in the
3. Do you pray un - to God the Fa - ther, "What wilt Thou have
4. Then go out through the streets and by - ways, Preach the Word to the

kind and true? He's the "Rock of your sal - va - tion!"
way that's new? Have you drunk from the liv - ing foun - tain?
me to do?" Nev - er fear, He will sure - ly an - swer,
man - y or few; Say to ev - 'ry fall - en broth - er,

There's Hon - ey in the Rock for you. O there's Hon-ey in the Rock, my

broth-er, There's Hon - ey in the Rock for you; Leave your
my broth-er, for you;

sins for the blood to cov - er, There's Hon-ey in the Rock for you. for you.

rit.

267 Yes, I Know!

ANNA W. WATERMAN

ANNA W. WATERMAN

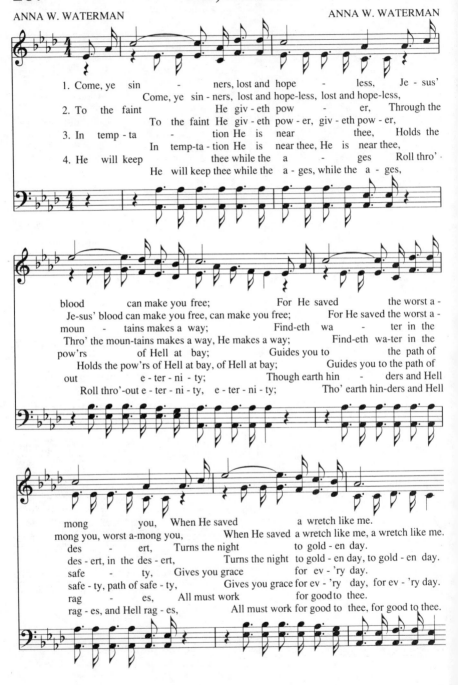

1. Come, ye sin - ners, lost and hope - less, Je - sus'
   Come, ye sin - ners, lost and hope-less, lost and hope-less,
2. To the faint He giv - eth pow - er, Through the
   To the faint He giv - eth pow - er, giv - eth pow - er,
3. In temp - ta - tion He is near thee, Holds the
   In temp-ta - tion He is near thee, He is near thee,
4. He will keep thee while the a - ges Roll thro' -
   He will keep thee while the a - ges, while the a - ges,

blood can make you free; For He saved the worst a -
Je-sus' blood can make you free, can make you free; For He saved the worst a -
moun - tains makes a way; Find-eth wa - ter in the
Thro' the moun-tains makes a way, He makes a way; Find-eth wa-ter in the
pow'rs of Hell at bay; Guides you to the path of
Holds the pow'rs of Hell at bay, of Hell at bay; Guides you to the path of
out e - ter - ni - ty; Though earth hin - ders and Hell
Roll thro'-out e - ter - ni - ty, e - ter - ni - ty; Tho' earth hin-ders and Hell

mong you, When He saved a wretch like me.
mong you, worst a-mong you, When He saved a wretch like me, a wretch like me.
des - ert, Turns the night to gold - en day.
des - ert, in the des - ert, Turns the night to gold - en day, to gold - en day.
safe - ty, Gives you grace for ev - 'ry day.
safe - ty, path of safe - ty, Gives you grace for ev - 'ry day, for ev - 'ry day.
rag - es, All must work for good to thee.
rag - es, and Hell rag - es, All must work for good to thee, for good to thee.

And I know, (I sure-ly know), yes, I know, (I sure-ly know), Je-sus'

blood can make the vil-est sin-ner clean.

1. vil-est sin-ner clean.

2. clean. vil-est sin-ner clean.

What Did He Do? 268

J. M. GRAY

W. OWEN

1. O lis-ten to our won-drous sto-ry, Count-ed once a-mong the lost;
2. Will you sur-ren-der to the Sav-iour? To His scep-ter hum-bly bow?

Yes, One came down from Heav-en's glo-ry, Sav-ing us at aw-ful cost!
You, too, shall come to know His fav-or, He will save you, save you now.

Who saved us from e-ter-nal loss? What did He do?
Who but God's Son up-on the cross? He

Where is He now? In Heav-en in-ter-ced - ing!
died for you! Be - lieve it, thou, In

269

Why Do You Wait?

GEORGE F. ROOT

GEORGE F. ROOT

1. Why do you wait, dear broth-er, Oh, why do you tar-ry so long?
2. What do you hope, dear broth-er, to gain by a fur-ther de-lay?
3. Do you not feel, dear broth-er, His Spir-it now striv-ing with-in?
4. Why do you wait, dear broth-er? The har-vest is pass-ing a-way;

Your Sav-iour is wait-ing to give you a place in His sanc-ti-fied throng.
There's no one to save you but Je-sus, There's no oth-er way but His way.
Oh, why not ac-cept His sal-va-tion, And throw off your bur-den of sin?
Your Sav-iour is long-ing to bless you, There are dan-ger and death in de-lay.

1. *2.*

Why not? why not? Why not come to Him now? now?

270

Just as I Am

CHARLOTTE ELLIOTT

WILLIAM B. BRADBURY

1. Just as I am, with-out one plea, But that Thy blood was shed for me,
2. Just as I am, and wait-ing not To rid my soul of one dark blot,
3. Just as I am, tho' tossed a-bout With many a con-flict, many a doubt,
4. Just as I am, poor, wretch-ed, blind; Sight, rich-es, heal-ing of the mind,
5. Just as I am, Thou wilt re-ceive, Wilt wel-come, par-don, cleanse, re-lieve;

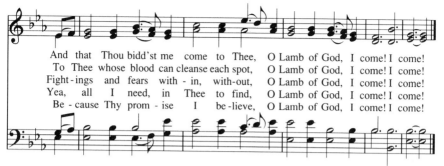

And that Thou bidd'st me come to Thee, O Lamb of God, I come! I come!
To Thee whose blood can cleanse each spot, O Lamb of God, I come! I come!
Fight-ings and fears with - in, with-out, O Lamb of God, I come! I come!
Yea, all I need, in Thee to find, O Lamb of God, I come! I come!
Be - cause Thy prom - ise I be - lieve, O Lamb of God, I come! I come!

Lord, I'm Coming Home 271

WILLIAM J. KIRKPATRICK

WILLIAM J. KIRKPATRICK

1. I've wan-dered far a - way from God, Now I'm com-ing home;
2. I've wast - ed man - y pre - cious years, Now I'm com-ing home:
3. I've tired of sin and stray - ing, Lord, Now I'm com-ing home;
4. My soul is sick, my heart is sore, Now I'm com-ing home;

Fine

The paths of sin too long I've trod, Lord, I'm com-ing home.
I now re - pent with bit - ter tears, Lord, I'm com-ing home.
I'll trust Thy love, be - lieve Thy Word, Lord, I'm com-ing home.
My strength re - new, my hope re - store, Lord, I'm com-ing home.

D.S. O - pen wide Thine arms of love, Lord, I'm com-ing home.

D.S.

Com-ing home, com-ing home, Nev - er-more to roam.

272

Jesus, I Come

WILLIAM T. SLEEPER

GEORGE C. STEBBINS

1. Out of my bond-age, sor-row and night, Je-sus, I come, Je-sus, I come;
2. Out of my shame-ful fail-ure and loss, Je-sus, I come, Je-sus, I come;
3. Out of un-rest and ar-ro-gant pride, Je-sus, I come, Je-sus, I come;
4. Out of the fear and dread of the tomb, Je-sus, I come, Je-sus, I come;

In - to Thy free-dom, glad-ness and light, Je-sus, I come to Thee.
In - to the glo-rious gain of Thy cross, Je-sus, I come to Thee.
In - to Thy bless-ed will to a-bide, Je-sus, I come to Thee.
In - to the joy and light of Thy Home, Je-sus, I come to Thee.

Out of my sick-ness in-to Thy health, Out of my want and in-to Thy
Out of earth's sor-rows in-to Thy balm, Out of life's storms and in-to Thy
Out of my-self to dwell in Thy love, Out of de-spair in-to rap-tures a-
Out of the depths of ru-in un-told, In-to the peace of Thy shel-ter-ing

wealth, Out of my sin and in-to Thy-self, Je-sus, I come to Thee.
calm, Out of dis-tress to ju-bi-lant psalm, Je-sus, I come to Thee.
bove, Up-ward for aye on wings like a dove, Je-sus, I come to Thee.
fold, Ev-er Thy glo-rious face to be-hold, Je-sus, I come to Thee.

What Will You Do With Jesus? 273

AUTHOR UNKNOWN

M. L. STOCKS

1. Je - sus is stand - ing in Pi - late's hall, Friend-less, for - sak - en, be -
2. Je - sus is stand - ing on tri - al still, You can be false to Him
3. Will you e - vade Him as Pi - late tried? Or will you choose Him, what -
4. Will you, like Pe - ter, your Lord de - ny? Or will You scorn from His
5. "Je - sus, I give Thee my heart to - day! Je - sus, I'll fol - low Thee

trayed by all: Hark - en! what mean - eth the sud - den call!
if you will, You can be faith - ful thro' good or ill:
e'er be - tide? Vain - ly you strug - gle from Him to hide:
foes to fly, Dar - ing for Je - sus to live or die?
all the way, Glad - ly o - bey - ing Thee!" Will you say:

"What will you do with Je - sus?"
What will you do with Je - sus?
What will you do with Je - sus? What will you do with Je - sus?
What will you do with Je - sus?
"This will I do with Je - sus!"

Neu - tral you can - not be; Some-day your heart will be

ask - ing, "What will He do with me?"

274 Come Unto Me

CHARLES P. JONES   CHARLES P. JONES

1. Hear the bless-ed Sav-iour call-ing the op-pressed, "O ye heav-y la-den, come to Me and rest; Come, no lon-ger tar-ry, I your load will bear, Bring Me ev-'ry bur-den, bring Me ev-'ry care."
2. Are you dis-ap-point-ed, wan-d'ring here and there, Drag-ging chains of doubt and load-ed down with care? Do un-ho-ly feel-ings strug-gle in your breast? Bring your case to Je-sus, He will give you rest.
3. Stum-bling on the moun-tains dark with sin and shame, Stum-bling tow'rd the pit of Hell's con-sum-ing flame, By the pow'rs of sin de-lud-ed and op-pressed, Hear the ten-der Shep-herd, "Come to Me and rest."
4. Have you by temp-ta-tion of-ten con-quered been, Has a sense of weak-ness brought dis-tress with-in? Christ will sanc-ti-fy you, if you'll claim His best, In the Ho-ly Spir-it, He will give you rest.

Come un-to Me; I ———————— will give you
Come un-to Me, Come un-to Me, I will give you rest,

275 Almost Persuaded

PHILIP P. BLISS

PHILIP P. BLISS

1. "Al-most per-suad-ed," now to be-lieve; "Al-most per-suad-ed,"
2. "Al-most per-suad-ed," come, come to-day; "Al-most per-suad-ed,"
3. "Al-most per-suad-ed," har-vest is past! "Al-most per-suad-ed,"

Christ to re-ceive; Seems now some soul to say, "Go, Spir-it,
turn not a-way; Je-sus in-vites you here, An-gels are
doom comes at last! "Al-most" can-not a-vail; "Al-most" is

go Thy way, Some more con-ven-ient day On... Thee I'll call."
ling-'ring near, Prayers rise from hearts so dear, O... wan-d'rer, come.
but to fail! Sad, sad, that bit-ter wail, "Al-most," but lost.

276 Where He Leads Me

E. W. BLANDLY

J. S. NORRIS

1. I can hear my Sav-iour call-ing, I can hear my Sav-iour call-ing,
2. I'll go with Him thro' the gar-den, I'll go with Him thro' the gar-den,
3. I'll go with Him thro' the judg-ment, I'll go with Him thro' the judg-ment,
4. He will give me grace and glo-ry, He will give me grace and glo-ry,

REF.: Where He leads me   I will fol-low, Where He leads me   I will fol-low,

D.C. for Ref.

I can hear my Sav-iour call-ing, "Take thy cross and fol-low, fol-low Me."
I'll go with Him thro' the gar-den, I'll go with Him, with Him all the way.
I'll go with Him thro' the judg-ment, I'll go with Him, with Him all the way.
He will give me grace and glo-ry, And go with me, with me all the way.

Where He leads me I will fol-low, I'll go with Him, with Him all the way.

Only Trust Him 277

JOHN H. STOCKTON   JOHN H. STOCKTON

1. Come, ev - 'ry soul by sin op-pressed, There's mer - cy with the Lord,
2. For Je - sus shed His pre-cious blood, Rich bless-ings to be - stow;
3. Yes, Je - sus is the Truth, the Way, That leads you in - to rest:
4. Come, then, and join this ho - ly band, And on to Glo - ry go,

And He will sure - ly give you rest By trust-ing in His Word.
Plunge now in - to the crim - son flood That wash - es white as snow.
Be - lieve in Him with-out de - lay, And you are ful - ly blest.
To dwell in that ce - les - tial Land, Where joys im - mor - tal flow.

1.
2.

On - ly trust Him, on - ly trust Him, On - ly trust Him now.
He will save you, He will save you, He will (Omit ....) save you now.

278 Jesus Is Calling

FANNY J. CROSBY

GEORGE C. STEBBINS

1. Je - sus is ten - der - ly call - ing thee home — Call - ing to - day,
2. Je - sus is call - ing the wear - y to rest — Call - ing to - day,
3. Je - sus is wait - ing; O come to Him now — Wait - ing to - day,
4. Je - sus is plead - ing; O list to His voice: Hear Him to - day,

call - ing to - day; Why from the sun - shine of love wilt thou roam
call - ing to - day; Bring Him thy bur - den and thou shalt be blest:
wait - ing to - day; Come with thy sins; at His feet low - ly bow;
hear Him to - day; They who be - lieve on His name shall re - joice;

Far - ther and far - ther a - way?___
He will not turn thee a - way.___ Call - ing to - day, ___
Come, and no lon - ger de - lay. ___
Quick - ly a - rise and a - way. ___ Call-ing, call-ing to - day, to - day,

Call - ing to - day, ___ Je - sus is
Call - ing, call - ing, to - day, to - day, Je - sus is ten - der - ly

call - ing, is ten - der - ly call - ing to - day. ___
call - ing to - day,

Let Jesus Come Into Your Heart 279

LEILA N. MORRIS   LEILA N. MORRIS

1. If you are tired of the load of your sin, Let Je - sus come
2. If 'tis for pu - ri - ty now that you sigh, Let Je - sus come
3. If there's a tem-pest your voice can - not still, Let Je - sus come
4. If you would join the glad songs of the blest, Let Je - sus come

in - to your heart; If you de - sire a new life to be - gin,
in - to your heart; Foun-tains for cleans-ing are flow-ing, near by,
in - to your heart; If there's a void this world nev - er can fill,
in - to your heart; If you would en - ter the man-sions of rest,

Let Je - sus come in - to your heart. Just now your

doubt-ings give o'er; Just now, re - ject Him no more; Just now, throw

o - pen the door; Let Je - sus come in - to your heart.

280 Softly and Tenderly Jesus Is Calling

WILL L. THOMPSON

WILL L. THOMPSON

1. Soft - ly and ten-der - ly Je - sus is call-ing, Call-ing for
2. Why should we tar - ry when Je - sus is plead-ing, Plead-ing for
3. Time is now fleet-ing, the mo-ments are pass-ing, Pass-ing from
4. Oh! for the won-der - ful love He has prom-ised, Prom-ised for

you and for me; See, on the por-tals He's wait - ing and watch-ing,
you and for me? Why should we ling - er and heed not His mer-cies,
you and from me; Sha - dows are gath - er - ing, death-beds are com-ing,
you and for me; Tho' we have sinned, He has mer - cy and par-don,

p

Watch-ing for you and for me.
Mer-cies for you and for me? Come home, come home,
Com-ing for you and for me. Come home, come home,
Par-don for you and for me.

cresc. *pp* *ppp*

Ye who are wear - y, come home; Ear - nest-ly, ten-der - ly,

rit.   *pp*

Je - sus is call - ing, Call - ing, O sin - ner, come home!

Pass Me Not, O Gentle Saviour   281

FANNY J. CROSBY

WILLIAM H. DOANE

1. Pass me not, O gen - tle Sav - iour, Hear my hum - ble cry;
2. Let me at a throne of mer - cy Find a sweet re - lief;
3. Trust - ing on - ly in Thy mer - it, Would I seek Thy face;
4. Thou the Spring of all my com - fort, More than life to me,

While on oth - ers Thou art call - ing, Do not pass me by.
Kneel - ing there in deep con - tri - tion, Help my un - be - lief.
Heal my wound - ed, bro - ken spir - it, Save me by Thy grace.
Whom have I on earth be - side Thee? Whom in Heav'n but Thee?

Sav - iour, Sav - iour, Hear my hum - ble cry;

While on oth - ers Thou art call - ing, Do not pass me by.

Favorite song of Dr. Charles Billington.

282 Why Not Now?

DANIEL W. WHITTLE

CHARLES C. CASE

1. While we pray and while we plead, While you see your soul's deep need,
2. You have wan - dered far a - way; Do not risk an - oth - er day;
3. In the world you've failed to find Aught of peace for troub - led mind;
4. Come to Christ, con - fes-sion make; Come to Christ, and par - don take;

While our Fa - ther calls you home, Will you not, my broth- er, come?
Do not turn from God thy face, But to - day ac - cept His grace.
Come to Christ, on Him be - lieve, Peace and joy you shall re - ceive.
Trust in Him from day to day, He will keep you all the way.

Why not now? Why not now? Why not come to Je - sus now?
Why not now? Why not now?

Why not now? Why not now? Why not come to Je - sus now?
Why not now? Why not now?

Have You Any Room for Jesus?   283

SOURCE UNKNOWN
Arr. by Daniel W. Whittle

C. C. WILLIAMS

1. Have you an-y room for Je-sus, He who bore your load of sin?
2. Room for pleas-ure, room for busi-ness, But for Christ the Cru-ci-fied,
3. Have you an-y room for Je-sus, As in grace He calls a-gain?
4. Room and time now give to Je-sus, Soon will pass God's day of grace;

As He knocks and asks ad-mis-sion, Sin-ner, will you let Him in?
Not a place that He can en-ter, In the heart for which He died?
O to-day is time ac-cept-ed, To-mor-row you may call in vain.
Soon thy heart left cold and si-lent, And thy Sav-iour's plead-ing cease.

Room for Je-sus, King of Glo-ry! Has-ten now His Word o-bey;

Swing the heart's door wide-ly o-pen, Bid Him en-ter while you may.

284   Who at My Door Is Standing?

MARY B. C. SLADE   ASA B. EVERETT

1. Who at my door is stand-ing, Pa-tient-ly draw-ing near,
2. Lone-ly with-out He's stay-ing: Lone-ly with-in am I;
3. All through the dark hours drea-ry, Knock-ing a-gain is He;
4. Door of my heart, I has-ten! Thee will I o-pen wide.

En-trance with-in de-mand-ing? Whose is the voice I hear?
While I am still de-lay-ing, Will He not pass me by?
Je-sus, art Thou not wea-ry, Wait-ing so long for me?
Tho' He re-buke and chas-ten, He shall with me a-bide.

Sweet-ly the tones are fall-ing: "O-pen the door for Me!

If thou wilt heed My call-ing, I will a-bide with thee."

Into My Heart

285

HARRY D. CLARKE

HARRY D. CLARKE

1. Come in-to my heart, bless-ed Je - sus, Come in-to my heart,
2. Come in-to my heart, bless-ed Je - sus, I need Thee thro' life's drear - y
3. Come in-to my heart, bless-ed Je - sus, And take all my guilt a-
4. Come in-to my heart, bless-ed Je - sus, O cleanse and il - lu-mine my

I pray; My soul is so troub-led and wea-ry, Come in-to my heart to-
way; The bur-den of sin is so heav-y, Come in-to my heart to
way; Then spot-less I'll stand in Thy pres-ence, When breaks the e - ter - nal
soul; Fill me with Thy won-der-ful Spir-it, Come in and take full con-

day.
stay. In - to my heart, in - to my heart, Come
day.
trol.

in - to my heart, Lord Je - sus; Come in to-day, Come

in to stay, Come in-to my heart, Lord Je - sus.

286 The Nail-Scarred Hand

BAYLUS B. McKINNEY

BAYLUS B. McKINNEY

1. Have you failed in your plan of your storm-tossed life? Place your hand in the
2. Are you walk-ing a - lone through the shad-ows dim? Place your hand in the
3. Would you fol - low the will of the ris - en Lord? Place your hand in the
4. Is your soul bur-dened down with its load of sin? Place your hand in the

nail-scarred hand; Are you wea - ry and worn from its toil and strife?
nail-scarred hand; Christ will com - fort your heart, put your trust in Him,
nail-scarred hand; Would you live in the light of His bless - ed Word?
nail-scarred hand; Throw your heart o - pen wide, let the Sav - iour in,

Place your hand in the nail-scarred hand. Place your hand in the nail-scarred

hand, Place your hand in the nail-scarred hand; He will keep to the

end, He's your dear - est Friend, Place your hand in the nail-scarred hand.

Open Your Heart's Door

JOHN R. RICE

JOHN R. RICE

1. Je - sus is here, Je - sus is here, Here on the door-step He's
2. Who - so - e'er will, Who - so - e'er will, May take the wa - ter of
3. "Don't turn a - way, Don't turn a - way From the soft warn-ing," your
4. Je - sus, come in; Je - sus, come in; Oh, lift the bur - den, for -

wait - ing so near, Not far a - way, but read - y to - day, Your poor
life to your fill. Je - sus has paid, His life down He laid, For all
con-science would say, God's brok-en laws, your sin and your fall, Oh, do
give all my sin. Con-quer, O mild One, my heart so wild, Take now

lost soul this mo-ment to save.
your sins, a - tone-ment He made.
not grieve God's Spir - it who calls.
and cleanse and make me God's child.

O - pen your heart's door to Je - sus,

He's stand-ing near, wait - ing to hear your heart's con - fes - sion and

He'll take pos - ses-sion, So o - pen your heart's door and let Him come in.

288

I Am Resolved

PALMER HARTSOUGH

JAMES H. FILLMORE

1. I am re-solved no lon - ger to lin - ger, Charmed by the world's de - light;
2. I am re-solved to go to the Sav-iour, Leav - ing my sin and strife;
3. I am re-solved to fol - low the Sav-iour, Faith - ful and true each day;

Things that are high - er, things that are no - bler, These have al - lured my sight.
He is the true One, He is the just One, He hath the words of life.
Heed what He say - eth, do what He will - eth, He is the liv - ing way.

I will has - ten to Him, Has-ten so glad and free;
I will has - ten, has - ten to Him, Has-ten so glad and free;

Has-ten glad and free;

Je - sus, Great - est, High - est, I will come to Thee.
Je - sus, Je - sus,

Come, Sinner, Come! 289

W. E. WITTER

H. R. PALMER

1. {
While Je - sus whis - pers to you, Come, sin - ner, come!
While we are pray - ing for you, *(Omit ....)*
}

2. {
Are you too heav - y la - den? Come, sin - ner, come!
Je - sus will bear your bur - den, *(Omit ....)*
}

3. {
Oh, hear His ten - der plead - ing, Come, sin - ner, come!
Come and re - ceive the bless - ing, *(Omit ....)*
}

Come, sin - ner, come!

Come, sin - ner, come!

Come, sin - ner, come!

{
Now is the time to own Him,
Now is the time to know Him,
}
{
Je - sus will not de - ceive you,
Je - sus can now re - deem you,
}
{
While Je - sus whis - pers to you,
While we are pray - ing for you,
}

Come, sin - ner, come!
(Omit ....)
Come, sin - ner, come!
(Omit ....)
Come, sin - ner, come!
(Omit ....)

Come, sin - ner, come!

Come, sin - ner, come!

Come, sin - ner, come!

290

Let Him In

JONATHAN B. ATCHINSON   EDWIN O. EXCELL

1. There's a Sav-iour at the door, Let Him
2. O - pen now to Him your heart, Let Him
3. Hear you now His lov - ing voice? Let Him
4. Now ad - mit the heav'n - ly Guest, Let Him
   Let the Sav-iour in,

in;   He has been there oft be - fore,
in;   If you wait He will de - part,
in;   Now, oh, now make Him your choice,
in;   He will make for you a feast,
Let the Sav - iour in;

Let Him in;   Let Him in, ere He is
Let Him in;   Let Him in, He is your
Let Him in;   He is stand - ing at your
Let Him in;   He will speak your sins for -
Let the Sav-iour in,   Let the Sav-iour in;

gone, Let Him in, the Ho - ly One, Je - sus Christ, the Fa - ther's
Friend, He your soul will sure de - fend, He will keep you to the
door, Joy to you He will re - store, And His name you will a -
giv'n, And when earth ties are all riv'n, He will take you Home to

I Am Coming, Lord   291

LEWIS HARTSOUGH   LEWIS HARTSOUGH

292 His Way With Thee

CYRUS S. NUSBAUM

CYRUS S. NUSBAUM

1. Would you live for Je - sus, and be al-ways pure and good? Would you walk with
2. Would you have Him make you free, and fol - low at His call? Would you know the
3. Would you in His king-dom find a place of con-stant rest? Would you prove Him

Him with - in the nar - row road? Would you have Him bear your bur-den, car - ry
peace that comes by giv - ing all? Would you have Him save you, so that you can
true in prov - i - den - tial test? Would you in His serv - ice la - bor al - ways

all your load?
nev - er fall? Let Him have His way with thee. His pow'r can make you what you
at your best?

ought to be; His blood can cleanse your heart and make you free; His love can fill your

soul, and you will see 'Twas best for Him to have His way with thee.

rit.

Is Your All on the Altar?

293

ELISHA A. HOFFMAN

ELISHA A. HOFFMAN

1. You have longed for sweet peace, and for faith to in-crease, And have ear-nest-ly
2. Would you walk with the Lord, in the light of His Word, And have peace and con-
3. O we nev-er can know what the Lord will be-stow Of the bless-ings for
4. Who can tell all the love He will send from a-bove, And how hap-py our

fer-vent-ly prayed; But you can-not have rest or be per-fect-ly blest
tent-ment al-way? You must do His sweet will, to be free from all ill,
which we have prayed, Till our bod-y and soul He doth ful-ly con-trol,
hearts will be made, Of the fel-low-ship sweet we shall share at His feet,

Un-til all on the al-tar is laid.
On the al-tar your all you must lay.
And our all on the al-tar is laid.
When our all on the al-tar is laid.

Is your all on the al-tar of

sac-ri-fice laid? Your heart, does the Spir-it con-trol? You can on-ly be

blest and have peace and sweet rest, As you yield Him your bod-y and soul.

294 Stepping in the Light

ELIZA E. HEWITT

WILLIAM J. KIRKPATRICK

1. Try - ing to walk in the steps of the Sav-iour, Try - ing to fol - low our
2. Press - ing more close-ly to Him who is lead - ing, When we are tempt-ed to
3. Walk - ing in foot-steps of gen - tle for-bear-ance, Foot-steps of faith-ful-ness,
4. Try - ing to walk in the steps of the Sav-iour, Up-ward, still up-ward we'll

Sav - iour and King; Shap - ing our lives by His bless-ed ex - am - ple,
turn from the way; Trust - ing the arm that is strong to de-fend us,
mer - cy and love, Look - ing to Him for the grace free - ly prom - ised,
fol - low our Guide; When we shall see Him, "the King in His beau - ty,"

Hap-py, how hap-py, the songs that we bring.
Hap-py, how hap-py, our prais-es each day. How beau-ti - ful to walk in the
Hap-py, how hap-py, our jour-ney a-bove.
Hap-py, how hap-py, our place at His side.

steps of the Sav - iour, Step-ping in the light, Step-ping in the light; How

beau-ti - ful to walk in the steps of the Sav-iour, Led in paths of light.

Back to Bethel

295

B. B. McKINNEY

B. B. McKINNEY

1. Back to the Bi-ble, the true Liv-ing Word, Sweet-est old sto-ry that
2. Back to the beau-ti-ful path I once trod, Back to the church and the
3. Back to the giv-ing of mon-ey and time, Back to the life of con-
4. Back to the prayer-life in Christ I once knew, Back to its beau-ti-ful

ev-er was heard; Back to the joy-life my soul longs to know,
peo-ple of God; Out of the cold world of sin and its woe,
tent-ment sub-lime, Back to pro-tec-tion the world can-not know,
life-cleans-ing dew, Back to help oth-ers to con-quer each foe,

Beth-el is call-ing, and I must go. Back to Beth-el
I must go, Back where the riv-ers of sweet wa-ters flow, Back to the
true life my soul longs to know, Beth-el is call-ing, and I must go.

296 Follow On

W. O. CUSHING

ROBERT LOWRY

1. Down in the val-ley with my Sav-iour I would go, Where the flow'rs are
2. Down in the val-ley with my Sav-iour I would go, Where the storms are
3. Down in the val-ley, or up - on the moun-tain steep, Close be-side my

bloom-ing and the sweet wa-ters flow; Ev - 'ry-where He leads me I would
sweep-ing and the dark wa-ters flow; With His hand to lead me I will
Sav-iour would my soul ev - er keep; He will lead me safe - ly in the

fol-low, fol-low on, Walk-ing in His foot-steps till the crown be won.
nev-er, nev-er fear, Dan-ger can-not fright me if my Lord is near.
path that He has trod, Up to where they gath-er on the hills of God.

Fol-low! fol - low! I would fol-low Je - sus! An-y-where, ev - 'ry-where,

I would fol - low on! Fol - low! fol - low! I would fol - low

Je - sus! Ev - 'ry-where He leads me I would fol - low on!

Close to Thee

297

FANNY J. CROSBY

SILAS J. VAIL

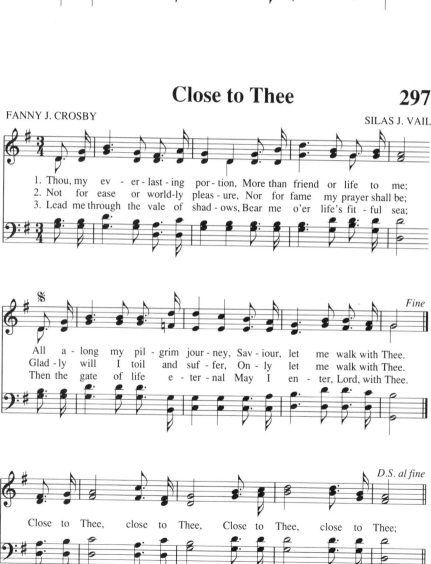

1. Thou, my ev - er - last - ing por - tion, More than friend or life to me;
2. Not for ease or world-ly pleas - ure, Nor for fame my prayer shall be;
3. Lead me through the vale of shad - ows, Bear me o'er life's fit - ful sea;

Fine

All a - long my pil - grim jour - ney, Sav - iour, let me walk with Thee.
Glad - ly will I toil and suf - fer, On - ly let me walk with Thee.
Then the gate of life e - ter - nal May I en - ter, Lord, with Thee.

D.S. al fine

Close to Thee, close to Thee, Close to Thee, close to Thee;

298 More Like the Master

CHARLES H. GABRIEL

CHARLES H. GABRIEL

1. More like the Mas-ter I would ev - er be, More of His meek-ness,
2. More like the Mas-ter is my dai - ly prayer; More strength to car - ry
3. More like the Mas-ter I would live and grow; More of His love to

more hu-mil-i - ty; More zeal to la-bor, more cour-age to be true;
cross-es I must bear; More ear-nest ef-fort to res-cue souls from sin;
oth-ers I would show; More self de - ni - al, like His in Gal - i - lee,

More con-se - cra-tion for work He bids me do.
More of His Spir-it, the wan-der-er to win.
More like the Mas-ter I long to ev - er be.

Take Thou my heart, I would be Thine a - lone;
take my heart, I would be Thine a-lone;

Take Thou my heart
Take my heart, O take my heart and

make it all Thine own; Purge me from sin, O Lord, I now im-
make it all Thine own; Purge Thou me from ev-'ry sin, O Lord, I

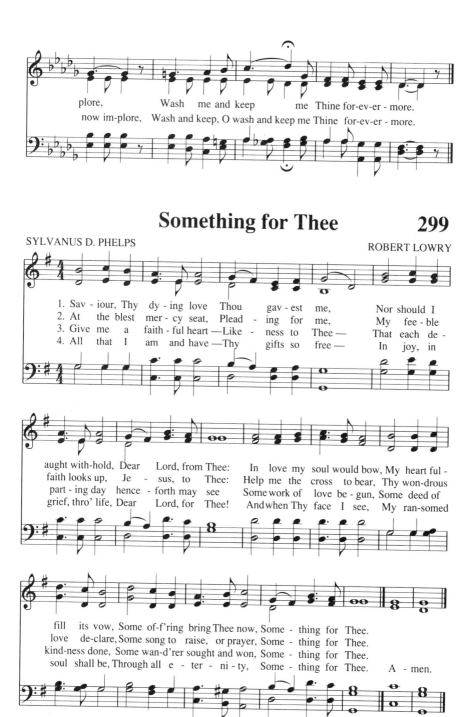

plore, Wash me and keep me Thine for-ev-er - more.
now im-plore, Wash and keep, O wash and keep me Thine for-ev-er - more.

Something for Thee

299

SYLVANUS D. PHELPS

ROBERT LOWRY

1. Sav - iour, Thy dy - ing love Thou gav - est me, Nor should I
2. At the blest mer - cy seat, Plead - ing for me, My fee - ble
3. Give me a faith - ful heart —Like - ness to Thee — That each de -
4. All that I am and have —Thy gifts so free — In joy, in

aught with-hold, Dear Lord, from Thee: In love my soul would bow, My heart ful -
faith looks up, Je - sus, to Thee: Help me the cross to bear, Thy won-drous
part - ing day hence - forth may see Some work of love be - gun, Some deed of
grief, thro' life, Dear Lord, for Thee! And when Thy face I see, My ran-somed

fill its vow, Some of-f'ring bring Thee now, Some - thing for Thee.
love de-clare, Some song to raise, or prayer, Some - thing for Thee.
kind-ness done, Some wan-d'rer sought and won, Some - thing for Thee.
soul shall be, Through all e - ter - ni - ty, Some - thing for Thee. A - men.

300 Ashamed of Jesus

JOSEPH GRIGGS

EDWIN O. EXCELL

1. Je - sus, and shall it ev - er be, A mor - tal
2. A - shamed of Je - sus! soon - er far Let eve - ning
3. A - shamed of Je - sus! that dear Friend, On whom my
4. A - shamed of Je - sus! yes, I may, When I've no

man a - shamed of Thee? A - shamed of Thee, whom
blush to own a star; He sheds the beams of
hopes of Heav'n de - pend? No! when I blush be
guilt to wash a - way, No tear to wipe, no

an - gels praise, Whose glo - ries shine through end - less days?
light di - vine O'er this be - night - ed soul of mine.
this my shame, That I no more re - vere His name.
good to crave, No fears to quell, no soul to save.

A - shamed of Je - sus, I nev - er, I nev - er will
A - shamed of Je - sus, a - shamed of Je - sus,

be; For Je - sus, my Sav - iour, my
nev - er will be; Je - sus my Sav - iour, for

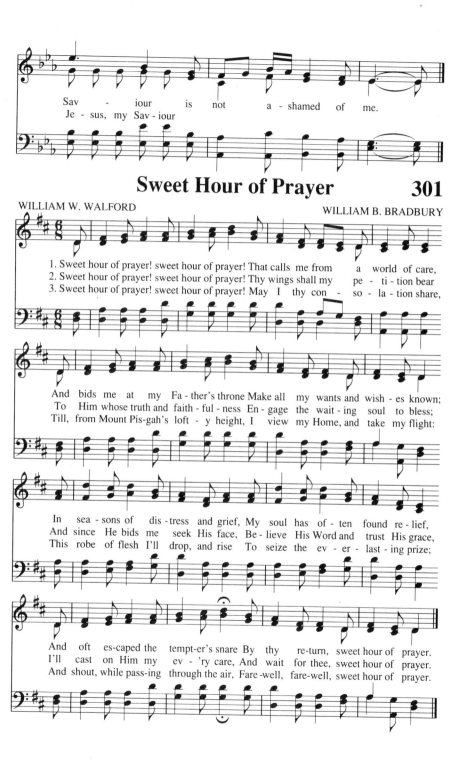

Sav - iour is not a - shamed of me.
Je - sus, my Sav - iour

Sweet Hour of Prayer 301

WILLIAM W. WALFORD

WILLIAM B. BRADBURY

1. Sweet hour of prayer! sweet hour of prayer! That calls me from a world of care,
2. Sweet hour of prayer! sweet hour of prayer! Thy wings shall my pe - ti - tion bear
3. Sweet hour of prayer! sweet hour of prayer! May I thy con - so - la - tion share,

And bids me at my Fa - ther's throne Make all my wants and wish - es known;
To Him whose truth and faith - ful - ness En - gage the wait - ing soul to bless;
Till, from Mount Pis - gah's loft - y height, I view my Home, and take my flight:

In sea - sons of dis - tress and grief, My soul has of - ten found re - lief,
And since He bids me seek His face, Be - lieve His Word and trust His grace,
This robe of flesh I'll drop, and rise To seize the ev - er - last - ing prize;

And oft es - caped the tempt - er's snare By thy re - turn, sweet hour of prayer.
I'll cast on Him my ev - 'ry care, And wait for thee, sweet hour of prayer.
And shout, while pass - ing through the air, Fare - well, fare - well, sweet hour of prayer.

302 Sweet Will of God

LEILA N. MORRIS

LEILA N. MORRIS

1. My stub-born will at last hath yield-ed; I would be Thine, and
2. I'm tired of sin, foot-sore and wea-ry, The dark-some path hath
3. Thy pre-cious will, O con - qu'ring Sav - iour, Doth now em - brace and
4. Shut in with Thee, O Lord, for - ev - er, My way-ward feet no

Thine a - lone; And this the prayer my lips are bring-ing,
drear - y grown, But now a light has ris'n to cheer me;
com - pass me; All dis-cords hushed, my peace a riv - er,
more to roam; What pow'r from Thee my soul can sev - er?

"Lord, let in me Thy will be done."
I find in Thee my Star, my Sun.
My soul a pris-oned bird set free.
The cen-ter of God's will my home.

Sweet will of God, still

fold me clos - er, Till I am whol - ly lost in Thee; Sweet

will of God, still fold me clos - er, Till

I am whol - ly lost in Thee.

My Faith Looks Up to Thee   303

RAY PALMER

LOWELL MASON

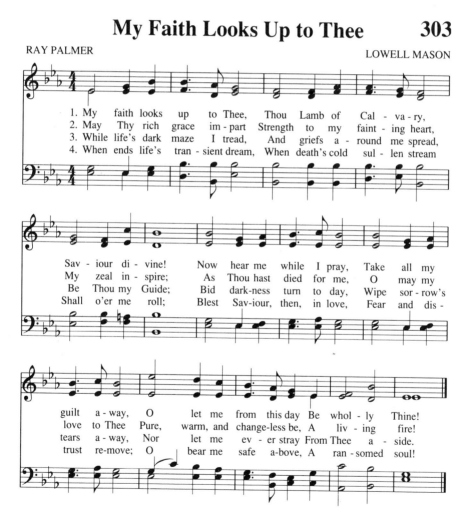

1. My faith looks up to Thee, Thou Lamb of Cal - va - ry,
2. May Thy rich grace im - part Strength to my faint - ing heart,
3. While life's dark maze I tread, And griefs a - round me spread,
4. When ends life's tran - sient dream, When death's cold sul - len stream

Sav - iour di - vine! Now hear me while I pray, Take all my
My zeal in - spire; As Thou hast died for me, O may my
Be Thou my Guide; Bid dark - ness turn to day, Wipe sor - row's
Shall o'er me roll; Blest Sav - iour, then, in love, Fear and dis -

guilt a - way, O let me from this day Be whol - ly Thine!
love to Thee Pure, warm, and change-less be, A liv - ing fire!
tears a - way, Nor let me ev - er stray From Thee a - side.
trust re-move; O bear me safe a-bove, A ran - somed soul!

304 Nothing Between

C. A. TINDLEY

C. A. TINDLEY
Arranged by F. A. Clark

1. Noth-ing be-tween my soul and the Sav-iour, Naught of this world's de-
2. Noth-ing be-tween like world - ly pleas-ure; Hab-its of life, though
3. Noth-ing be-tween, like pride or like sta-tion; Self or friends shall
4. Noth-ing be-tween, e'en man-y hard tri-als, Though the whole world a-

lu - sive dream: I have re-nounced all sin - ful pleas-ure,
harm-less they seem, Must not my heart from Him ev-er sev-er—
not in - ter - vene; Though it may cost me much trib-u-la-tion,
gainst me con-vene; Watch-ing with prayer and much self-de-ni-al, I'll

Je - sus is mine, there's noth-ing be-tween.
He is my all, there's noth-ing be-tween.
I am re-solved, there's noth-ing be-tween.
tri-umph at last, with noth-ing be-tween.

Noth-ing be-tween my soul and the

Sav-iour, So that His bless-ed face may be seen; Noth-ing pre-vent-ing the

least of His fa-vor, Keep the way clear! Let noth-ing be-tween.

Yield Not to Temptation

305

HORATIO R. PALMER

HORATIO R. PALMER

1. Yield not to temp-ta - tion, For yield-ing is sin, Each vic-t'ry will
2. Shun e - vil com - pan - ions, Bad lan-guage dis - dain, God's name hold in
3. To him that o'er-com - eth God giv - eth a crown, Through faith we shall

help you Some oth - er to win; Fight man-ful - ly on - ward,
rev - 'rence, Nor take it in vain; Be thought-ful and ear - nest,
con - quer, Though of - ten cast down; He who is our Sav - iour,

Dark pas-sions sub -due,
Kind-heart-ed and true, Look ev - er to Je - sus, He will car-ry you through.
Our strength will re - new,

Ask the Sav - iour to help you, Com-fort, strength-en, and keep you,

He is will - ing to aid you, He will car - ry you through.

306

Have Thine Own Way, Lord!

ADELAIDE A. POLLARD

GEORGE C. STEBBINS

1. Have Thine own way, Lord! Have Thine own way! Thou art the
2. Have Thine own way, Lord! Have Thine own way! Search me and
3. Have Thine own way, Lord! Have Thine own way! Wound-ed and
4. Have Thine own way, Lord! Have Thine own way! Hold o'er my

Pot - ter; I am the clay. Mold me and make me Af - ter Thy
try me, Mas-ter, to - day! Whit - er than snow, Lord, wash me just
wea - ry, Help me, I pray! Pow-er—all pow - er— Sure - ly is
be - ing Ab - so-lute sway! Fill with Thy Spir - it Till all shall

will, While I am wait - ing, Yield-ed and still.
now, As in Thy pres - ence Hum-bly I bow.
Thine! Touch me and heal me, Sav-iour di - vine!
see Christ on - ly, al - ways, Liv-ing in me!

307

Jesus Calls Us

Mrs. CECIL F. ALEXANDER

WILLIAM H. JUDE

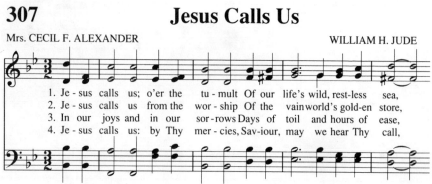

1. Je - sus calls us; o'er the tu - mult Of our life's wild, rest-less sea,
2. Je - sus calls us from the wor - ship Of the vain world's gold-en store,
3. In our joys and in our sor-rows Days of toil and hours of ease,
4. Je - sus calls us: by Thy mer - cies, Sav-iour, may we hear Thy call,

Day by   day His sweet voice sound - eth, Say-ing, "Chris-tian, fol - low Me."
From each   i - dol that would keep us, Say-ing, "Chris-tian, love Me more."
Still He   calls, in cares and pleas - ures, "Chris-tian, love Me more than these."
Give our   hearts to Thy o - be-dience, Serve and love Thee best of all.

I Surrender All 308

JUDSON W. VAN DeVENTER   WINFIELD S. WEEDEN

1. All   to Je - sus   I   sur-ren-der, All   to Him I   free - ly give;
2. All   to Je - sus   I   sur-ren-der, Hum - bly at His   feet I bow,
3. All   to Je - sus   I   sur-ren-der, Make   me, Sav-iour, whol-ly Thine;
4. All   to Je - sus   I   sur-ren-der, Lord,   I give my - self to Thee;

I   will ev - er   love   and trust Him, In   His pres-ence dai - ly live.
World - ly pleas-ures all   for-sak - en, Take   me, Je - sus, take me now.
Let   me feel the Ho - ly Spir - it — Tru - ly know that Thou art mine.
Fill   me with Thy love   and pow - er, Let   Thy bless-ing fall on me.

I   sur-ren-der all,   I   sur-ren-der all.
      I   sur-ren-der all,   I   sur-ren-der all.

All   to Thee, my   bless - ed Sav - iour,   I   sur - ren - der   all.

Favorite song of Dr. Fred D. Jarvis.

309 — Dare to Be a Daniel

PHILIP P. BLISS

PHILIP P. BLISS

1. Stand-ing by a pur-pose true, Heed-ing God's com-mand,
2. Man - y might-y men are lost, Dar - ing not to stand,
3. Man - y gi-ants, great and tall, Stalk-ing through the land,
4. Hold the gos-pel ban-ner high! On to vic-t'ry grand!

Hon-or them, the
Who for God had
Head-long to the
Sa - tan and his

faith-ful few! All hail to Dan-iel's Band!
been a host, By join-ing Dan-iel's Band!
earth would fall, If met by Dan-iel's Band!
host de - fy, And shout for Dan-iel's Band!

Dare to be a Dan - iel,

Dare to stand a - lone! Dare to have a pur-pose firm! Dare to make it known!

310 — Footprints of Jesus

MARY B. C. SLADE

ASA B. EVERETT

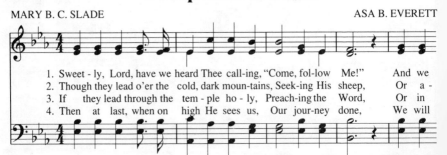

1. Sweet - ly, Lord, have we heard Thee call-ing, "Come, fol-low Me!" And we
2. Though they lead o'er the cold, dark moun-tains, Seek-ing His sheep, Or a -
3. If they lead through the tem - ple ho - ly, Preach-ing the Word, Or in
4. Then at last, when on high He sees us, Our jour-ney done, We will

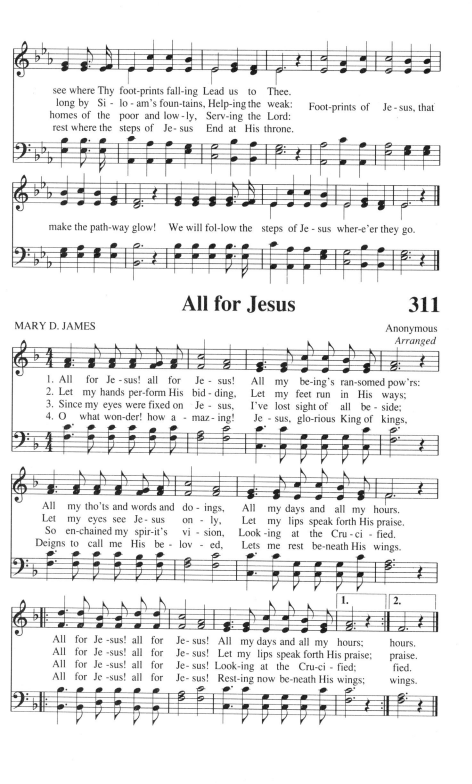

see where Thy foot-prints fall-ing Lead us to Thee.
long by Si - lo - am's foun-tains, Help-ing the weak:
homes of the poor and low-ly, Serv-ing the Lord:
rest where the steps of Je- sus End at His throne.

Foot-prints of Je - sus, that

make the path-way glow! We will fol-low the steps of Je - sus wher-e'er they go.

All for Jesus 311

MARY D. JAMES

Anonymous
Arranged

1. All for Je - sus! all for Je - sus! All my be-ing's ran-somed pow'rs:
2. Let my hands per-form His bid - ding, Let my feet run in His ways;
3. Since my eyes were fixed on Je - sus, I've lost sight of all be - side;
4. O what won-der! how a - maz - ing! Je - sus, glo-rious King of kings,

All my tho'ts and words and do - ings, All my days and all my hours.
Let my eyes see Je - sus on - ly, Let my lips speak forth His praise.
So en-chained my spir-it's vi - sion, Look-ing at the Cru - ci - fied.
Deigns to call me His be - lov - ed, Lets me rest be-neath His wings.

1.   **2.**

All for Je -sus! all for Je - sus! All my days and all my hours; hours.
All for Je -sus! all for Je - sus! Let my lips speak forth His praise; praise.
All for Je -sus! all for Je - sus! Look-ing at the Cru-ci-fied; fied.
All for Je -sus! all for Je - sus! Rest-ing now be-neath His wings; wings.

312 Open My Eyes, That I May See

CLARA H. SCOTT

CLARA H. SCOTT

1. O - pen my eyes, that I may see Glimps-es of truth Thou hast for me;
2. O - pen my ears, that I may hear Voi-ces of truth Thou send-est clear;
3. O - pen my mouth, and let me bear Glad-ly the warm truth ev - 'ry-where;

Place in my hands the won-der-ful key That shall un-clasp and set me free.
And while the wave-notes fall on my ear, Ev-'ry-thing false shall dis - ap-pear.
O - pen my heart, and let me pre-pare Love with Thy chil-dren thus to share.

Si - lent - ly now I wait for Thee, Read-y, my God, Thy will to see;
Si - lent - ly now I wait for Thee, Read-y, my God, Thy will to see;
Si - lent - ly now I wait for Thee, Read-y, my God, Thy will to see;

O - pen my eyes, il - lu - mine me, Spir - it di - vine!
O - pen my ears, il - lu - mine me, Spir - it di - vine!
O - pen my heart, il - lu - mine me, Spir - it di - vine!

313 I'll Be True, Precious Jesus

Anonymous

ELIZABETH PATE

1. I'll be true, pre-cious Je - sus, I'll be true, I'll be true, pre-cious
2. I'll go thro', pre-cious Je - sus, I'll go through, I'll go thro', pre-cious

Je-sus, I'll be true;
Je-sus, I'll go through; There's a race to be run, There's a

vic-t'ry to be won. Ev-'ry hour, by Thy pow-er, I'll be true.

More Love to Thee   314

ELIZABETH P. PRENTISS

WILLIAM H. DOANE

1. More love to Thee, O Christ, More love to Thee! Hear Thou the
2. Once earth-ly joy I craved, Sought peace and rest; Now Thee a-
3. Let sor-row do its work, Send grief and pain; Sweet are Thy
4. Then shall my lat-est breath Whis-per Thy praise; This be the

prayer I make on bend-ed knee; This is my ear-nest plea:
lone I seek, Give what is best; This all my prayer shall be:
mes-sen-gers, Sweet their re-frain, When they can sing with me,
part-ing cry My heart shall raise; This still its prayer shall be:

More love, O Christ, to Thee, More love to Thee, More love to Thee!

315   Take My Life, and Let It Be

FRANCES R. HAVERGAL

CÆSAR H. A. MALAN

1. Take my life, and let it be Con-se - cra - ted, Lord, to
2. Take my feet, and let them be Swift and beau - ti - ful for
3. Take my sil - ver and my gold, Not a mite would I with -
4. Take my will, and make it Thine, It shall be no long - er

Thee; Take my hands, and let them move At the im - pulse
Thee; Take my voice, and let me sing, Al - ways, on - ly,
hold; Take my mo - ments and my days, Let them flow in
mine; Take my heart, it is Thine own; It shall be Thy

of Thy love, At the im - pulse of Thy love.
for my King, Al - ways, on - ly, for my King.
cease - less praise, Let them flow in cease- less praise.
roy - al throne, It shall be Thy roy - al throne.

316   I Have Decided to Follow Jesus

Attributed to an Indian prince
As sung in Garo, Assam

Indian Folk Melody
Arranged by Norman Johnson

1. I have de - cid - ed to fol-low Je - sus, I have de - cid - ed
2. Tho' none go with me, still I will fol - low, Tho' none go with me,
3. The world be - hind me, the cross be -fore me, The world be- hind me,

to fol-low Je - sus, I have de - cid - ed to fol-low Je - sus—
still I will fol - low, Tho' none go with me, still I will fol - low—
the cross be - fore me, The world be - hind me, the cross be - fore me—

No turn - ing back, no turn - ing back.
No turn - ing back,

I'll Live for Him 317

RALPH E. HUDSON

C. R. DUNBAR

1. My life, my love I give to Thee, Thou Lamb of God who died for me;
2. I now be-lieve Thou dost re-ceive, For Thou hast died that I might live;
3. O Thou who died on Cal - va - ry, To save my soul and make me free,

Chorus: I'll live for Him who died for me, How hap - py then my life shall be!

D.C.

O may I ev - er faith - ful be, My Sav-iour and my God!
And now hence-forth I trust in Thee, My Sav-iour and my God!
I'll con - se-crate my life to Thee, My Sav-iour and my God!

I'll live for Him who died for me, My Sav-iour and my God!

318 Give Me Thy Heart

ELIZA E. HEWITT

WILLIAM J. KIRKPATRICK

1. "Give Me thy heart," says the Fa-ther a-bove— No gift so pre-cious to Him as our love; Soft-ly He whis-pers wher-ev-er thou art, "Grate-ful-ly trust Me and give Me thy heart."

2. "Give Me thy heart," says the Sav-iour of men, Call-ing in mer-cy a-gain and a-gain; "Trust in Me on-ly, I'll nev-er de-part— Have I not died for thee? give Me thy heart."

3. "Give Me thy heart," says the Spir-it di-vine; "All that thou hast to My keep-ing re-sign; Grace more a-bound-ing is Mine to im-part— Make full sur-ren-der and give Me thy heart."

"Give Me thy heart, Give Me thy heart"—Hear the soft whis-per, wher-ev-er thou art; From this dark world He would draw thee a-part, Speak-ing so ten-der-ly, "Give Me thy heart."

Just a Closer Walk With Thee 319

Anonymous

Anonymous
Arranged for John T. Benson

1. I am weak, but Thou art strong, (Thou art strong,) Je - sus keep me from all
2. Through this world of toil and snares, (toil and snares,) If I fal - ter, Lord, who
3. When my fee - ble life is o'er, (life is o'er,) Time for me will be no

wrong; (from all wrong;) I'll be sat - is-fied as long, (just as long,) As I walk let me
cares? (Lord, who cares?) Who with me my burden shares? (burden shares?) None but Thee, dear
more; (be no more;) Guide me gen-tly, safe-ly o'er, (safe-ly o'er,) To Thy king-dom

walk close to Thee. (close to Thee.)
Lord, none but Thee. (none but Thee.) Just a clos-er walk with Thee, (walk with Thee,)
shore, to Thy shore. (to Thy shore.)

Grant it, Je - sus, is my plea; (hum-ble plea;) Dai - ly walk-ing close to

Thee, (close to Thee,) Let it be, dear Lord, let it be. (let it be.)

320 O to Be Like Thee!

THOMAS O. CHISHOLM   WILLIAM J. KIRKPATRICK

1. O to be like Thee! bless-ed Re-deem-er, This is my con-stant
2. O to be like Thee! full of com-pas-sion, Lov-ing, for-giv-ing,
3. O to be like Thee! low-ly in spir-it, Ho-ly and harm-less,
4. O to be like Thee! Lord, I am com-ing, Now to re-ceive a-
5. O to be like Thee! while I am plead-ing, Pour out Thy Spir-it,

long-ing and prayer; Glad-ly I'll for-feit all of earth's treas-ures,
ten-der and kind, Help-ing the help-less, cheer-ing the faint-ing,
pa-tient and brave; Meek-ly en-dur-ing cru-el re-proach-es,
noint-ing di-vine; All that I am and have I am bring-ing.
fill with Thy love; Make me a tem-ple meet for Thy dwell-ing,

Je-sus, Thy per-fect like-ness to wear.
Seek-ing the wan-d'ring sin-ner to find.
Will-ing to suf-fer oth-ers to save.   O to be like Thee!
Lord, from this mo-ment all shall be Thine.
Fit me for life and Heav-en a-bove.

O to be like Thee, Bless-ed Re-deem-er, pure as Thou art; Come in Thy

sweet-ness, come in Thy full-ness; Stamp Thine own im-age deep on my heart.

Where He Leads I'll Follow

321

WILLIAM A. OGDEN

WILLIAM A. OGDEN

1. Sweet are the prom - is - es, Kind is the word, Dear-er far than
2. Sweet is the ten - der love Je - sus hath shown, Sweet-er far than
3. List to His lov - ing words, "Come un - to Me"; Wea - ry, heav - y -

an - y mes-sage man ev - er heard; Pure was the mind of Christ,
an - y love that mor - tals have known; Kind to the err - ing one,
la - den, there is sweet rest for thee; Trust in His prom - is - es,

Sin - less I see; He the great ex - am -ple is, and pat - tern for me.
Faith-ful is He; He the great ex - am -ple is, and pat - tern for me.
Faith-ful and sure; Lean up - on the Sav-iour, and thy soul is se - cure.

Where He leads I'll fol - low,
Where He leads I'll fol - low, Where He leads I'll fol - low,

1. Fol - low all the way.
Fol-low all the way, yes, fol-low all the way.

2. Fol-low Je-sus ev-'ry day.

322 Living for Jesus

THOMAS O. CHISHOLM

C. HAROLD LOWDEN

1. Liv - ing for Je - sus a life that is true, Striv - ing to
2. Liv - ing for Je - sus who died in my place, Bear - ing on
3. Liv - ing for Je - sus wher - ev - er I am, Do - ing each
4. Liv - ing for Je - sus through earth's lit - tle while, My dear - est

please Him in all that I do; Yield-ing al - le - giance, glad -
Cal - v'ry my sin and dis - grace; Such love con - strains me to
du - ty in His ho - ly name; Will - ing to suf - fer af -
treas-ure, the light of His smile; Seek - ing the lost ones He

heart-ed and free, This is the path-way of bless-ing for me.
an-swer His call, Fol - low His lead-ing and give Him my all.
flic-tion and loss, Deem-ing each tri - al a part of my cross.
died to re - deem, Bring-ing the wea - ry to find rest in Him.

O Je - sus, Lord and Sav - iour, I give my - self to Thee, For

Thou, in Thy a - tone-ment, Didst give Thy-self for me; I

own no oth - er Mas - ter, My heart shall be Thy throne, My

life I give, hence - forth to live, O Christ, for Thee a - lone.

More About Jesus   323

ELIZA E. HEWITT

JOHN R. SWENEY

1. More a-bout Je - sus would I know, More of His grace to oth - ers show;
2. More a-bout Je - sus let me learn, More of His ho - ly will dis-cern;
3. More a-bout Je - sus; in His Word, Hold-ing com-mun - ion with my Lord;
4. More a-bout Je - sus on His throne, Rich-es in Glo - ry all His own;

More of His sav - ing full - ness see, More of His love who died for me.
Spir - it of God, my Teach - er be, Show-ing the things of Christ to me.
Hear-ing His voice in ev - 'ry line, Mak-ing each faith - ful say - ing mine.
More of His king-dom's sure in-crease; More of His com - ing, Prince of Peace.

Fine

D.S. *More of His sav - ing full - ness see, More of His love who died for me.*

D.S. al fine

More, more a - bout Je - sus, More, more a - bout Je - sus;

324 Draw Me Nearer

FANNY J. CROSBY

WILLIAM H. DOANE

1. I am Thine, O Lord, I have heard Thy voice, And it told Thy love to me; But I long to rise in the arms of faith, And be clos - er drawn to Thee.
2. Con - se - crate me now to Thy ser - vice, Lord, By the pow'r of grace di - vine; Let my soul look up with a stead-fast hope, And my will be lost in Thine.
3. O the pure de - light of a sin - gle hour That be - fore Thy throne I spend, When I kneel in prayer, and with Thee, my God, I com - mune as friend with friend!
4. There are depths of love that I can - not know Till I cross the nar - row sea; There are heights of joy that I may not reach Till I rest in peace with Thee.

Draw me near - er, near-er, bless-ed Lord, To the cross where Thou hast died; Draw me near - er, near - er, near - er, bless-ed Lord, To Thy pre - cious bleed - ing side.

Trust and Obey

JOHN H. SAMMIS

DANIEL B. TOWNER

1. When we walk with the Lord In the light of His Word, What a glo-ry He
2. Not a shad-ow can rise, Not a cloud in the skies, But His smile quick-ly
3. Not a bur-den we bear, Not a sor-row we share, But our toil He doth
4. But we nev-er can prove The de-lights of His love Un-til all on the
5. Then in fel-low-ship sweet We will sit at His feet, Or we'll walk by His

sheds on our way! While we do His good will, He a-bides with us still,
drives it a-way; Not a doubt or a fear, Not a sigh nor a tear,
rich-ly re-pay; Not a grief nor a loss, Not a frown nor a cross,
al-tar we lay; For the fa-vor He shows, And the joy He be-stows,
side in the way; What He says we will do, Where He sends we will go,—

And with all who will trust and o-bey.
Can a-bide while we trust and o-bey.
But is blest if we trust and o-bey. Trust and o-bey, for there's no oth-er
Are for them who will trust and o-bey.
Nev-er fear, on-ly trust and o-bey.

way To be hap-py in Je-sus, But to trust and o-bey.

326
Christ Is All

W. A. WILLIAMS

W. A. WILLIAMS

1. I en-tered once a home of care, For age and pen - u - ry were there, Yet peace and joy with - al; I asked the lone - ly moth - er whence Her help - less wid - ow-hood's de - fense; She told me, "Christ is all." Christ is

2. I stood be - side a dy - ing bed, Where lay a child with ach - ing head, Wait - ing for Je - sus' call; I marked his smile, 'twas sweet as May, And as his spir - it passed a - way, He whis-pered, "Christ is all." Christ is

3. I saw the mar - tyr at the stake, The flames could not his cour - age shake, Nor death his soul ap - pall; I asked him whence his strength was giv'n — He looked tri - umph - ant - ly to Heav'n, And an-swered, "Christ is all." Christ is

4. I saw the gos - pel her - ald go To Af - ric's sand and Green-land's snow, To save from Sa - tan's thrall; Nor home nor life he count - ed dear, Midst wants and per - ils owned no fear, He felt that "Christ is all." Christ is

5. I dreamed that hoar - y time had fled, And earth and sea gave up their dead, A fire dis - solved this ball; I saw the church's ran - somed throng, I heard the bur - den of their song, 'Twas "Christ is all in all." Christ is

6. Then come to Christ, O come to - day, The Fa - ther, Son, and Spir - it say; The Bride re - peats the call; For He will cleanse your guil - ty stains, His love will soothe your wea - ry pains, For "Christ is all in all." Christ is

all, all in all, She told me, "Christ is all."
all, all in all, He whis-pered, "Christ is all."
all, all in all, And an-swered, "Christ is all."
all, all in all, He felt that "Christ is all."
all, all in all, 'Twas "Christ is all in all."
all, all in all, For "Christ is all in all."

Higher Ground 327

JOHNSON OATMAN, JR.

CHARLES H. GABRIEL

1. I'm press-ing on the up-ward way, New heights I'm gain-ing ev-'ry day;
2. My heart has no de-sire to stay Where doubts a-rise and fears dis-may;
3. I want to live a-bove the world, Tho' Sa-tan's darts at me are hurled;
4. I want to scale the ut-most height, And catch a gleam of Glo-ry bright;

Still pray-ing as I'm on-ward bound, "Lord, plant my feet on high-er ground."
Tho' some may dwell where these a-bound, My prayer, my aim is high-er ground.
For faith has caught the joy-ful sound, The song of saints on high-er ground.
But still I'll pray till Heav'n I've found, "Lord, lead me on to high-er ground."

Lord, lift me up and let me stand, By faith, on Heav-en's ta-ble-land,

A high-er plane than I have found; Lord, plant my feet on high-er ground.

328 I Want That Mountain!

BILL HARVEY   BILL HARVEY

1. I saw the giant of Prayer-less-ness up - on the moun-tain
2. There was a giant of Laz - i - ness who said I would - n't
3. One faith - less giant up - on the crest of He-bron's loft - y
4. Let ev - 'ry gi - ant of dis-tress and un - be - lief and

high; He laughed so hard at my un - bend - ed knee. No
go And wit - ness for the One who set me free. I'll
height Has vowed that he's the one to make me flee. I'll
sin Get read - y now to va - cate, for you see: I've

long - er in the wil - der - ness I'll stay, and so I cry: I
come from out the wil - der - ness, I'll wit - ness now I know; I
climb from out the wil - der - ness And trust Je - ho - vah's might! I
come from out the wil - der - ness! I know I'm going to win! I

want that moun-tain, It be - longs to me!
want that moun-tain, It be - longs to me!
want that moun-tain, It be - longs to me!   I want that
want that moun-tain, It be - longs to me!

moun-tain!   I want that moun-tain!   Where the milk and hon - ey

flow, Where the grapes of Esh - col grow. I want that moun-tain!

I want that moun-tain! The moun-tain that my Lord has giv - en me.

Take Time to Be Holy 329

WILLIAM D. LONGSTAFF

GEORGE C. STEBBINS

1. Take time to be ho - ly, Speak oft with thy Lord; A - bide in Him
2. Take time to be ho - ly, The world rush-es on; Spend much time in
3. Take time to be ho - ly, Let Him be thy Guide; And run not be-
4. Take time to be ho - ly, Be calm in thy soul; Each thought and each

al - ways, And feed on His Word. Make friends of God's chil - dren;
se - cret With Je - sus a - lone; By look-ing to Je - sus,
fore Him, What - ev - er be - tide; In joy or in sor - row,
mo - tive Be - neath His con - trol; Thus led by His Spir - it

Help those who are weak; For - get-ting in noth - ing His bless-ing to seek.
Like Him thou shalt be; Thy friends in thy con - duct His like-ness shall see.
Still fol-low thy Lord, And look-ing to Je - sus, Still trust in His Word.
To foun-tains of love, Thou soon shalt be fit - ted For ser-vice a - bove.

330 I Would Be Like Jesus

JAMES ROWE

BENTLEY D. ACKLEY

1. Earth-ly pleas-ures vain-ly call me; I would be like Je - sus;
2. He has bro-ken ev-'ry fet-ter; I would be like Je - sus;
3. All the way from earth to Glo-ry, I would be like Je - sus;
4. That in Heav-en He may meet me, I would be like Je - sus;
   would be like Je - sus;

Noth-ing world-ly shall en-thrall me; I would be like Je - sus.
That my soul may serve Him bet-ter, I would be like Je - sus.
Tell-ing o'er and o'er the sto - ry, I would be like Je - sus.
That His words, "Well done," may greet me, I would be like Je - sus.
   would be like Je - sus.

Be like Je - sus, this my song, In the home and in the throng;

Be like Je - sus all day long! I would be like Je - sus.

Wherever He Leads I'll Go 331

B. B. McKINNEY

B. B. McKINNEY

1. "Take up thy cross and fol-low Me," I heard my Mas-ter say;
2. He drew me clos-er to His side, I sought His will to know,
3. It may be through the shad-ows dim, Or o'er the storm-y sea,
4. My heart, my life, my all I bring To Christ who loves me so;

"I gave My life to ran-som thee, Sur-ren-der your all to-day."
And in that will I now a-bide, Wher-ev-er He leads I'll go.
I take my cross and fol-low Him, Wher-ev-er He lead-eth me.
He is my Mas-ter, Lord, and King, Wher-ev-er He leads I'll go.

Wher-ev-er He leads I'll go, Wher-ev-er He leads I'll go,

I'll fol-low my Christ who loves me so, Wher-ev-er He leads I'll go.

332 Channels Only

MARY E. MAXWELL

ADA R. GIBBS

1. How I praise Thee, pre-cious Sav - iour, That Thy love laid hold of me;
2. Emp-tied that Thou should-est fill me, A clean ves - sel in Thy hand;
3. Wit-ness-ing Thy pow'r to save me, Set-ting free from self and sin;
4. Je - sus, fill now with Thy Spir - it Hearts that full sur - ren - der know;

Thou hast saved and cleansed and filled me That I might Thy chan-nel be.
With no pow'r but as Thou giv - est Gra-cious - ly with each com-mand.
Thou who bought-est to pos - sess me, In Thy full - ness, Lord, come in.
That the streams of liv - ing wa - ter From our in - ner man may flow.

Chan-nels on - ly, bless-ed Mas - ter, But with all Thy won-drous pow'r

Flow-ing through us, Thou canst use us Ev - 'ry day and ev - 'ry hour.

Give Me Jesus

333

FANNY J. CROSBY

JOHN R. SWENEY

1. Take the world, but give me Je - sus, All its joys are but a name;
2. Take the world, but give me Je - sus, Sweet-est com - fort of my soul;
3. Take the world, but give me Je - sus, Let me view His con-stant smile;
4. Take the world, but give me Je - sus, In His cross my trust shall be;

But His love a - bid - eth ev - er, Through e - ter - nal years the same.
With my Sav - iour watch-ing o'er me, I can sing though bil-lows roll.
Then through-out my pil - grim jour - ney Light will cheer me all the while.
Till, with clear - er, bright-er vi - sion, Face to face my Lord I see.

O the height and depth of mer - cy! O the length and breadth of love!

O the full - ness of re - demp-tion, Pledge of end - less life a - bove!

334 Make Me a Blessing

IRA. B. WILSON

GEORGE S. SCHULER

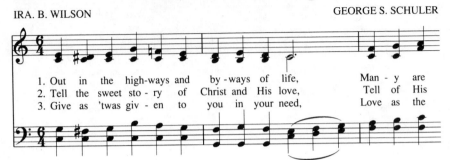

1. Out in the high-ways and by-ways of life, Man-y are
2. Tell the sweet sto-ry of Christ and His love, Tell of His
3. Give as 'twas giv-en to you in your need, Love as the

wea-ry and sad;
    are wea-ry and sad;
pow'r to for-give;
    His pow'r to for-give;
Mas-ter loved you;
    the Mas-ter loved you;

Car-ry the sun-shine where dark-ness is
Oth-ers will trust Him if on-ly you
Be to the help-less a help-er in-

rit.

Men or Unison

rife, Mak-ing the sor-row-ing glad.
prove True, ev-'ry mo-ment you live.
deed, Un-to your mis-sion be true.

Make me a bless-ing,

Make me a bless - ing, Out of my life may
Out of my life

Je - sus shine; Make me a bless -

ing, O Sav - iour, I pray. Make me a
I pray Thee, my Sav - iour,

bless - ing to some - one to - day.

335 If Jesus Goes With Me

C. AUSTIN MILES

C. AUSTIN MILES

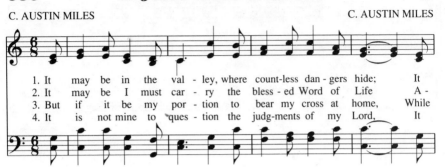

1. It may be in the val - ley, where count-less dan - gers hide; It
2. It may be I must car - ry the bless - ed Word of Life A -
3. But if it be my por - tion to bear my cross at home, While
4. It is not mine to ques - tion the judg-ments of my Lord, It

may be in the sun - shine that I, in peace, a - bide; But
cross the burn - ing des - erts to those in sin - ful strife; And
oth - ers bear their bur - dens be - yond the bil - low's foam; I'll
is but mine to fol - low the lead - ings of His Word; But

this one thing I know — if it be dark or fair, If Je - sus is
though it be my lot to bear my col - ors there, If Je - sus goes
prove my faith in Him — con - fess His judg-ment fair, And, if He stays
if to go or stay, or wheth-er here or there, I'll be, with my

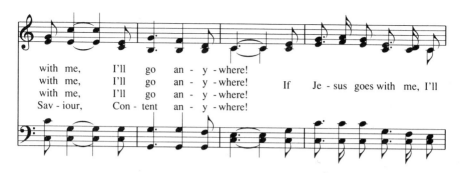

with me, I'll go an - y - where!
with me, I'll go an - y - where!
with me, I'll go an - y - where! If Je - sus goes with me, I'll
Sav - iour, Con - tent an - y - where!

go An - y - where! 'Tis Heav-en to me, Wher -e're I may be, If
I'll go

He is there! I count it a priv - i - lege here His cross to
His cross, His cross, His

bear; If Je - sus goes with me, I'll go An - y - where!
cross to bear;

336   Constantly Abiding

MRS. WILL L. MURPHY   MRS. WILL L. MURPHY

1. There's a peace in my heart that the world nev-er gave, A
2. All the world seemed to sing of a Sav-iour and King, When
3. This treas-ure I have in a tem-ple of clay, While

peace it can-not take a-way; Tho' the tri-als of
peace sweet-ly came to my heart; Trou-bles all fled a-
here on His foot-stool I roam; But He's com-ing to

life may sur-round like a cloud, I've a peace that has come there to
way and my night turned to day, Bless-ed Je-sus, how glo-rious Thou
take me some glo-ri-ous day, O-ver there to my heav-en-ly

stay!   Con - stant-ly a-bid - ing,
art!   Con-stant-ly a-bid - ing, con-stant-ly a-bid-ing,
Home!

337   Ho! Every One That Is Thirsty

LUCY J. RIDER   LUCY J. RIDER

1. Ho! ev-'ry one that is thirst-y in spir-it, Ho! ev-'ry one that is wea-ry and sad, Come to the foun-tain, there's full-ness in Je-sus, All that you're long-ing for, come and be glad.

2. Child of the world, are you tired of your bon-dage? Wea-ry of earth-joys, so false, so un-true; Thirst-ing for God, and His full-ness of bless-ing? List to the prom-ise, a mes-sage for you.

3. Child of the king-dom, be filled with the Spir-it, Noth-ing but full-ness thy long-ing can meet. 'Tis the en-due-ment for life and for ser-vice; Thine is the prom-ise, so cer-tain, so sweet.

"I will pour wa-ter on him who is thirst-y, I will pour floods up-on the dry ground; O-pen your heart for the gift I am

bring - ing, While ye are seek - ing Me, I will be found."

Holy Ghost, With Light Divine   338

ANDREW REED

LOUIS M. GOTTSCHALK
Arr. by EDWIN P. PARKER

1. Ho - ly Ghost, with light di - vine, Shine up - on this
2. Ho - ly Ghost, with pow'r di - vine, Cleanse this guilt - y
3. Ho - ly Ghost, with joy di - vine, Cheer this sad - dened
4. Ho - ly Spir - it, all di - vine, Dwell with - in this

heart of mine; Chase the shade of night a - way,
heart of mine; Long has sin, with - out con - trol,
heart of mine; Bid my man - y woes de - part,
heart of mine; Cast down ev - 'ry i - dol - throne,

Turn my dark - ness in - to day.
Held do - min - ion o'er my soul.
Heal my wound - ed, bleed - ing heart.
Reign su - preme, and reign a - lone. A - men.

339 Spirit of God, Descend Upon My Heart

GEORGE CROLY

FREDERICK C. ATKINSON

1. Spir - it of God, de - scend up - on my heart;
2. Hast Thou not bid us love Thee, God and King?
3. Teach me to feel that Thou art al - ways nigh;
4. Teach me to love Thee as Thine an - gels love,

Wean it from earth, through all its puls - es move;
All, all Thine own, soul, heart and strength and mind;
Teach me the strug - gles of the soul to bear,
One ho - ly pas - sion fill - ing all my frame;

Stoop to my weak - ness, might - y as Thou art,
I see Thy cross, there teach my heart to cling:
To check the ris - ing doubt, the reb - el sigh;
The bap - tism of the heav'n - de - scend - ed Dove,

And make me love Thee as I ought to love.
O let me seek Thee, and O let me find.
Teach me the pa - tience of un - an - swered prayer.
My heart an al - tar, and Thy love the flame. A - men.

Blessed Quietness

340

MANIE P. FERGUSON

W. S. MARSHALL
Arr. by JAMES M. KIRK

1. Joys are flow - ing like a riv - er, Since the Com - fort - er has
2. Bring-ing life and health and glad - ness, All a - round this heav'n-ly
3. Like the rain that falls from heav - en, Like the sun - light from the
4. See, a fruit - ful field is grow - ing, Bless - ed fruit of right-eous-
5. What a won - der - ful sal - va - tion, Where we al - ways see His

come; He a - bides with us for - ev - er, Makes the trust - ing heart His
Guest, Ban-ished un - be - lief and sad - ness, Changed our wea - ri - ness to
sky, So the Ho - ly Ghost is giv - en, Com - ing on us from on
ness; And the streams of life are flow - ing In the lone - ly wil - der -
face! What a per - fect hab - i - ta - tion, What a qui - et rest - ing

home.
rest.
high. Bless-ed qui - et - ness, ho - ly qui - et - ness, What as - sur-ance in my
ness.
place!

soul! On the storm-y sea, He speaks peace to me, How the bil-lows cease to roll!

rit. _ _ _ _ _ _ _ _ _

341 Pentecostal Power

CHARLOTTE G. HOMER

CHAS. H. GABRIEL

1. Lord, as of old at Pen - te - cost Thou didst Thy pow'r dis - play,
2. For might - y works for Thee pre - pare, And strength-en ev - 'ry heart;
3. All self con-sume, all sin de - stroy! With ear - nest zeal en - due
4. Speak, Lord! be - fore Thy throne we wait, Thy prom - ise we be - lieve,

With cleans-ing, pu - ri - fy - ing flame De - scend on us to - day.
Come, take pos - ses - sion of Thine own, And nev - er-more de - part.
Each wait - ing heart to work for Thee; O Lord, our faith re - new!
And will not let Thee go un - til The bless - ing we re - ceive.

Lord, send the old - time pow'r, the Pen - te - cos - tal pow'r! Thy

flood - gates of bless - ing on us throw o - pen wide! Lord,

send the old - time pow'r, the Pen - te - cos - tal pow'r, That

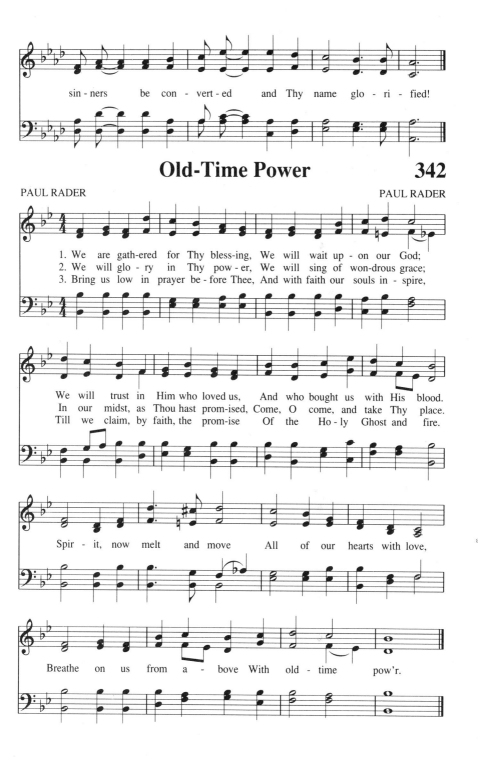

sin - ners   be con - vert - ed   and Thy name glo - ri - fied!

Old-Time Power

342

PAUL RADER

PAUL RADER

1. We are gath-ered for Thy bless-ing, We will wait up - on our God;
2. We will glo - ry in Thy pow - er, We will sing of won-drous grace;
3. Bring us low in prayer be - fore Thee, And with faith our souls in - spire,

We will trust in Him who loved us, And who bought us with His blood.
In our midst, as Thou hast prom-ised, Come, O come, and take Thy place.
Till we claim, by faith, the prom-ise Of the Ho - ly Ghost and fire.

Spir - it, now melt and move All of our hearts with love,

Breathe on us from a - bove With old - time pow'r.

343 Revive Us Again

WILLIAM P. MACKAY

JOHN J. HUSBAND

1. We praise Thee, O God! for the Son of Thy love, For Je - sus who
2. We praise Thee, O God! for Thy Spir - it of light, Who has shown us our
3. All glo - ry and praise to the Lamb that was slain, Who has borne all our
4. Re - vive us a - gain; fill each heart with Thy love; May each soul be re -

died, and is now gone a - bove.
Sav-iour, and scat - tered our night. Hal - le - lu - jah! Thine the glo - ry; Hal - le -
sins, and has cleansed ev - 'ry stain.
kin-dled with fire from a - bove.

lu - jah! A - men! Hal - le - lu - jah! Thine the glo - ry; Re - vive us a - gain.

344 Fall Fresh on Me

Arr. by B. B. McKINNEY

Spir - it of the liv - ing God, fall fresh on me, Spir - it of the

D.S. — Spir - it of the

Fine

liv - ing God, fall fresh on me. Melt me, mold me, fill me, use me.

liv - ing God, fall fresh on me.

Breathe on Me 345

EDWIN HATCH

B. B. McKINNEY

1. Ho - ly Spir - it, breathe on me, Un - til my heart is clean;
2. Ho - ly Spir - it, breathe on me, My stub-born will sub - due;
3. Ho - ly Spir - it, breathe on me, Fill me with power di - vine;
4. Ho - ly Spir - it, breathe on me, Till I am all Thine own,

Let sun-shine fill its in - most part, With not a cloud be - tween.
Teach me in words of liv - ing flame What Christ would have me do.
Kin - dle a flame of love and zeal With - in this heart of mine.
Un - til my will is lost in Thine, To live for Thee a - lone.

Breathe on me, breathe on me, Ho - ly Spir-it, breathe on me;

Take Thou my heart, cleanse ev-'ry part, Ho - ly Spir - it, breathe on me.

346   Bring Your Vessels, Not a Few

LEILA N. MORRIS   LEILA N. MORRIS

1. Are you look-ing for the full-ness of the bless-ing of the Lord
2. Bring your emp-ty earth-en ves-sels, clean thro' Je - sus' pre-cious blood,
3. Like the cruse of oil un-fail-ing is His grace for - ev - er-more,

In your heart and life to - day? Claim the prom-ise of your Fa - ther,
Come, ye need - y, one and all; And in hu - man con - se - cra - tion
And His love un-chang-ing still; And ac - cord - ing to His prom-ise

come ac-cord-ing to His Word, In the bless-ed old-time way.
wait be-fore the throne of God, Till the Ho - ly Ghost shall fall.
with the Ho-ly Ghost and pow'r, He will ev - 'ry ves - sel fill.

He will fill your heart to-day to o - ver-flow - ing, As the
He will fill   your   heart to o - ver-flow-ing,

Lord com-mand-eth you, "Bring your ves-sels, not a few"; He will fill your heart to-
He will fill

day to o - ver - flow - ing With the Ho - ly Ghost and pow'r.
your heart to o - ver - flow-ing,

Fill Me Now 347

ELWOOD H. STOKES

JOHN R. SWENEY

1. Hov - er o'er me, Ho - ly Spir - it, Bathe my trem-bling heart and brow;
2. Thou canst fill me, gra-cious Spir - it, Though I can - not tell Thee how;
3. I am weak-ness full of weak-ness, At Thy sa - cred feet I bow;
4. Cleanse and com-fort, bless and save me, Bathe, O bathe my heart and brow;

Fill me with Thy hal-lowed pres-ence, Come, O come and fill me now.
But I need Thee, great - ly need Thee, Come, O come and fill me now.
Blest, di - vine, e - ter - nal Spir - it, Fill with pow'r and fill me now.
Thou art com - fort - ing and sav - ing, Thou art sweet - ly fill - ing now.

Fill me now, fill me now, Je - sus, come and fill me now,

Fill me with Thy hal-lowed pres-ence, Come, O come and fill me now.

348   Come, Holy Spirit

JOHN R. RICE   JOHN R. RICE

1. Pow-er, might-y pow'r Je-sus prom-ised from on high; Pow-er
2. Then came Pen-te-cost and the Ho-ly Ghost was giv'n; And they
3. Sa-tan-blind-ed men must con-vict-ed be, a-waked! More than
4. Na-ked, fruit-less Chris-tians we toil with-out God's pow'r. Fields are
5. Thirst-y are our hearts, so we wait up-on the Lord. Ear-nest-

souls to win, souls to save from sin. O Thou breath of God,
all were filled, all em-pow-ered till Mul-ti-tudes were saved,
hu-man pow'r, for God's work this hour. Un-seen pow'rs of Hell
wast-ing white, wait-ing for God's might. O Thou Ho-ly Spir-
ly we plead, this our ut-most need. Then with God's a-noint-

come up-on the hearts that cry, Wit-ness-ing to poor, lost men.
turned to Christ and were for-giv'n; We too should be Spir-it-filled.
shat-tered till men fear and quake, By the Spir-it's might-y pow'r.
it, come crum-ble Sa-tan's tower, Souls we'll reap be-fore the night.
ing we'll car-ry men the Word, Sow a-broad the fruit-ful seed.

Come, Ho-ly Spir-it, fill me; I need Thee, I seek Thee;

Come, Ho-ly Spir-it, fill me; Lord, fill me with the Ho-ly Ghost.

The Comforter Has Come

349

FRANK BOTTOME

WILLIAM J. KIRKPATRICK

1. O spread the ti-dings 'round, wher-ev-er man is found, Wher-
2. The long, long night is past, the morn-ing breaks at last, And
3. Lo, the great King of kings, with heal-ing in His wings, To
4. O bound-less love di-vine! how shall this tongue of mine To

ev-er hu-man hearts and hu-man woes a-bound; Let ev-'ry Christian
hushed the dread-ful wail and fu-ry of the blast, As o'er the gold-en
ev-'ry cap-tive soul a full de-liv-'rance brings; And thro' the va-cant
won-d'ring mor-tals tell the match-less grace di-vine - That I, a child of

D.S.: Ho-ly Ghost from Heav'n, The Fa-ther's prom-ise giv'n; O spread the ti-dings

tongue pro-claim the joy-ful sound: The Com-fort-er has come!
hills the day ad-vanc-es fast! The Com-fort-er has come!
cells the song of tri-umph rings; The Com-fort-er has come!
Hell, should in His im-age shine! The Com-fort-er has come!

Fine

'round, wher-ev-er man is found — The Com-fort-er has come!

The Com-fort-er has come, The Com-fort-er has come! The

D.S.

350 Revive Thy Work

ALFRED MIDLANE

JAMES McGRANAHAN

1. Re - vive Thy work, O Lord! Thy might - y arm make bare;
2. Re - vive Thy work, O Lord! Dis - turb this sleep of death;
3. Re - vive Thy work, O Lord! Cre - ate soul-thirst for Thee;
4. Re - vive Thy work, O Lord! Ex - alt Thy pre-cious name;

Speak with the voice that wakes the dead, And make Thy peo - ple hear.
Quick - en the smol-d'ring em - bers now By Thine al - might - y breath.
But hun-g'ring for the Bread of Life, Oh, may our spir - its be!
And, by the Ho - ly Ghost, our love For Thee and Thine in - flame.

Re - vive! re - vive! And give re - fresh-ing show'rs;
Re - vive Thy work! re - vive Thy work! And give, oh, give re - fresh-ing show'rs;

The glo - ry shall be all Thine own; The bless-ing shall be ours.

Tell It to Jesus

351

JEREMIAH E. RANKIN

EDMUND S. LORENZ

1. Are you wea-ry, are you heav-y-heart-ed? Tell it to Je-sus,
2. Do the tears flow down your cheeks un-bid-den? Tell it to Je-sus,
3. Do you fear the gath-'ring clouds of sor-row? Tell it to Je-sus,
4. Are you troub-led at the thought of dy-ing? Tell it to Je-sus,

Tell it to Je-sus; Are you griev-ing o-ver joys de-part-ed?
Tell it to Je-sus; Have you sins that to men's eyes are hid-den?
Tell it to Je-sus; Are you anx-ious what shall be to-mor-row?
Tell it to Je-sus; For Christ's com-ing King-dom are you sigh-ing?

Tell it to Je-sus a-lone. Tell it to Je-sus, tell it to Je-sus,

He is a Friend that's well known; You've no oth-er

such a friend or broth-er, Tell it to Je-sus a-lone.

352 Have You Prayed It Through?

W. C. POOLE

B. D. ACKLEY

1. Have you prayed all night, Till the break of day, And the morn-ing light
2. Did you pray it through Till the an-swer came? There's a prom-ise true
3. As the Mas-ter prayed In the gar-den lone, Let your prayer be made

Drove the dark a - way? Did you lin-ger there, Till the morn-ing dew,
For your faith to claim; At the place of prayer Je - sus waits for you,
To the Fa - ther's throne; If you seek His will He will an-swer you;

In pre - vail - ing prayer Did you pray it through?
Did you meet Him there, Did you pray it through? Did you
Are you trust - ing still, Have you prayed it through?

pray till the an-swer came, Did you plead in the Sav-iour's
till it came,

name? Have you prayed all night till the morn - ing
in His name?

light, Did you pray till the an - swer came?

From Every Stormy Wind 353

HUGH STOWELL

THOMAS HASTINGS

1. From ev - 'ry storm - y wind that blows, From ev - 'ry swell - ing
2. There is a place where Je - sus sheds The oil of glad - ness
3. There is a scene where spir - its blend, Where friend holds fel - low -
4. There, there on ea - gles' wings we soar, And sin and sense mo -

tide of woes, There is a calm, a sure re -
on our heads; A place than all be - sides more
ship with friend: Tho' sun - dered far, by faith they
lest no more, And Heav'n comes down our souls to

treat: 'Tis found be - neath the mer - cy seat.
sweet: It is the blood - bought mer - cy seat.
meet A - round one com - mon mer - cy seat.
greet, When glo - ry crowns the mer - cy seat.

354   I Am Praying for You

S. O'MALEY CLUFF

IRA D. SANKEY

1. I have a Sav-iour, He's plead-ing in Glo-ry, A dear, lov-ing
2. I have a Fa-ther; to me He has giv-en A hope for e-
3. I have a robe: 'tis re-splen-dent in white-ness, A-wait-ing in
4. When Je-sus has found you, tell oth-ers the sto-ry, That your lov-ing

Sav-iour, tho' earth-friends be few; And now He is watch-ing in
ter-ni-ty, bless-ed and true; And soon will He call me to
Glo-ry my won-der-ing view; Oh, when I re-ceive it all
Sav-iour is their Sav-iour, too; Then pray that your Sav-iour may

ten-der-ness o'er me, But, oh, that my Sav-iour were your Sav-iour,
meet Him in Heav-en, But, oh, that He'd let me bring you with me,
shin-ing in bright-ness, Dear friend, could I see you re-ceiv-ing one,
bring them to Glo-ry, And prayer will be an-swered-'twas an-swered for

f   *p*

too.
too!   For you I am pray-ing, For you I am pray-ing, For
too!
you!

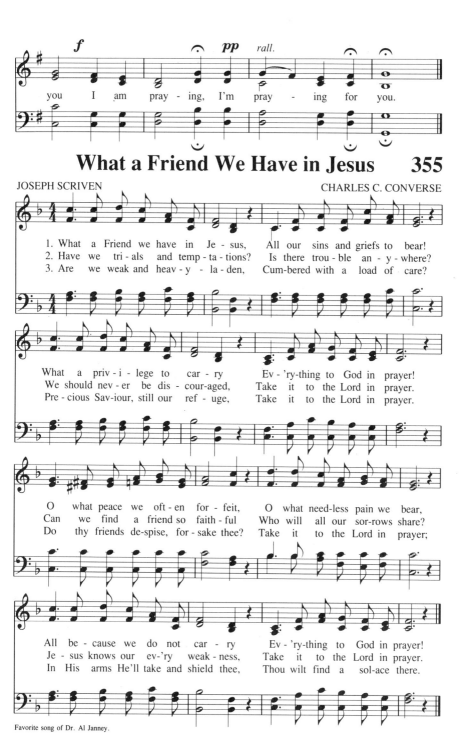

you I am pray - ing, I'm pray - ing for you.

What a Friend We Have in Jesus   355

JOSEPH SCRIVEN   CHARLES C. CONVERSE

1. What a Friend we have in Je - sus,   All our sins and griefs to bear!
2. Have we tri - als and temp - ta - tions?   Is there trou - ble an - y - where?
3. Are we weak and heav - y - la - den,   Cum - bered with a load of care?

What a priv - i - lege to car - ry   Ev - 'ry-thing to God in prayer!
We should nev - er be dis - cour-aged,   Take it to the Lord in prayer.
Pre - cious Sav-iour, still our ref - uge,   Take it to the Lord in prayer.

O what peace we oft - en for - feit,   O what need-less pain we bear,
Can we find a friend so faith - ful   Who will all our sor-rows share?
Do thy friends de-spise, for - sake thee?   Take it to the Lord in prayer;

All be - cause we do not car - ry   Ev - 'ry-thing to God in prayer!
Je - sus knows our ev - 'ry weak - ness,   Take it to the Lord in prayer.
In His arms He'll take and shield thee,   Thou wilt find a sol-ace there.

Favorite song of Dr. Al Janney.

356   I Must Tell Jesus

ELISHA A. HOFFMAN   ELISHA A. HOFFMAN

1. I must tell Jesus all of my trials; I cannot bear these burdens alone; In my distress He kindly will help me; He ever loves and cares for His own.

2. I must tell Jesus all of my troubles; He is a kind, compassionate Friend; If I but ask Him, He will deliver, Make of my troubles quickly an end.

3. Tempted and tried I need a great Saviour, One who can help my burdens to bear; I must tell Jesus, I must tell Jesus; He all my cares and sorrows will share.

4. O how the world to evil allures me! O how my heart is tempted to sin! I must tell Jesus, and He will help me Over the world the vic't'ry to win.

I must tell Jesus! I must tell Jesus! I cannot bear my burdens alone; I must tell Jesus! I must tell Jesus! Jesus can help me, Jesus alone.

Favorite song of Mr. Lindsay Terry.

Ask and Seek and Knock 357

JOHN R. RICE

JOHN R. RICE

1. Is there an-y-thing too hard for God to do?
2. Do you think He does not love e-nough to give
3. When we read the Book of God we see His grace
4. We may ask "in Je-sus' name," or "ask in faith,"

Is there aught be-yond His pow'r? He com-mand-ed us to
All His chil-dren want and need? His be-lov-ed Son He
In His prom-is-es all through. Ev-'ry word re-veals that
Pray u-nit-ed or a-lone. We may pray with trem-bling

o-pen wide our mouth, We should ask our needs this hour.
gave to save our souls; He would give all else in-deed!
God does an-swer prayer. We should claim each prom-ise true.
faith, but pray we should, We should plead till it is done!

We should ask and seek, Keep knock-ing at the door, at Je-sus' feet.

We have not our needs, Be-cause we do not plead with Je-sus.

358   'Tis the Blessed Hour of Prayer

FANNY J. CROSBY

WILLIAM H. DOANE

1. 'Tis the bless-ed hour of prayer, when our hearts low-ly bend,
2. 'Tis the bless-ed hour of prayer, when the Sav-iour draws near,
3. 'Tis the bless-ed hour of prayer, when the tempt-ed and tried
4. At the bless-ed hour of prayer, trust-ing Him we be-lieve

And we gath-er to Je-sus, our Sav-iour and Friend; If we
With a ten-der com-pas-sion His chil-dren to hear; When He
To the Sav-iour who loves them their sor-row con-fide; With a
That the bless-ings we're need-ing we'll sure-ly re-ceive; In the

come to Him in faith, His pro-tec-tion to share, What a balm for the
tells us we may cast at His feet ev-ery care, What a balm for the
sym-pa-thiz-ing heart He re-moves ev-ery care, What a balm for the
full-ness of this trust we shall lose ev-ery care, What a balm for the

wea-ry! O how sweet to be there! Bless-ed hour of prayer, Bless-ed

hour of prayer; What a balm for the wea-ry! O how sweet to be there!

Thy Word Have I Hid in My Heart — 359

From Psalm 119
Adapted by Ernest O. Sellers

ERNEST O. SELLERS

1. Thy Word is a lamp to my feet, A light to my path al-
2. For - ev - er, O Lord, is Thy Word Es - tab-lished and fixed on
3. At morn - ing, at noon, and at night I ev - er will give Thee
4. Thru Him whom Thy Word hath fore - told, The Sav-iour and Morn-ing

way, To guide and to save me from sin And show me the heav'n-ly
high; Thy faith - ful-ness un - to all men A - bid-eth for - ev - er
praise; For Thou art my por - tion, O Lord, And shall be thru all my
Star, Sal - va - tion and peace have been brought To those who have strayed a-

way.
nigh. Thy Word have I hid in my heart, (in my heart,) That I might not
days!
far.

sin a - gainst Thee; (a - gainst Thee;) That I might not sin, that

I might not sin, Thy Word have I hid in my heart.

360 Pray About Everything

JOY RICE MARTIN   JOY RICE MARTIN

1. Once I was bur-dened with man - y a care; Prob-lems too
2. Ask of your Fa - ther, He lov - eth to please; Un - lock His
3. Doubt-ing and fret - ting can on - ly bring shame; Wor - ry and
4. Rich - es in Je - sus, a - bun-dant and free, Needs in our

hard for my weak soul to bear; Then in God's Word came a
treas - ure, He gives us the keys; Claim-ing this prom - ise, I
fear will dis - hon - or His name; Go to your Sav - iour His
work or what - ev - er it be; Ours for the ask - ing! This

mes - sage so clear;   Pray a - bout ev - 'ry - thing.
dropped to my knees: (ev - 'ry - thing.)
prom - ise to claim:
on - ly His plea:

Prayer is a won - der - ful treas - ure; Prayer is a won - der - ful

thing.   Bless - ing all ours with - out meas - ure; So

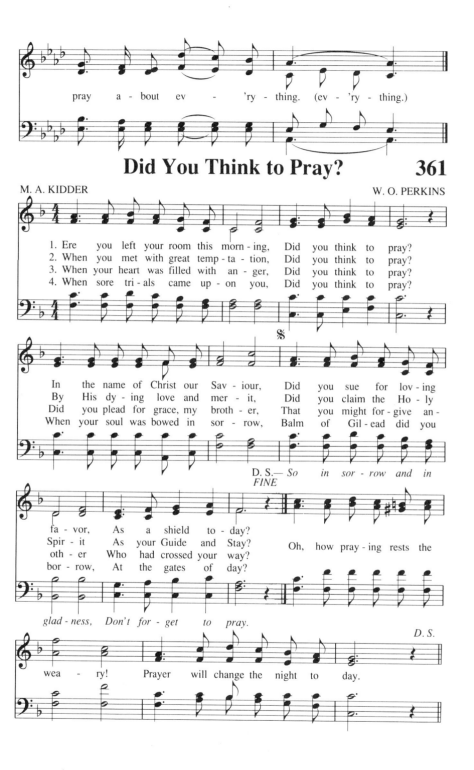

pray a - bout ev - 'ry - thing. (ev - 'ry - thing.)

Did You Think to Pray?   361

M. A. KIDDER

W. O. PERKINS

1. Ere you left your room this morn - ing, Did you think to pray?
2. When you met with great temp - ta - tion, Did you think to pray?
3. When your heart was filled with an - ger, Did you think to pray?
4. When sore tri - als came up - on you, Did you think to pray?

In the name of Christ our Sav - iour, Did you sue for lov - ing
By His dy - ing love and mer - it, Did you claim the Ho - ly
Did you plead for grace, my broth - er, That you might for - give an -
When your soul was bowed in sor - row, Balm of Gil - ead did you

D. S.— So in sor - row and in
FINE

fa - vor, As a shield to - day?
Spir - it As your Guide and Stay?
oth - er Who had crossed your way?
bor - row, At the gates of day?

Oh, how pray - ing rests the

glad - ness, Don't for - get to pray.

D. S.

wea - ry! Prayer will change the night to day.

362 I'm Leaning on Jesus

JOHN R. RICE

JOHN R. RICE

1. Cast all your care on Him, He car - eth for you; His prom - ise is
2. God spared not His Son, but de - liv - ered Him up; To pay our trans -
3. How large is your bur - den? Then make loud your call! Re - sour - ces are
4. Lean on Him in sor - row, in pov - er - ty's woes; He feels our temp -

gi - ven, His Word it is true; He cloth - eth the li - lies, the
gres - sions, no price was too much; How shall He not with Him give
bound - less, His pow - er, His all Are pledged; He ex - ceed - ing a -
ta - tions, in pi - ty He knows; The Fa - ther His chil - dren in

spar - rows He feeds, So tell Him your bur - dens and needs.
all things in - deed? So bold - ly His mer - cy we plead.
bun - dant will prove, Your moun - tains He's a - ble to move.
mer - cy doth hear, And lifts up the fall - en ones dear.

I'm lean - ing on Je - sus, He walks with me
I'm lean - ing on Je - sus, on Je - sus my Sav - iour

o - ver life's road. I'm lean - ing on
life's rug - ged road. I'm lean - ing on Je - sus, on

Je - sus, He car - ries, He car - ries my load.
Je - sus my Sav - iour my heav - y load.

Wonderful Words of Life
363

PHILIP P. BLISS

PHILIP P. BLISS

1. Sing them o - ver a - gain to me, Won-der - ful words of Life;
2. Christ, the bless-ed One, gives to all, Won-der - ful words of Life;
3. Sweet - ly ech - o the gos - pel call, Won-der - ful words of Life;

Let me more of their beau - ty see, Won - der - ful words of Life.
Sin - ner, list to the lov - ing call, Won - der - ful words of Life.
Of - fer par - don and peace to all, Won - der - ful words of Life.

Words of life and beau - ty, Teach me faith and du - ty:
All so free - ly giv - en, Woo - ing us to Heav - en:
Je - sus, on - ly Sav - iour, Sanc - ti - fy for - ev - er:

Beau-ti - ful words, won-der-ful words, Won-der-ful words of Life. Life.

364 Standing on the Promises

R. KELSO CARTER

R. KELSO CARTER

1. Stand-ing on the prom-is-es of Christ my King, Thro' e - ter - nal a - ges
2. Stand-ing on the prom-is-es that can - not fail, When the howl-ing storms of
3. Stand-ing on the prom-is-es of Christ the Lord, Bound to Him e - ter - nal -
4. Stand-ing on the prom-is-es I can - not fall, Lis-t'ning ev - 'ry mo-ment

let His prais - es ring; Glo-ry in the high - est I will shout and sing,
doubt and fear as - sail, By the liv - ing Word of God I shall pre - vail,
ly by love's strong cord, O-ver-com-ing dai - ly with the Spir - it's sword,
to the Spir - it's call, Rest-ing in my Sav-iour, as my all in all,

Stand-ing on the prom-is-es of God. Stand - ing,
Stand-ing on the prom-is - es,

stand - ing, Stand-ing on the prom - is - es of
stand - ing on the prom - is - es,

God my Sav - iour; Stand - ing; stand -
Stand-ing on the prom - is - es, stand - ing on the

ing,   I'm stand - ing on the prom - is - es of God.
prom - is - es,

Break Thou the Bread of Life   365

MARY ANN LATHBURY

WILLIAM F. SHERWIN

1. Break Thou the bread of life, Dear Lord, to me, As Thou didst
2. Bless Thou the truth, dear Lord, to me, to me, As Thou didst
3. Thou art the Bread of life, O Lord, to me, Thy ho - ly
4. O send Thy Spir - it, Lord, Now un - to me, That He may

break the loaves Be - side the sea; Be - yond the sa - cred page
bless the bread By Gal - i - lee; Then shall all bond - age cease,
Word the truth That sav - eth me; Give me to eat and live
touch my eyes, And make me see; Show me the truth con-cealed

I seek Thee, Lord; My spir - it pants for Thee, O liv - ing Word.
All fet - ters fall; And I shall find my peace, My All in All.
With Thee a - bove; Teach me to love Thy truth, For Thou art love.
With - in Thy Word, And in Thy Book re - vealed I see the Lord.

366 The Old Book and the Old Faith

GEORGE H. CARR

GEORGE H. CARR

1. 'Mid the storms of doubt and un-be-lief we fear, Stands a Book e-
2. 'Tis the Book that tells us of the Fa-ther's love, When He sent His
3. 'Tis the Book that tells us of the will of God And the Sav-iour's

ter-nal that the saints hold dear; Thru the rest-less a-ges it re-
Son to us from Heav'n a-bove, Who by rich-est prom-ise cre-ates
teach-ings while the earth He trod-How He soothed earth's sor-rows and re-

mains the same -'Tis the Book of God, and the Bi-ble is its name!
hope with-in, For 'tis thru His blood we are saved from ev-'ry sin!
lieved its woe, Thru whom strength is giv-en to con-quer ev-'ry foe!

The old Book and the old Faith Are the Rock on which I stand!
The grand old Book and the dear old Faith on which I stand!

The old Book and the old Faith Are the bul-wark of the land!
The grand old Book and the dear old Faith

Thru storm and stress they stand the test, In ev-'ry clime and na-tion blest;

The old Book and the old Faith Are the hope of ev-'ry land!
The grand old Book and the dear old Faith

GRAND CHORUS AT CLOSE
(May be omitted)

O the grand old Book and the dear old Faith Are the Rock on which I stand!

O the grand old Book and the dear old Faith Are the hope of ev-'ry land!

367 My Mother's Bible

M.B. WILLIAMS

CHARLIE D. TILLMAN

Duet

1. { There's a dear and pre-cious Book, Tho' it's worn and fad-ed now, Which re-
   { When I stood at Moth-er's knee, With her hand up-on my brow, and I

2. { As she read the sto-ries o'er, Of those might-y men of old, Of
   { Of lit-tle Da-vid bold, Who be-came a king at last; Of

3. { Then she read of Je-sus' love, As He blest the chil-dren dear, How He
   { Of His heav-y load of care, Then she dried my flow-ing tears With her

4. { Well, those days are past and gone, But their mem-'ry lin-gers still, And the
   { And I seek to do His will, As my moth-er taught me then, And

1.

calls those hap-py days of long a-go;
Jo-seph, and of Dan-iel and their trials;
suf-fered, bled and died up-on the tree;
dear old Book each day has been my guide;

2.

heard her voice in gen-tle tones and low.
Sa-tan with his man-y wick-ed wiles.
kiss-es as she said it was for me.
ev-er in my heart His words a-bide.

Bless-ed

Book, pre-cious Book, On thy dear old tear-stained
Bless-ed Book, pre-cious Book,

leaves I love to look; love to look; Thou art sweet-er day by day, As I

walk the nar-row way That leads at last to that bright Home a - bove.

Holy Bible, Book Divine 368

JOHN BURTON

Wm. B. BRADBURY

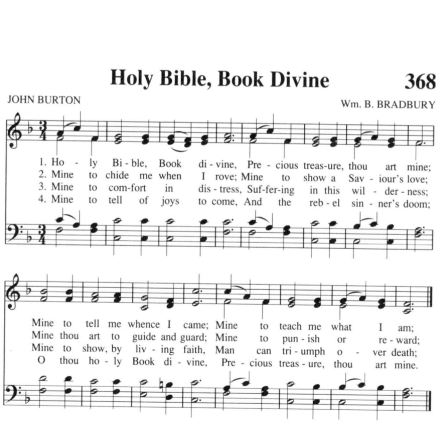

1. Ho - ly Bi - ble, Book di - vine, Pre - cious treas-ure, thou art mine;
2. Mine to chide me when I rove; Mine to show a Sav - iour's love;
3. Mine to com-fort in dis - tress, Suf-fer-ing in this wil - der - ness;
4. Mine to tell of joys to come, And the reb - el sin - ner's doom;

Mine to tell me whence I came; Mine to teach me what I am;
Mine thou art to guide and guard; Mine to pun - ish or re - ward;
Mine to show, by liv - ing faith, Man can tri - umph o - ver death;
O thou ho - ly Book di - vine, Pre - cious treas-ure, thou art mine.

369   I Know the Bible Is True

GENE ROUTH   B. B. McKINNEY

1. I know the Bi-ble was sent from God, The Old, as well as the New;
2. I know the sto-ry of Christ is true, His vir-gin, glo-ri-ous birth,
3. I know the Bi-ble is whol-ly true, For peace it gave me with-in;
4. Tho' foes de-ny with a spir-it bold The mes-sage old, but still new,

In-spired and ho-ly, the liv-ing Word, I know the Bi-ble is true.
His life, His death, and the o-pen tomb, And His re-turn to the earth.
It finds me, com-forts me day by day, And gives me vic-t'ry o'er sin.
Its truth is sweet-er each time 'tis told, I know the Bi-ble is true.

I know,   I know,   I know the Bi-ble is true;
    I know,   I know,   is true;

Di-vine-ly in-spired the whole way thro', I know the Bi-ble is true.

Throw Out the Life-Line 370

EDWARD S. UFFORD

EDWARD S. UFFORD
Arranged by George C. Stebbins

1. Throw out the Life-Line a - cross the dark wave, There is a broth-er whom
2. Throw out the Life-Line with hand quick and strong: Why do you tar - ry, why
3. Throw out the Life-Line to dan-ger-fraught men, Sink-ing in an-guish where
4. Soon will the sea - son of res - cue be o'er, Soon will they drift to e -

some -one should save; Some-bod - y's broth-er! O who then will dare To
lin - ger so long? See! he is sink - ing; O has - ten to - day — And
you've nev - er been; Winds of temp-ta - tion and bil - lows of woe Will
ter - ni - ty's shore; Haste then, my broth-er, no time for de - lay, But

throw out the Life-Line, his per - il to share?
out with the Life-Boat! a - way, then, a - way!
soon hurl them out where the dark wa - ters flow.
throw out the Life-Line and save them to - day.

Throw out the Life-Line!

Throw out the Life-Line! Some-one is drift-ing a - way; Throw out the

Life-Line! Throw out the Life-Line! Some-one is sink-ing to - day.

371   O Bring Your Loved Ones

JOHN R. RICE

JOHN R. RICE

1. How can I meet Him with-out my loved ones, How can I smile and
2. Time now for warn-ing, time now for plead-ing, Time now to weep, to
3. Sol-emn ac-count-ing, fac-ing our Sav-iour. Re-wards re-ceiv-ing,
4. How poor in-vest-ment, in land or bus-'ness; What cheap re-turns we'll
5. How glad the greet-ing, prais-es and sing-ing, When we meet Je-sus,

know they are lost, When I see Je-sus, up in the glo-ry
cling to the cross. Too late in Heav-en, to win our loved ones;
suf-fer-ing loss! Judg-ment seat, fac-ing Je-sus in Heav-en;
have for our pains! But how the wise will shine in their glo-ry,
with all our own! Then will our la-bor seem but a tri-fle,

With-out the souls He bought at such cost?
Too late to pray, to weep o'er the lost.
Wood, hay and stub-ble, burn-ing as dross.
When souls ap-pear, what e-ter-nal gain!
And all our tears, and toil-ing be done!

O bring your loved ones,

Bring them to Je-sus! Bring ev-'ry broth-er and sis-ter to

Him! When come the reap-ers, Home with the har-vest,

May all our dear ones be safe gath - ered in!

Let the Lower Lights Be Burning 372

PHILIP P. BLISS

PHILIP P. BLISS

1. Bright-ly beams our Fa-ther's mer - cy From His light-house ev - er - more,
2. Dark the night of sin has set - tled, Loud the an - gry bil-lows roar;
3. Trim your fee - ble lamp, my broth-er; Some poor sail - or temp-est-tossed,

But to us He gives the keep-ing Of the lights a - long the shore.
Ea - ger eyes are watch-ing, long-ing, For the lights a - long the shore.
Try - ing now to make the har - bor, In the dark-ness may be lost.

Let the low - er lights be burn-ing! Send a gleam a-cross the wave!

Some poor faint - ing, strug-gling sea-man You may res - cue, you may save.

373 So Send I You

E. MARGARET CLARKSON

JOHN W. PETERSON

1. So send I you to la-bor un-re-ward-ed, To serve un-
2. So send I you to bind the bruised and bro-ken, O'er wan-d'ring
3. So send I you to lone-li-ness and long-ing, With heart a-
4. So send I you to leave your life's am-bi-tion, To die to
5. So send I you to hearts made hard by hat-red, To eyes made

paid, un-loved, un-sought, un-known, To bear re-buke, to suf-fer
souls to work, to weep, to wake, To bear the bur-dens of a
hun-g'ring for the loved and known, For-sak-ing home and kin-dred,
dear de-sire, self-will re-sign, To la-bor long, and love where
blind be-cause they will not see, To spend, though it be blood, to

scorn and scoff-ing — So send I you to toil for Me a-lone.
world a-wea-ry — So send I you to suf-fer for My sake.
friend and dear one — So send I you to know My love a-lone.
men re-vile you — So send I you to lose your life in Mine.
spend and spare not — So send I you to taste of Cal-va-ry.

*
"As the Fa-ther hath sent me, So send I you."

Effective if sung only after the last verse.

© Copyright 1954 by Singspiration, Inc. All rights reserved. Used by permission.

Send the Light

374

CHARLES H. GABRIEL

CHARLES H. GABRIEL

1. There's a call comes ring-ing o'er the rest-less wave, "Send the light!
2. We have heard the Mac-e-do-nian call to-day, "Send the light!
3. Let us pray that grace may ev-'ry-where a-bound; Send the light!
4. Let us not grow wea-ry in the work of love, Send the light!

Send the light!

Send the light!"   There are souls to res-cue, there are souls to save,
Send the light!"   And a gold-en of-f'ring at the cross we lay,
Send the light!   And a Christ-like spir-it ev-'ry-where be found,
Send the light!   Send the light! Let us gath-er jew-els for a crown a-bove,

Send the light!   Send the light!   Send the light!   the
Send the light!   Send the light!   Send the light!

1.

bless-ed gos - pel light; Let it shine from shore to
the bless-ed gos-pel light; Let it shine

2.

shore!   shine   for-ev-er-more.
from shore to shore!   Let it shine   for-ev-er-more.

375 Work, for the Night Is Coming

ANNIE L. COGHILL
Altered by Lowell Mason

LOWELL MASON

1. Work, for the night is com - ing, Work through the morn-ing hours;
2. Work, for the night is com - ing, Work through the sun - ny noon;
3. Work, for the night is com - ing, Un - der the sun - set skies;

Work while the dew is spark - ling; Work 'mid spring-ing flow'rs.
Fill bright-est hours with la - bor, Rest comes sure and soon.
While their bright tints are glow - ing, Work, for day - light flies.

Work when the day grows bright - er, Work in the glow - ing sun;
Give ev - 'ry fly - ing min - ute Some-thing to keep in store;
Work till the last beam fad - eth, Fad - eth to shine no more;

Work, for the night is com - ing, When man's work is done.
Work, for the night is com - ing, When man works no more.
Work, while the night is dark - 'ning, When man's work is o'er.

376 In Christ There Is No East or West

JOHN OXENHAM

ALEXANDER R. REINAGLE

1. In Christ there is no East or West, In Him no South or North;
2. In Him shall true hearts ev - 'ry-where Their high com-mun-ion find;
3. Join hands, then, broth-ers of the faith, What-e'er your race may be;
4. In Christ now meet both East and West, In Him meet South and North;

Words from "Bees in Amber," by John Oxenham. Used by permission of Miss Erica Oxenham.

But   one great fel-low - ship of love Through-out the whole wide   earth.
His   serv-ice is the   gold-en cord Close-bind-ing all man -   kind.
Who   serves my Fa-ther   as   a son Is   sure-ly kin to   me.
All   Christ-ly souls are   one in Him Through-out the whole wide   earth.

Rescue the Perishing   377

FANNY J. CROSBY

WILLIAM H. DOANE

1. Res - cue the per - ish - ing, Care for the dy - ing, Snatch them in pit - y from
2. Though they are slight-ing Him, Still He is wait - ing, Wait - ing the pen - i - tent
3. Down in the hu - man heart, Crushed by the tempt-er, Feel-ings lie bur - ied that
4. Res - cue the per - ish - ing, Du - ty de-mands it; Strength for thy la - bor the

sin and the grave;   Weep o'er the er - ring ones, Lift up the fall - en,
child to re-ceive;   Plead with them ear-nest - ly, Plead with them gen - tly,
grace can re-store;   Touched by a   lov-ing heart, Wak-ened by kind-ness,
Lord will pro-vide;   Back to the nar-row way   Pa - tient-ly win them;

Tell them of Je - sus the might - y to save.
He will for - give if they on - ly be-lieve.
Chords that are bro - ken will vi - brate once more.   Res - cue the per - ish-ing,
Tell the poor wan-d'rer a   Sav-iour has died.

Care for the   dy - ing; Je - sus is mer -ci -ful, Je - sus will save.

378   A Passion for Souls

HERBERT G. TOVEY

FOSS L. FELLERS

1. Give me a pas-sion for souls, dear Lord, A pas-sion to save the lost;
2. Though there are dan-gers un - told and stern Con - front-ing me in the way,
3. How shall this pas-sion for souls be mine? Lord, make Thou the an - swer clear;

O that Thy love were by all a-dored, And wel-comed at an - y cost.
Will-ing-ly still would I go, nor turn, But trust Thee for grace each day.
Help me to throw out the old Life-Line To those who are strug - gling near.

Je - sus, I long, I long to be win - ning Men who are

lost, and con - stant - ly sin - ning; O may this hour be

one of be - gin - ning The sto - ry of par - don to tell.

Bringing in the Sheaves 379

KNOWLES SHAW

GEORGE A. MINOR

1. Sow-ing in the morn-ing, sow-ing seeds of kind-ness, Sow-ing in the
2. Sow-ing in the sun-shine, sow-ing in the shad-ows, Fear-ing nei-ther
3. Go-ing forth with weep-ing, sow-ing for the Mas-ter, Though the loss sus-

noon-tide and the dew-y eve; Wait-ing for the har-vest,
clouds nor win-ter's chill-ing breeze; By and by the har-vest,
tained our spir-it of-ten grieves; When our weep-ing's o-ver,

and the time of reap-ing, We shall come re-joic-ing, bring-ing in the sheaves.
and the la-bor end-ed, We shall come re-joic-ing, bring-ing in the sheaves.
He will bid us wel-come, We shall come re-joic-ing, bring-ing in the sheaves.

Bring-ing in the sheaves, bring-ing in the sheaves, We shall come re-joic-

1.
ing, bring-ing in the sheaves;

2.
ing, bring-ing in the sheaves.

380

He Was Not Willing

LUCY R. MEYER

LUCY R. MEYER

1. "He was not will-ing that an - y should per - ish"; Je - sus en-throned in the
2. "He was not will-ing that an - y should per - ish"; Clothed in our flesh with His
3. Plen -ty for pleas-ure, but lit - tle for Je - sus; Time for the world with its
4. "He was not will-ing that an - y should per - ish"; Am I His fol - low - er,

Glo - ry a - bove, Saw our poor fall -en world, pit - ied our sor - rows,
sor - row and pain, Came He to seek the lost, com - fort the mourn - er,
trou-bles and toys, No time for Je - sus' work, feed - ing the hun - gry,
and can I live Long - er at ease with a soul go-ing down-ward,

Poured out His life for us, won - der - ful love! Per - ish-ing! Per - ish-ing!
Heal the heart bro - ken by sor - row and shame. Per - ish-ing! Per - ish - ing!
Lift - ing lost souls to e - ter - ni - ty's joys. Per - ish-ing! Per - ish - ing!
Lost for the lack of the help I might give? Per - ish-ing! Per - ish - ing!

Throng-ing our path - way, Hearts break with bur-dens too heav - y to bear;
Har - vest is pass - ing, Reap-ers are few and the night draw-eth near;
Hark, how they call us: "Bring us your Sav-iour, O tell us of Him!
Thou wast not will - ing; Mas -ter, for - give, and in - spire us a - new;

Je - sus would save, but there's no one to tell them,
Je - sus is call - ing thee, haste to the reap - ing,
We are so wea - ry, so heav - i - ly la - den,
Ban - ish our world - li - ness, help us to ev - er

No one to lift them from sin and des - pair.
Thou shalt have souls, pre - cious souls for thy hire.
And with long weep - ing our eyes have grown dim."
Live with e - ter - ni - ty's val - ues in view.

Fight the Good Fight 381

JOHN S. B. MONSELL

WILLIAM BOYD

1. Fight the good fight with all thy might! Christ is thy strength, and
2. Run the straight race through God's good grace, Lift up thine eyes, and
3. Cast care a - side, lean on thy Guide, His bound-less mer - cy
4. Faint not nor fear, His arms are near, He chang-eth not, and

Christ thy right; Lay hold on life, and it shall be
seek His face; Life with its way be - fore us lies,
will pro - vide; Trust, and thy trust - ing soul shall prove
thou art dear; On - ly be - lieve, and thou shalt see

Thy joy and crown e - ter - nal - ly.
Christ is the path, and Christ the prize.
Christ is its life, and Christ its love.
That Christ is all in all to thee. A - men.

382 Seeking the Lost

WILLIAM A. OGDEN   WILLIAM A. OGDEN

1. Seek - ing the lost, yes, kind - ly en - treat - ing Wan - der - ers
2. Seek - ing the lost and point - ing to Je - sus Souls that are
3. Thus I would go on mis - sions of mer - cy, Fol - low - ing

on the moun - tain a - stray; "Come un - to Me," His
weak and hearts that are sore, Lead - ing them forth in
Christ from day un - to day, Cheer - ing the faint and

mes - sage re - peat - ing, Words of the Mas - ter speak - ing to - day.
ways of sal - va - tion, Show - ing the path to life ev - er - more.
rais - ing the fall - en, Point - ing the lost to Je - sus, the Way.

Go - ing a - far up - on the moun - tain,
In - to the fold of my Re - deem - er,

Go - ing a - far up - on the moun - tain, Bring - ing the
In - to the fold of my Re - deem - er, Je - sus the

1.
Bring - ing the wan - d'rer back a - gain, back a - gain,
Je - sus, the Lamb for sin - ners

2.
slain, for sin - ners slain.

wan - d'rer back a - gain,
Lamb for sin - ners slain.

Make Me a Channel of Blessing 383

H. G. SMYTH

H. G. SMYTH

1. Is your life a chan-nel of bless - ing? Is the love of God flow-ing through you? Are you tell - ing the lost of the Sav - iour? Are you read - y His serv-ice to do?

2. Is your life a chan-nel of bless - ing? Are you bur-dened by those that are lost? Have you urged up - on those who are stray - ing, The Sav-iour who died on the cross?

3. Is your life a chan-nel of bless - ing? Is it dai - ly tell - ing for Him? Have you spo - ken the word of sal - va - tion To those who are dy-ing in sin?

4. We can-not be chan-nels of bless - ing If our lives are not free from known sin; We will bar - ri - ers be and a hin-drance To those we are try-ing to win.

Make me a chan-nel of bless-ing to-day,
Make me a chan-nel of bless-ing, I pray; My life pos - sess-ing,
my serv - ice bless-ing, Make me a chan-nel of bless-ing to - day.

rit.

384   In the Service of the King

ALFRED H. ACKLEY

BENTLEY D. ACKLEY

1. I am hap-py in the serv-ice of the King, I am hap-py, O so hap-py; I have peace and joy that noth-ing else can bring, In the serv-ice of the King.

2. I am hap-py in the serv-ice of the King, I am hap-py, O so hap-py; Through the sun-shine and the shad-ow I can sing, In the serv-ice of the King.

3. I am hap-py in the serv-ice of the King, I am hap-py, O so hap-py; All that I pos-sess to Him I glad-ly bring, In the serv-ice of the King.

In the serv-ice of the King, Ev-'ry tal-ent I will bring; I have peace and joy and bless-ing In the serv-ice of the King.

Go Ye Into All the World

385

JAMES McGRANAHAN

JAMES McGRANAHAN

1. Far, far a-way, in hea-then dark-ness dwell-ing, Mil - lions of souls for -
2. See o'er the world wide - o -pen doors in - vit - ing, Sol- diers of Christ, a -
3. "Why will ye die?" the voice of God is call - ing; "Why will ye die?" re -
4. God speed the day, when those of ev -'ry na - tion, "Glo - ry to God!" tri -

ev - er may be lost; Who, who will go, sal - va-tion's sto - ry tell - ing,
rise and en - ter in! Chris-tians, a-wake! your forc - es all u - nit - ing,
ech - o in His name; Je - sus hath died to save from death ap-pal - ling,
um-phant-ly shall sing; Ran-somed, re-deemed, re-joic - ing in sal - va - tion,

Look-ing to Je-sus, mind-ing not the cost?
Send forth the Gos-pel, break the chains of sin. "All pow'r is giv-en un - to Me,
Life and sal-va-tion there-fore go pro - claim.
Shout, "Hal-le-lu-jah!" for the Lord is King.

All pow'r is giv - en un - to Me, Go ye in - to all the world, and

preace the Gos - pel, And lo, I am with you al - way."

386 It Pays to Serve Jesus

FRANK C. HUSTON

FRANK C. HUSTON

1. The serv-ice of Je-sus true pleas-ure af-fords, In
2. It pays to serve Je-sus what-e'er may be-tide, It
3. Though some-times the shad-ows may hang o'er the way, And

Him there is joy with-out an al-loy; 'Tis Heav-en to
pays to be true what-e'er you may do; 'Tis rich-es of
sor-rows may come to beck-on us Home, Our pre-cious Re-

trust Him and rest on His words; It pays to serve Je-sus each
mer-cy in Him to a-bide; It pays to serve Je-sus each
deem-er each toil will re-pay; It pays to serve Je-sus each

day.
day. It pays to serve Je-sus, it pays ev-'ry
day.

day, It pays ev-'ry step of the way; Though the
ev-'ry step of the way;

path - way to Glo - ry may some-times be drear, You'll be

hap - py each step of the way.

Must I Go, and Empty-Handed? 387

C. C. LUTHER

GEORGE C. STEBBINS

1. "Must I go, and emp -ty-hand - ed," Thus my dear Re- deem - er meet?
2. Not at death I shrink nor fal -ter, For my Sav - iour saves me now;
3. O the years in sin-ning wast - ed, Could I but re - call them now,
4. O ye saints, a -rouse, be ear-nest, Up and work while yet 'tis day;

Not one day of serv - ice give Him, Lay no tro - phy at His feet?
But to meet Him emp - ty-hand - ed, Thought of that now clouds my brow.
I would give them to my Sav-iour, To His will I'd glad - ly bow.
Ere the night of death o'er-take thee, Strive for souls while still you may.

"Must I go, and emp - ty - hand - ed?" Must I meet my Sav-iour so?

Not one soul with which to greet Him: Must I emp - ty - hand - ed go?

388 Speak, My Lord

GEORGE BENNARD   GEORGE BENNARD

1. Hear the Lord of har-vest sweet-ly call-ing, "Who will go and
2. When the coal of fire had touched the proph-et, Mak-ing him as
3. Mil-lions now in sin and shame are dy-ing; Lis-ten to their
4. Soon the time for reap-ing will be o-ver; Soon we'll gath-er

work for Me to-day? Who will bring to Me the lost and dy-ing?
pure, as pure can be; When the voice of God said, "Who'll go for us?"
sad and bit-ter cry; Has-ten, broth-er, has-ten to the res-cue;
for the har-vest-home; May the Lord of har-vest smile up-on us,

Who will point them to the nar-row way?"   Speak, my Lord,   speak, my
Then he an-swered, "Here I am, send me."   Speak, my Lord,
Quick-ly an-swer, "Mas-ter, here am I."
May we hear His bless-ed, "Child, well done."

Lord,   Speak, and I'll be quick to an-swer Thee;   Speak, my
speak, my Lord,   to an-swer Thee;

Lord, speak, my Lord, Speak, and I will an-swer, "Lord, send me."

Speak, my Lord, "Lord, send me."

Bring Them In 389

ALEXCENAH THOMAS

WILLIAM A. OGDEN

1. Hark! 'tis the Shep-herd's voice I hear, Out in the des-ert dark and drear,
2. Who'll go and help this Shep-herd kind, Help Him the wan-d'ring ones to find?
3. Out in the des-ert hear their cry, Out on the moun-tains wild and high;

Call-ing the sheep who've gone a-stray Far from the Shep-herd's fold a-way.
Who'll bring the lost ones to the fold, Where they'll be shel-tered from the cold?
Hark! 'tis the Mas-ter speaks to thee, "Go find My sheep wher-e'er they be."

Bring them in, bring them in, Bring them in from the fields of sin;

Bring them in, bring them in, Bring the wan-d'ring ones to Je - sus.

390　Have I Done My Best for Jesus?

EDWIN YOUNG   HARRY E. STORRS

1. I wonder, have I done my best for Jesus, Who died upon the cru-el tree? To think of His great sac-ri-fice at Cal-v'ry! I know my Lord ex-pects the best from me.

2. The hours that I have wast-ed are so man-y, The hours I've spent for Christ so few; Be-cause of all my lack of love for Je-sus, I won-der if His heart is break-ing too.

3. I wonder, have I cared e-nough for oth-ers, Or have I let them die a-lone? I might have helped a wan-d'rer to the Sav-iour, The seed of pre-cious Life I might have sown.

4. No long-er will I stay with-in the val-ley — I'll climb to moun-tain heights a-bove; The world is dy-ing now for want of some-one To tell them of the Sav-iour's match-less love.

How man-y are the lost that I have lift-ed? How man-y are the chained I've helped to free? I

won-der, have I done my best for Je - sus, When He has done so much for me?

Ready 391

A. C. PALMER

A. C. PALMER

1. Read-y to suf - fer grief or pain, Read-y to stand the test;
2. Read-y to go, read - y to bear, Read-y to watch and pray;
3. Read-y to speak, read - y to think, Read-y with heart and mind;
4. Read-y to speak, read - y to warn, Read-y o'er souls to yearn;

Read-y to stay at home and send Oth- ers if He sees best.
Read-y to stand a - side and give Till He shall clear the way.
Read-y to stand where He sees fit, Read-y His will to find.
Read-y in life or read - y in death, Read-y for His re - turn.

Read - y to go, read - y to stay, Read-y my place to fill;

Read - y for serv - ice low -ly or great, Read-y to do His will.

392 A Soul Winner for Jesus

J. W. FERRILL   J. W. FERRILL

1. I want to be a soul win-ner for Je-sus ev-'ry day, He does so much for me; I want to aid the lost sin-ner to leave his err-ing way, And be from bond-age free. A soul win-ner for Je-sus, A soul win-ner for Je-sus, O let me be each day; A soul win-ner for Je-sus, A

2. I want to be a soul win-ner and bring the lost to Christ, That they His grace may know; I want to live for Christ ev-er, and do His bless-ed will, Be-cause He loves me so. win-ner for Je-sus Christ the Lord, win-ner for Je-sus Christ the Lord,

3. I want to be a soul win-ner till Je-sus calls for me, To lay my bur-dens down; I want to hear Him say, "Ser-vant, you've gath-ered man-y sheaves, Re-ceive a star-ry crown."

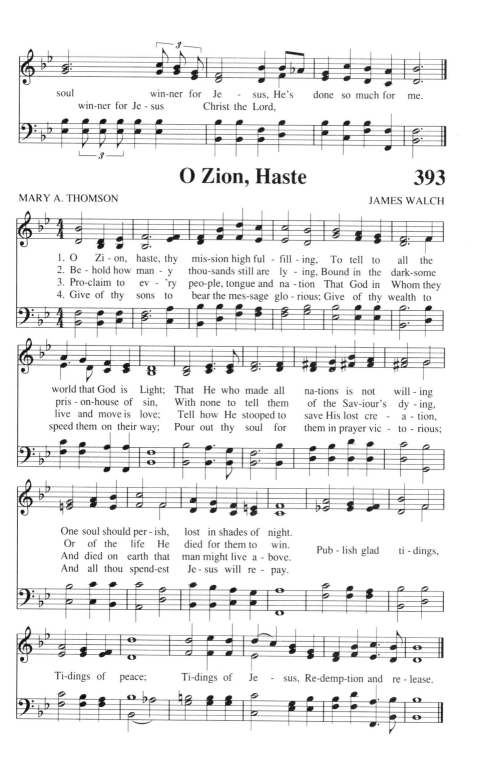

soul winner for Je - sus, He's done so much for me.
win-ner for Je - sus Christ the Lord,

O Zion, Haste 393

MARY A. THOMSON

JAMES WALCH

1. O Zi - on, haste, thy mis-sion high ful - fill - ing, To tell to all the
2. Be - hold how man - y thou-sands still are ly - ing, Bound in the dark-some
3. Pro-claim to ev - 'ry peo-ple, tongue and na - tion That God in Whom they
4. Give of thy sons to bear the mes-sage glo - rious; Give of thy wealth to

world that God is Light; That He who made all na-tions is not will - ing
pris - on-house of sin, With none to tell them of the Sav-iour's dy - ing,
live and move is love; Tell how He stooped to save His lost cre - a - tion,
speed them on their way; Pour out thy soul for them in prayer vic - to - rious;

One soul should per - ish, lost in shades of night.
Or of the life He died for them to win.
And died on earth that man might live a - bove.   Pub - lish glad ti - dings,
And all thou spend-est Je - sus will re - pay.

Ti-dings of peace; Ti-dings of Je - sus, Re-demp-tion and re - lease.

394 To the Work!

FANNY J. CROSBY

WILLIAM H. DOANE

1. To the work! to the work! we are ser-vants of God, Let us fol-low the
2. To the work! to the work! let the hun-gry be fed, To the foun-tain of
3. To the work! to the work! there is la-bor for all, For the king-dom of
4. To the work! to the work! in the strength of the Lord, And a robe and a

path that our Mas - ter hath trod; With the balm of His coun - sel our
Life let the wea - ry be led; In the cross and its ban - ner our
dark - ness and er - ror shall fall; And the name of Je - ho - vah ex -
crown shall our la - bor re-ward When the Home of the faith - ful our

strength to re-new, Let us do with our might what our hands find to do.
glo - ry shall be, While we her - ald the ti - dings, "Sal - va - tion is free!"
alt - ed shall be, In the loud swell-ing cho - rus, "Sal - va - tion is free!"
dwell-ing shall be And we shout with the ran-somed, "Sal - va - tion is free!"

Toil -ing on, toil - ing on, Toil - ing
Toil -ing on, toil - ing on,

on, toil - ing on; Let us hope,
Toil -ing on, toil - ing on; and trust,

let us watch And la-bor till the Mas-ter comes.

and pray,

Help Somebody Today   395

CARRIE E. BRECK

CHARLES H. GABRIEL

1. Look all a-round you, find some-one in need, Help some-bod-y to - day!
2. Man - y are wait-ing a kind, lov-ing word, Help some-bod-y to - day!
3. Man - y have bur-dens too heav-y to bear, Help some-bod-y to - day!
4. Some are dis-cour-aged and wea-ry in heart, Help some-bod-y to - day!

Though it be lit - tle — a neigh-bor-ly deed —Help some-bod-y to - day!
Thou hast a mes-sage, O let it be heard, Help some-bod-y to - day!
Grief is the por-tion of some ev-'ry-where, Help some-bod-y to - day!
Some-one the jour-ney to Heav-en should start, Help some-bod-y to - day!

Help some-bod-y to - day, Some-bod-y a-long life's way; Let

to-day, Home - ward way;

sor-row be end-ed, The friend-less be-friend-ed, O help some-bod-y to - day!

396

So Little Time

JOHN R. RICE

JOHN R. RICE

1. So lit-tle time! The har-vest will be o-ver, Our reap-ing
2. How man-y times I should have strong-ly plead-ed; How of-ten
3. De-spite the heat, the cease-less toil, the hard-ship, The bro-ken
4. A day of pleas-ure, or a feast of friend-ship; A house or
5. The har-vest white, with reap-ers few is wast-ing And man-y

done, we reap-ers tak-en Home, Re-port our work to Je-sus, Lord of
did I feel to strict-ly warn. The Spir-it moved, O had I pled for
heart o'er those we can-not win; Mis-un-der-stood be-cause we're oft pe-
car or gar-ments fair or fame, Will all be trash, when souls are brought to
souls will die and nev-er know The love of Christ, the joy of sins for-

har-vest, And hope He'll smile and that He'll say, "Well done!"
Je-sus! The grain is fall-en, lost ones not re-born.
cul-iar, Still no re-grets we'll have but for our sin. To-day we
Heav-en, And then how sad to face the slack-er's blame!
giv-en, O let us weep and love and pray and go!

reap, or miss our gold-en har-vest! To-day is giv-en us lost souls to

win. O then to save some dear ones from the burn-ing, To-

day we'll go to bring some sin - ner in.

Little Is Much When God Is in It 397

Mrs. F. W. SUFFIELD

Mrs. F. W. SUFFIELD

1. In the har - vest field now rip-ened There's a work for all to do.
2. Does the place you're called to la - bor Seem so small and lit - tle known?
3. Are you laid a - side from serv-ice, Bod - y worn from toil and care?
4. When the con - flict here is end- ed, And our race on earth is run,

Hark! the voice of God is call-ing, To the har - vest call - ing you.
It is great if God is in it, And He'll not for-get His own.
You can still be in the bat - tle, In the sa - cred place of prayer.
He will say, to all the faith-ful, "Wel-come Home, My child; well done."

Lit - tle is much when God is in it; La - bor not for wealth or fame.

There's a crown, and you can win it If you'll go in Je - sus' name.

8va

398 Tell It Again

MARY B. C. SLADE

R. M. McINTOSH

1. In - to the tent where a gyp- sy boy lay, Dy -ing a - lone at the
2. "Did He so love me, a poor lit - tle boy? Send un - to me the good
3. Bend - ing we caught the last words of his breath, Just as he en-tered the
4. Smil - ing he said, as his last sigh he spent, "I am so glad that for

close of the day, News of sal - va - tion we car - ried, said he:
ti - dings of joy? Need I not per - ish? my hand will He hold?
val - ley of death: "God sent His Son! 'Who-so - ev - er,' said He:
me He was sent!" Whis-pered, while low sank the sun in the West,

"No - bod - y ev - er has told it to me!"
No - bod - y ev - er the sto - ry has told!"
Then I am sure that He sent Him for me!"
"Lord, I be - lieve, tell it now to the rest!"

Tell it a - gain!

Tell it a - gain! Sal - va-tion's sto - ry re - peat o'er and o'er, Till none can

say of the chil-dren of men, "No-bod - y ev - er has told me be-fore."

Shall I Empty-Handed Be? 399

N. A. McAULAY and MAUD FRAZER

JOHN P. HILLIS

1. Shall I emp-ty-hand-ed be When be-side the crys-tal sea I shall stand be-fore the ev-er-last-ing throne? Must I have a heart of shame As I an-swer to my name, With no works that my Re-deem-er there can own? (there can own?)

2. What re-gret must then be mine When I meet my Lord di-vine, If I've wast-ed all the tal-ents He doth lend? If no soul to me can say, "I am glad you passed my way; For 'twas you who told me of the sin-ner's Friend. (sin-ner's Friend.)

3. If my grat-i-tude I'd show Un-to Him who loves me so, Let me la-bor till the ev-'ning shad-ows fall; That some lit-tle gift of love I may bear to realms a-bove, And not emp-ty-hand-ed be when comes the call. (comes the call.)

4. When the har-vest days are past, Shall I hear Him say at last, "Wel-come, toil-er, I've pre-pared for thee a place?" Shall I bring Him gold-en sheaves, Ri-pened fruit, not fad-ed leaves, When I see the bless-ed Sav-iour face to face? (face to face?)

5. When the books are o-pened wide, And the deeds of all are tried, May I have a rec-ord whit-er than the snow; When my race on earth is run, May I hear Him say, "Well done! Take the crown that love im-mor-tal doth be-stow." (doth be-stow.")

400   I'll Wish I Had Given Him More

GRACE REESE ADKINS   GRACE REESE ADKINS

1. By and by when I look on His face, Beau-ti-ful face, thorn-shad-owed face; By and by when I look on His face, I'll wish I had giv-en Him more. More, so much more, More of my life than I e'er gave be-fore — By and by when I look on His face, I'll wish I had giv-en Him more.

2. By and by when He holds out His hands, Wel-com-ing hands, nail-riv-en hands; By and by when He holds out His hands, I'll wish I had giv-en Him more. More, so much more, More of my love than I e'er gave be-fore — By and by when He holds out His hands, I'll wish I had giv-en Him more.

3. In the light of that heav-en-ly place, Light from His face, beau-ti-ful face; In the light of that heav-en-ly place, I'll wish I had giv-en Him more. More, so much more, Treas-ures un-bound-ed for Him I a-dore — By and by when I look on His face, I'll wish I had giv-en Him more.

Set My Soul Afire

401

GENE BARTLETT

GENE BARTLETT

1. Set my soul a - fire, Lord, for Thy ho - ly Word, Burn it deep with-
2. Set my soul a - fire, Lord, for the lost in sin, Give to me a
3. Set my soul a - fire, Lord, in my dai - ly life, Far too long I've

in me, let your voice be heard; Mil-lions grope in dark - ness,
pas - sion as I seek to win; Help me not to fal - ter,
wan - dered in this day of strife; Noth - ing else will mat - ter

in this day and hour, I will be Your wit - ness, fill me with Thy pow'r.
nev-er let me fail, Fill me with Thy Spir - it, let Thy will pre - vail.
but to live for Thee. I will be Your wit - ness as You live in me.

Set my soul a - fire, Lord, set my soul a - fire, Make my life a

wit - ness of Thy sav - ing pow'r. Mil - lions grope in dark - ness,

wait-ing for Thy Word, Set my soul a - fire, Lord, Set my soul a - fire.

402 Our Best

S. C. KIRK

GRANT C. TULLAR

1. Hear ye the Mas-ter's call, "Give Me thy best!"
   For, be it great or small, That is His test. Do then the
   best you can, Not for re-ward, Not for the praise of men, But
   for the Lord. Ev - 'ry work for Je - sus will be
   blest, But He asks from ev - 'ry - one his best.
   Our tal - ents may be few, These may be small,

2. Wait not for men to laud, Heed not their slight;
   Win - ning the smile of God Brings its de - light! Aid - ing the
   good and true Ne'er goes un - blest, All that we think or do, Be
   it the best.

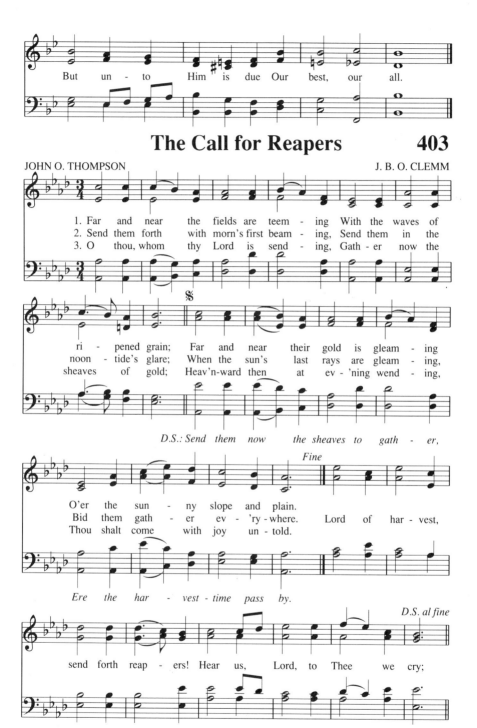

But un - to Him is due Our best, our all.

The Call for Reapers 403

JOHN O. THOMPSON

J. B. O. CLEMM

1. Far and near the fields are teem - ing With the waves of
2. Send them forth with morn's first beam - ing, Send them in the
3. O thou, whom thy Lord is send - ing, Gath - er now the

ri - pened grain; Far and near their gold is gleam - ing
noon - tide's glare; When the sun's last rays are gleam - ing,
sheaves of gold; Heav'n-ward then at ev - 'ning wend - ing,

D.S.: Send them now the sheaves to gath - er,

Fine

O'er the sun - ny slope and plain.
Bid them gath - er ev - 'ry - where. Lord of har - vest,
Thou shalt come with joy un - told.

Ere the har - vest - time pass by.

D.S. al fine

send forth reap - ers! Hear us, Lord, to Thee we cry;

404 When the Battle's Over

ISAAC WATTS

English. Arr. by WM. B. BLAKE

1. { Am I a sol-dier of the cross, A fol-lower of the Lamb,
   And shall I fear to own His cause, Or blush to speak His name? }

2. { Must I be car-ried to the skies On flow-ery beds of ease
   While oth-ers fought to win the prize, And sailed thro' blood-y seas? }

3. { Sure I must fight if I would reign, In-crease my cour-age, Lord;
   I'll bear the toil, en-dure the pain, Sup-port-ed by Thy Word. }

And when the bat-tle's o-ver we shall wear a crown! Yes,

we shall wear a crown! Yes, we shall wear a crown! And when the bat-tle's

o-ver we shall wear a crown In the new Je-ru-sa-lem.

FINE

D.S.

Wear a crown, wear a crown, Wear a bright and shin-ing crown;
Wear a crown, wear a crown,

The Banner of the Cross

405

DANIEL W. WHITTLE

JAMES McGRANAHAN

1. There's a roy - al ban - ner giv - en for dis - play To the sol - diers
2. Though the foe may rage and gath - er as the flood, Let the stand - ard
3. O - ver land and sea, wher - ev - er man may dwell, Make the glo - rious
4. When the glo - ry dawns - 'tis draw - ing ver - y near - It is has - t'ning

of the King; As an en - sign fair we lift it up to - day,
be dis - played: And be - neath its folds, as sol - diers of the Lord,
ti - dings known; Of the crim - son ban - ner now the sto - ry tell,
day by day — Then be - fore our King the foe shall dis - ap - pear,

While as ran - somed ones we sing.
For the Truth be not dis - mayed!
While the Lord shall claim His own!
And the cross the world shall sway!

March - ing on, march - ing
on, on,

on, For Christ count ev - 'ry - thing but loss! And to
on, on, ev - 'ry - thing, ev - 'ry - thing but loss!

crown Him King, toil and sing 'Neath the ban - ner of the cross!
we'll Be - neath

406 Who Is on the Lord's Side?

FRANCES R. HAVERGAL

C. LUISE REICHARDT
Arr. by John Goss

1. Who is on the Lord's side? Who will serve the King?
2. Not for weight of glo - ry, Not for crown and palm,
3. Je - sus, Thou hast bought us, Not with gold or gem,
4. Fierce may be the con - flict, Strong may be the foe,

Who will be His help - ers, Oth - er lives to bring?
En - ter we the ar - my, Raise the war - rior psalm;
But with Thine own life - blood, For Thy di - a - dem;
But the King's own ar - my None can o - ver - throw;

Who will leave the world's side? Who will face the foe?
But for Love that claim - eth Lives for whom He died:
With Thy bless - ing fill - ing Each who comes to Thee,
Round His stan - dard rang - ing, Vic - t'ry is se - cure,

Who is on the Lord's side? Who for Him will go?
He whom Je - sus nam - eth Must be on His side.
Thou hast made us will - ing, Thou hast made us free.
For His truth un - chang - ing Makes the tri - umph sure.

By Thy call of mer - cy,
By Thy love con - strain - ing, By Thy grace di - vine,
By Thy grand re - demp - tion,
Joy - ful - ly en - list - ing,

We are on the Lord's side, Sav-iour, we are Thine!

Faith of Our Fathers 407

FREDERICK W. FABER

HENRI F. HEMY
ALT. BY JAMES G. WALTON

1. Faith of our fa - thers! liv - ing still In spite of dung-eon,
2. Our fa - thers, chained in pri - sons dark, Were still in heart and
3. Faith of our fa - thers, we still strive To win all na - tions
4. Faith of our fa - thers! we will love Both friend and foe in

fire and sword: O how our hearts beat high with joy
con - science free: How sweet would be their chil - dren's fate,
un - to thee! And thro' the truth that comes from God
all our strife, And preach thee, too, as love knows how,

When-e'er we hear that glo - rious word! Faith of our fa - thers!
If they, like them, could die for thee! Faith of our fa - thers!
Man-kind shall then in - deed be free: Faith of our fa - thers!
By kind - ly words and vir - tuous life: Faith of our fa - thers!

ho - ly faith! We will be true to thee till death!
ho - ly faith! We will be true to thee till death!
ho - ly faith! We will be true to thee till death!
ho - ly faith! We will be true to thee till death!

408 Loyalty to Christ

E. TAYLOR CASSEL

FLORA H. CASSEL

1. From o - ver hill and plain There comes the sig - nal strain, 'Tis
2. O hear, ye brave, the sound That moves the earth a - round, 'Tis
3. Come, join our loy - al throng, We'll rout the gi - ant wrong, 'Tis
4. The strength of youth we lay At Je - sus' feet to - day, 'Tis

loy - al - ty, loy - al - ty, loy - al - ty to Christ; Its
loy - al - ty, loy - al - ty, loy - al - ty to Christ; A -
loy - al - ty, loy - al - ty, loy - al - ty to Christ; Where
loy - al - ty, loy - al - ty, loy - al - ty to Christ; His

mu - sic rolls a - long, The hills take up the song,
rise to dare and do, Ring out the watch-word true, Of
Sa - tan's ban - ners float We'll send the bu - gle note,
Gos - pel we'll pro - claim Thro' - out the world's do - main,

loy - al - ty, loy - al - ty, Yes, loy - al - ty to Christ.

"On to vic - to - ry! On to vic - to - ry!" Cries our

great Com-mand - er: "On!" We'll move at His com -
great Com-mand - er: "On!"

mand, We'll soon pos - sess the land, Thro' loy - al - ty,

loy - al - ty, Yes, loy - al - ty to Christ. A - men.

409 The Fight Is On

LEILA N. MORRIS   LEILA N. MORRIS

1. The fight is on — the trum-pet sound is ring-ing out, The cry "To
2. The fight is on — a-rouse, ye sol-diers brave and true! Je - ho-vah
3. The fight is lead - ing on to cer-tain vic-to-ry, The bow of

arms!" is heard a-far and near; The Lord of hosts is
leads, and vic-t'ry will as-sure; Go buck-le on the
prom-ise spans the east-ern sky; His glo-rious name in

march-ing on to vic-to-ry, The tri-umph of the Christ will soon ap-pear.
ar-mor God has giv-en you, And in His strength for-ev-er we'll en-dure.
ev-'ry land shall hon-ored be, The morn will break— the dawn of peace is nigh.

The fight is on, O Chris-tian sol-dier, And face to face in stern ar-

ray, With ar - mor gleam-ing and col - ors stream-ing, The right and

wrong en - gage to - day! The fight is on, but be not

wea - ry, Be strong and in His might hold fast; If God be

for us, His ban-ner o'er us, We'll sing the vic-tor's song at last!
for us, o'er us,

410 Faith Is the Victory!

JOHN H. YATES

IRA D. SANKEY

1. En-camped a-long the hills of light, Ye Chris-tian sol-diers, rise, And
2. His ban-ner o-ver us is love, Our sword the Word of God; We
3. On ev-'ry hand the foe we find Drawn up in dread ar-ray; Let
4. To him that o-ver-comes the foe, White rai-ment shall be giv'n; Be-

press the bat-tle ere the night Shall veil the glow-ing skies. A-
tread the road the saints a-bove With shouts of tri-umph trod. By
tents of ease be left be-hind, And on-ward to the fray. Sal-
fore the an-gels he shall know His name con-fessed in Heav'n. Then

gainst the foe in vales be-low Let all our strength be hurled; Faith
faith, they like a whirl-wind's breath, Swept on o'er ev-'ry field; The
va-tion's hel-met on each head, With truth all girt a-bout, The
on-ward from the hills of light, Our hearts will love a-flame; We'll

is the vic-to-ry, we know, That o-ver-comes the world.
faith by which they con-quered Death Is still our shin-ing shield.
earth shall trem-ble 'neath our tread, And ech-o with our shout.
van-quish all the hosts of night, In Je-sus' con-qu'ring name.

Faith is the vic-to-ry! Faith is the vic-to-ry!
Faith is the vic-to-ry! Faith is the vic-to-ry!

Oh, glo-ri-ous vic-to-ry, That o-ver-comes the world.

Hold the Fort 411

P. P. BLISS

P. P. BLISS

1. Ho, my com-rades! see the sig-nal, Wav-ing in the sky!
2. See the might-y host ad-vanc-ing, Sa-tan lead-ing on;
3. See the glo-rious ban-ner wav-ing! Hear the trum-pet blow!
4. Fierce and long the bat-tle rag-es, But our Help is near;

Re-in-force-ments now ap-pear-ing, Vic-to-ry is nigh.
Might-y men a-round us fall-ing, Cour-age al-most gone!
In our Lead-er's name we'll tri-umph O-ver ev-'ry foe.
On-ward comes our great Com-mand-er, Cheer, my com-rades, cheer.

"Hold the fort, for I am com-ing," Je-sus sig-nals still;

Wave the an-swer back to Heav-en, "By Thy grace we will."

412   Onward, Christian Soldiers

SABINE BARING-GOULD   ARTHUR S. SULLIVAN

1. On-ward, Chris-tian sol - diers, March-ing as to war,
2. At the sign of tri - umph Sa - tan's host doth flee,
3. Like a might-y ar - my Moves the Church of God;
4. On-ward, then, ye peo - ple, Join our hap-py throng;

With the cross of Je - sus Go-ing on be - fore!
On, then, Chris-tian sol - diers, On to vic - to - ry!
Broth-ers, we are tread - ing Where the saints have trod.
Blend with ours your voic - es In the tri - umph song.

Christ, the roy-al Mas - ter, Leads a-gainst the foe;
Hell's foun-da-tions quiv - er At the shout of praise;
We are not di - vid - ed, All one bod-y we —
Glo-ry, laud and hon - or Un-to Christ the King —

For-ward in-to bat - tle See His ban-ner go!
Broth-ers, lift your voic - es, Loud your an-thems raise!
One in hope and doc - trine, One in char-i-ty.
This thru count-less a - ges Men and an-gels sing.

On-ward, Chris-tian sol - diers, March-ing as to war,

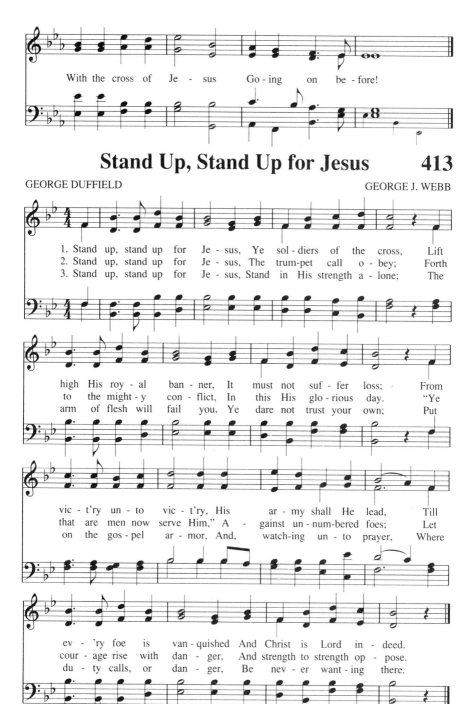

With the cross of Je - sus Go - ing on be - fore!

Stand Up, Stand Up for Jesus 413

GEORGE DUFFIELD

GEORGE J. WEBB

1. Stand up, stand up for Je - sus, Ye sol - diers of the cross, Lift
2. Stand up, stand up for Je - sus, The trum-pet call o - bey; Forth
3. Stand up, stand up for Je - sus, Stand in His strength a - lone; The

high His roy - al ban - ner, It must not suf - fer loss; From
to the might - y con - flict, In this His glo - rious day. "Ye
arm of flesh will fail you, Ye dare not trust your own; Put

vic - t'ry un - to vic - t'ry, His ar - my shall He lead, Till
that are men now serve Him," A - gainst un - num-bered foes; Let
on the gos - pel ar - mor, And, watch-ing un - to prayer, Where

ev - 'ry foe is van - quished And Christ is Lord in - deed.
cour - age rise with dan - ger, And strength to strength op - pose.
du - ty calls, or dan - ger, Be nev - er want - ing there.

414 Stand Up, Stand Up for Jesus

GEORGE DUFFIELD

ADAM GEIBEL

Unison

1. Stand up, stand up for Je - sus, Ye sol - diers of the
2. Stand up, stand up for Je - sus, The trum - pet call o -
3. Stand up, stand up for Je - sus, Stand in His strength a -
4. Stand up, stand up for Je - sus, The strife will not be

cross; Lift high His roy - al ban - ner, It
bey; Forth to the might - y con - flict, In
lone; The arm of flesh will fail you, Ye
long; This day the noise of bat - tle, The

must not suf - fer loss: From vic - t'ry un - to
this His glo - rious day: "Ye that are men now
dare not trust your own: Put on the gos - pel
next, the vic - tor's song: To Him that o - ver -

vic - t'ry His ar - my shall He lead, Till
serve Him" A - gainst un - num - bered foes; Let
ar - mor, Each piece put on with prayer; Where
com - eth, A crown of life shall be: He

415 Victory Through Grace

FANNY J. CROSBY

JOHN R. SWENEY

1. Con-quer-ing now and still to con - quer, Rid - eth the
2. Con-quer-ing now and still to con - quer, Who is this
3. Con-quer-ing now and still to con - quer, Je - sus Thou

King in His might! Lead - ing the host of all the
won - der - ful King? Whence are the ar - mies which He
Rul - er of all! Thrones and their scep - ters all shall

faith - ful In - to the midst of the fight; See them with
lead - eth, While of His glo - ry they sing? He is our
per - ish, Crowns and their splen - dor shall fall, Yet shall the

416 As a Volunteer

W. S. BROWN

CHARLES H. GABRIEL

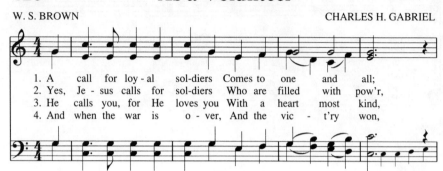

1. A call for loy-al sol-diers Comes to one and all;
2. Yes, Je-sus calls for sol-diers Who are filled with pow'r,
3. He calls you, for He loves you With a heart most kind,
4. And when the war is o-ver, And the vic-t'ry won,

Sol-diers for the con-flict, Will you heed the call?
Sol-diers who will serve Him Ev-'ry day and hour;
He whose heart was bro-ken, Bro-ken for man-kind;
When the true and faith-ful Gath-er one by one,

Will you an-swer quick-ly, With a read-y cheer,
He will not for-sake you, He is ev-er near,
Now, just now He calls you, Calls in ac-cents clear,
He will crown with glo-ry All who there ap-pear;

Will you be en-list-ed As a vol-un-teer? A vol-un-teer for

Je - sus, A sol - dier true! Oth - ers have en - list - ed,

Why not you? Je - sus is the Cap-tain, We will nev - er
O why not?

fear; Will you be en - list - ed As a vol-un-teer? A - men.

417 True-Hearted, Whole-Hearted

FRANCES R. HAVERGAL

GEORGE C. STEBBINS

1. True-heart-ed, whole-heart-ed, faith-ful and loy-al, King of our
2. True-heart-ed, whole-heart-ed, full-est al-le-giance Yield-ing hence-
3. True-heart-ed, whole-heart-ed, Sav-iour all glo-rious! Take Thy great

lives, by Thy grace we will be; Un-der the stan-dard ex-
forth to our glo-ri-ous King; Val-iant en-deav-or and
pow-er and reign there a-lone, O-ver our wills and af-

alt-ed and roy-al, Strong in Thy strength we will bat-tle for Thee.
lov-ing o-be-dience, Free-ly and joy-ous-ly now would we bring.
fec-tions vic-to-rious, Free-ly sur-ren-dered and whol-ly Thine own.

Peal out the watch-word! si-lence it nev-er! Song of our
Peal out the watch-word! si-lence it nev-er! Song of our

spir - its, re - joic - ing and free;   Peal   out the watch-word!
spir - its,   re-joic-ing and free;   Peal out the watch-word!

loy - al for - ev - er,   King   of our lives, by Thy grace we will be.
loy- al for - ev - er,   King of our lives, by Thy grace we will be.

Am I a Soldier of the Cross?   418

ISAAC WATTS

THOMAS A. ARNE

1. Am I a sol - dier of the cross, A fol - low'r of the Lamb?
2. Must I be car - ried to the skies On flow - 'ry beds of ease,
3. Are there no foes for me to face? Must I not stem the flood?
4. Sure I must fight, if I would reign; In - crease my cour - age, Lord;

And shall I fear to own His cause, Or blush to speak His name?
While oth - ers fought to win the prize, And sailed thro' blood - y seas?
Is this vile world a friend to grace, To help me on to God?
I'll bear the toil, en - dure the pain, Sup - port - ed by Thy Word.

419 Sound the Battle Cry

WILLIAM F. SHERWIN

WILLIAM F. SHERWIN

1. Sound the bat - tle cry! See, the foe is nigh; Raise the stan-dard high
2. Strong to meet the foe, March-ing on we go, While our cause we know,
3. O! Thou God of all, Hear us when we call, Help us one and all

For the Lord; Gird your ar-mor on, Stand firm, ev-'ry one; Rest your
Must pre - vail; Shield and ban-ner bright, Gleam-ing in the light, Bat - tling
By Thy grace; When the bat-tle's done, And the vic - t'ry's won, May we

cause up - on His ho - ly Word.
for the right We ne'er can fail. Rouse, then, sol-diers, ral - ly round the
wear the crown Be - fore Thy face.

ban-ner, Read-y, stead-y, pass the word a-long; On-ward, for-ward,

shout a-loud Ho-san - na! Christ is Cap-tain of the might - y throng.

There's a Song in the Air 420

JOSIAH G. HOLLAND

KARL P. HARRINGTON

1. There's a song in the air! There's a star in the sky! There's a
2. There's a tu-mult of joy O'er the won-der-ful birth, For the
3. In the light of that star Lie the a-ges im-pearled; And that
4. We re-joice in the light, And we ech-o the song That comes

moth-er's deep prayer, And a ba-by's low cry! And the
Vir-gin's sweet boy Is the Lord of the earth. Ay! the
song from a-far Has swept o-ver the world. Ev-'ry
down through the night From the heav-en-ly throng. Ay! we

star rains its fire while the beau-ti-ful sing, For the
star rains its fire while the beau-ti-ful sing, For the
hearth is a-flame, and the beau-ti-ful sing In the
shout to the love-ly e-van-gel they bring, And we

man-ger of Beth-le-hem cra-dles a King!
man-ger of Beth-le-hem cra-dles a King!
homes of the na-tions that Je-sus is King!
greet in His cra-dle our Sav-iour and King!

421

The First Noel

Old English Carol

Traditional melody from
W. Sandy's "Christmas Carols"

1. The first No - el the an-gel did say Was to cer-tain poor
2. And by the light of that same star, Three wise men
3. This star drew nigh to the north - west, O'er Beth - le -
4. Then en - tered in those wise men three, Full rev - 'rent -

shep-herds in fields where they lay; In fields where they lay
came from coun - try far; To seek for a King was
hem it took its rest, And there it did both
ly up - on their knee, And of - fered there in

keep-ing their sheep, On a cold win-ter's night that was so deep.
their in - tent, And to fol-low the star wher - ev - er it went.
stop and stay, Right o - ver the place where Je - sus lay.
His pres - ence, Their gold, and myrrh, and frank - in - cense.

No - el, No - el, No - el, No - el,

Born is the King of Is - ra - el.

Thou Didst Leave Thy Throne

422

EMILY E. S. ELLIOTT Margaret TIMOTHY R. MATTHEWS

1. Thou didst leave Thy throne And Thy king - ly crown, When Thou
2. Heav - en's arch - es rang When the an - gels sang, Pro -
3. The fox - es found rest, And the birds their nest In the
4. Thou cam - est, O Lord, With the liv - ing Word That should
5. When the heav - ens shall ring, And the an - gels sing, At Thy

cam - est to earth for me; But in Beth - le-hem's home
claim - ing Thy roy - al de - gree; But of low - ly birth
shade of the for - est tree; But Thy couch was the sod,
set Thy peo - ple free; But with mock - ing scorn,
com - ing to vic - to - ry, Let Thy voice call me Home,

Was there found no room For Thy ho - ly na - tiv - i - ty.
Didst Thou come to earth, And in great hu - mil - i - ty.
O Thou Son of God, In the des - erts of Gal - i - lee.
And with crown of thorn, They bore Thee to Cal - va - ry.
Say-ing, "Yet there is room, There is room at My side for thee."

1.—4. O come to my heart, Lord Je - sus, There is room in my heart for Thee.
5. My heart shall re-joice, Lord Je - sus, When Thou com-est and call - est for me.

423 Joy to the World!

ISAAC WATTS
Based on Psalm 98

Arranged from George F. Handel

1. Joy to the world! the Lord is come; Let earth re-
2. Joy to the world! the Sav-iour reigns; Let men their
3. No more let sins and sor-rows grow, Nor thorns in-
4. He rules the world with truth and grace, And makes the

ceive her King; Let ev - 'ry heart pre-pare Him room,
songs em-ploy; While fields and floods, rocks, hills, and plains
fest the ground; He comes to make His bless - ings flow
na - tions prove The glo - ries of His right - eous - ness,

And Heav'n and na - ture sing, And Heav'n and na - ture
Re - peat the sound-ing joy, Re - peat the sound-ing
Far as the curse is found, Far as the curse is
And won-ders of His love, And won-ders of His
1. And Heav'n and na - ture sing, And

sing, And Heav'n, and Heav'n and na - ture sing.
joy, Re - peat, re - peat the sound - ing joy.
found, Far as, far as the curse is found.
love, And won-ders, and won - ders of His love.
Heav'n and na - ture sing,

O Come, All Ye Faithful

424

LATIN HYMN
Translated by Frederick Oakeley

From John F. Wade's
"Cantus Diversi"

1. O come, all ye faith - ful, joy - ful and tri - um - phant, O
2. Sing, choirs of an - gels, sing in ex - ul - ta - tion, O
3. Yea, Lord, we greet Thee, born this hap - py morn - ing,

come ye, O come ye to Beth - le - hem;
sing, all ye bright hosts of Heav'n a - bove;
Je - sus, to Thee be all glo - ry giv'n;

Come and be - hold Him born the King of an - gels;
Glo - ry to God, all glo - ry in the high - est;
Word of the Fa - ther, now in flesh ap - pear - ing;

O come, let us a - dore Him, O come, let us a - dore Him, O

come, let us a - dore Him, Christ, the Lord.

425 No Room in the Inn

A. L. SKILTON

E. GRACE UPDEGRAFF

1. No beau-ti-ful cham-ber, No soft cra-dle bed,
2. No sweet con-se-cra-tion, No seek-ing His part,
3. No one to re-ceive Him, No wel-come while here,

No place but a man-ger, No-where for His head;
No hu-mil-i-a-tion No place in the heart;
No balm to re-lieve Him, No staff but a spear;

No prais-es of glad-ness, No thought of their sin,
No thought of the Sav-iour, No sor-row for sin,
No seek-ing His treas-ure, No weep-ing for sin,

rit.

No glo-ry but sad-ness, No room in the inn.
No prayer for His fa-vor, No room in the inn. No
No do-ing His pleas-ure, No room in the inn.

room, no room for Je-sus, O give Him wel-come free, Lest

you should hear at Heav-en's gate, "There is no room for thee."

I Heard the Bells on Christmas Day   426

HENRY W. LONGFELLOW

J. BAPTISTE CALKIN

1. I heard the bells on Christ-mas day, Their old fa-mil-iar car-ols play, And wild and sweet the words re-peat Of peace on earth, good-will to men.

2. I thought how, as the day had come, The bel-fries of all Chris-ten-dom Had rolled a-long th'un-bro-ken song Of peace on earth, good-will to men.

3. And in des-pair I bowed my head: "There is no peace on earth," I said, "For hate is strong, and mocks the song Of peace on earth, good-will to men."

4. Then pealed the bells more loud and deep: "God is not dead, nor doth He sleep; The wrong shall fail, the right pre-vail, With peace on earth, good-will to men:"

5. Till, ring-ing, sing-ing on its way, The world re-volved from night to day, A voice, a chime, a chant sub-lime, Of peace on earth, good-will to men!

427   We Three Kings of Orient Are

JOHN H. HOPKINS   JOHN H. HOPKINS

1. We three kings of O-ri-ent are, Bear-ing gifts we trav-erse a-far
2. Born a King on Beth-le-hem's plain, Gold I bring to crown Him a-gain,
3. Frank-in-cense to of-fer have I, In-cense owns a De-i-ty nigh;
4. Myrrh is mine; its bit-ter per-fume Breathes a life of gath-er-ing gloom;
5. Glo-rious now be-hold Him a-rise, King and God and Sac-ri-fice;

Field and foun-tain, moor and moun-tain, Fol-low-ing yon-der star.
King for-ev-er, ceas-ing nev-er O-ver us all to reign.
Prayer and prais-ing, all men rais-ing, Wor-ship Him, God on high.
Sor-rowing, sigh-ing, bleed-ing, dy-ing, Sealed in the stone-cold tomb.
Al-le-lu-ia, Al-le-lu-ia! Peals through the earth and skies.

O star of won-der, star of night, Star with roy-al beau-ty bright. West-ward lead-ing, still pro-ceed-ing, Guide us to thy per-fect light.

It Came Upon the Midnight Clear 428

EDMUND H. SEARS

RICHARD S. WILLIS

1. It came up-on the mid-night clear, That glo - rious song of old,
2. Still through the clo - ven skies they come, With peace-ful wings un - furled,
3. And ye, be-neath life's crush-ing load, Whose forms are bend - ing low,
4. For lo, the days are has-t'ning on, By proph - et bards fore -told,

From an - gels bend - ing near the earth, To touch their harps of gold:
And still their heav'n - ly mu - sic floats O'er all the wea - ry world:
Who toil a - long the climb-ing way With pain-ful steps and slow,
When with the ev - er - cir-cling years Comes round the age of gold;

"Peace on the earth, good-will to men, From Heav'n's all - gra - cious King":
A - bove its sad and low - ly plains They bend on hov - 'ring wing:
Look now! for glad and gold-en hours Come swift - ly on the wing;
When peace shall o - ver all the earth Its an - cient splen - dors fling.

The world in sol - emn still-ness lay To hear the an - gels sing.
And ev - er o'er its Ba-bel sounds The bless - ed an - gels sing.
O rest be-side the wea - ry road, And hear the an - gels sing.
And the whole world give back the song Which now the an - gels sing.

429   Hark! the Herald Angels Sing

CHARLES WESLEY

FELIX MENDELSSOHN-BARTHOLDY
Arranged by William H. Cummings

1. Hark! the her - ald an - gels sing, "Glo - ry to the new-born King:
2. Christ, by high - est Heav'n a -dored, Christ, the ev - er - last - ing Lord:
3. Hail the Heav'n-born Prince of Peace! Hail the Sun of right-eous-ness!
4. Come, De - sire of na - tions, come! Fix in us Thy hum-ble home:

Peace on earth, and mer - cy mild: God and sin - ners rec - on - ciled."
Late in time be - hold Him come, Off-spring of a vir - gin's womb.
Light and life to all He brings, Ris'n with heal - ing in His wings:
Rise, the wo - man's con-qu'ring Seed, Bruise in us the ser-pent's head;

Joy - ful, all ye na - tions, rise, Join the tri - umph of the skies;
Veiled in flesh the God-head see, Hail th'in-car - nate De - i - ty!
Mild He lays His glo - ry by, Born that man no more may die;
Ad - am's like-ness now ef -face, Stamp Thine im-age in its place:

With an - gel - ic hosts pro-claim, "Christ is born in Beth - le - hem."
Pleased as man with men to dwell, Je - sus our Im - man - u - el.
Born to raise the sons of earth; Born to give them sec - ond birth.
Sec - ond Ad - am from a - bove, Re - in - state us in Thy love.

Hark! the her - ald an - gels sing, "Glo - ry to the new-born King."

While Shepherds Watched Their Flocks 430

NAHUM TATE

GEORGE F. HANDEL

1. While shep-herds watched their flocks by night, All seat-ed on the
2. "Fear not!" said he; for might-y dread Had seized their trou - bled
3. "To you, in Dav - id's town this day, Is born of Dav - id's
4. "The heav'n-ly Babe you there shall find To hu-man view dis -
5. "All glo - ry be to God on high, And to the earth be

ground, The an - gel of the Lord came down, And
mind, "Glad ti - dings of great joy I bring, To
line, The Sav - iour who is Christ the Lord; And
played, All mean - ly wrapped in swath-ing bands, And
peace: Good will hence - forth from Heav'n to men, Be -

glo - ry shone a - round, And glo - ry shone a - round.
you and all man - kind, To you and all man - kind.
this shall be the sign: And this shall be the sign:
in a man-ger laid, And in a man - ger laid.
gin and nev - er cease, Be - gin and nev - er cease."

431 Silent Night! Holy Night!

JOSEPH MOHR

FRANZ GRÜBER

1. Si - lent night, ho - ly night, All is calm, all is bright
2. Si - lent night, ho - ly night, Shep-herds quake at the sight,
3. Si - lent night, ho - ly night, Son of God, love's pure light
4. Si - lent night, ho - ly night, Won-drous star, lend thy light;

Round yon vir - gin moth-er and child. Ho - ly in-fant so ten - der and mild.
Glo-ries stream from Heav-en a - far, Heav'n-ly hosts sing Al - le - lu - ia;
Ra-diant beams from Thy ho - ly face, With the dawn of re - deem - ing grace,
With the an - gels let us sing, Al - le - lu - ia to our King;

Sleep in heav - en - ly peace, Sleep in heav - en - ly peace.
Christ the Sav - iour is born! Christ the Sav - iour is born!
Je - sus, Lord, at Thy birth, Je - sus, Lord, at Thy birth.
Christ the Sav - iour is born. Christ the Sav - iour is born.

432 Angels, From the Realms of Glory

JAMES MONTGOMERY

HENRY SMART

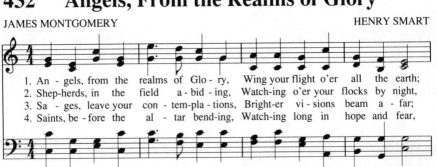

1. An - gels, from the realms of Glo - ry, Wing your flight o'er all the earth;
2. Shep-herds, in the field a - bid - ing, Watch-ing o'er your flocks by night,
3. Sa - ges, leave your con - tem-pla - tions, Bright-er vi - sions beam a - far;
4. Saints, be - fore the al - tar bend-ing, Watch-ing long in hope and fear,

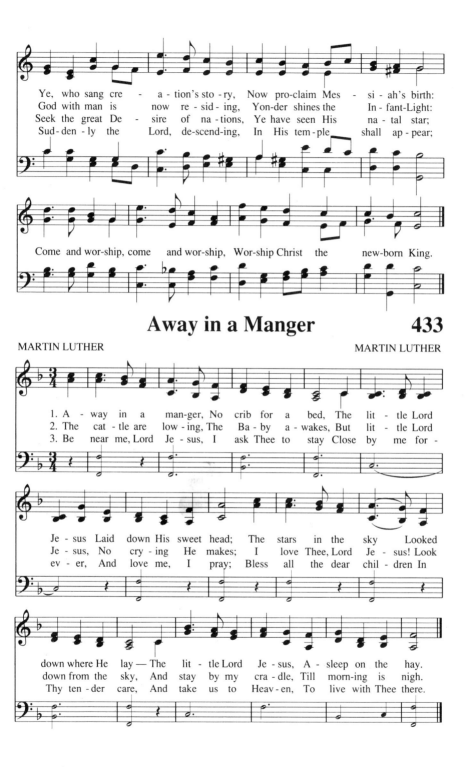

Ye, who sang cre - a - tion's sto - ry, Now pro-claim Mes - si - ah's birth:
God with man is now re - sid - ing, Yon-der shines the In - fant-Light:
Seek the great De - sire of na - tions, Ye have seen His na - tal star;
Sud - den - ly the Lord, de-scend-ing, In His tem - ple shall ap - pear;

Come and wor-ship, come and wor-ship, Wor-ship Christ the new-born King.

Away in a Manger 433

MARTIN LUTHER   MARTIN LUTHER

1. A - way in a man-ger, No crib for a bed, The lit - tle Lord
2. The cat - tle are low - ing, The Ba - by a - wakes, But lit - tle Lord
3. Be near me, Lord Je - sus, I ask Thee to stay Close by me for -

Je - sus Laid down His sweet head; The stars in the sky Looked
Je - sus, No cry - ing He makes; I love Thee, Lord Je - sus! Look
ev - er, And love me, I pray; Bless all the dear chil - dren In

down where He lay — The lit - tle Lord Je - sus, A - sleep on the hay.
down from the sky, And stay by my cra - dle, Till morn-ing is nigh.
Thy ten - der care, And take us to Heav - en, To live with Thee there.

434   O Little Town of Bethlehem

PHILLIPS BROOKS   LEWIS H. REDNER

1. O lit-tle town of Beth-le-hem, How still we see thee lie! A-
2. For Christ is born of Ma - ry; And gath-ered all a - bove, While
3. How si - lent - ly, how si - lent - ly The won-drous gift is giv'n! So
4. O ho - ly Child of Beth-le-hem, De- scend to us, we pray; Cast

bove thy deep and dream-less sleep The si - lent stars go by; Yet
mor - tals sleep, the an - gels keep Their watch of won-d'ring love. O
God im-parts to hu - man hearts The bless-ings of His Heav'n. No
out our sin and en - ter in, Be born in us to - day. We

in thy dark streets shin - eth The ev - er - last - ing Light; The
morn-ing stars, to - geth - er Pro - claim the ho - ly birth, And
ear may hear His com - ing; But in this world of sin, Where
hear the Christ - mas an - gels The great glad ti - dings tell — O

hopes and fears of all the years Are met in thee to - night.
prais - es sing to God the King, And peace to men on earth.
meek souls will re - ceive Him still, The dear Christ en - ters in.
come to us, a - bide with us, Our Lord Em - man - u - el.

O Beautiful for Spacious Skies 435

KATHERINE L. BATES

SAMUEL A. WARD

1. O beau - ti - ful for spa-cious skies, For am - ber waves of grain,
2. O beau - ti - ful for pil - grim feet, Whose stern, im-pas-sioned stress
3. O beau - ti - ful for he - roes proved In lib - er - at - ing strife,
4. O beau - ti - ful for pa-triot dream That sees be-yond the years

For pur - ple moun-tain maj - es -ties A - bove the fruit - ed plain!
A thor-ough-fare for free - dom beat A - cross the wil - der - ness!
Who more than self their coun - try loved, And mer - cy more than life!
Thine al - a-bas - ter cit - ies gleam, Un - dimmed by hu - man tears!

A - mer - i - ca! A - mer - i - ca! God shed His grace on thee,
A - mer - i - ca! A - mer - i - ca! God mend thine ev - 'ry flaw,
A - mer - i - ca! A - mer - i - ca! May God thy gold re - fine,
A - mer - i - ca! A - mer - i - ca! God shed His grace on thee,

And crown thy good with broth - er-hood From sea to shin - ing sea!
Con - firm thy soul in self con -trol, Thy lib - er - ty in law!
Till all suc-cess be no - ble - ness And ev - 'ry gain di - vine!
And crown thy good with broth - er-hood From sea to shin - ing sea!

436   The Star-Spangled Banner

FRANCIS SCOTT KEY   FRANCIS SCOTT KEY

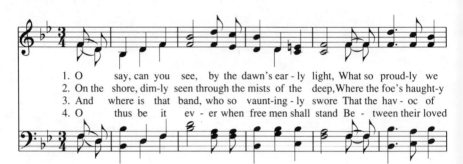

1. O   say, can you   see,   by the dawn's ear - ly light, What so proud-ly we
2. On the shore, dim-ly seen through the mists of the   deep, Where the foe's haught-y
3. And   where is that band, who so vaunt-ing - ly swore That the hav - oc of
4. O   thus be it   ev - er when free men shall stand Be - tween their loved

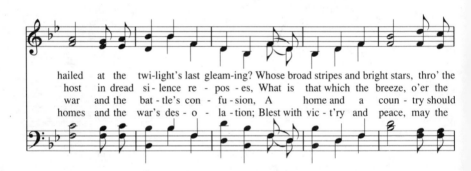

hailed   at the   twi-light's last gleam-ing? Whose broad stripes and bright stars, thro' the
host   in dread si - lence re - pos - es, What is   that which the breeze, o'er the
war   and the   bat - tle's con - fu - sion, A   home and a   coun - try should
homes   and the   war's des - o - la - tion; Blest with vic - t'ry and   peace, may the

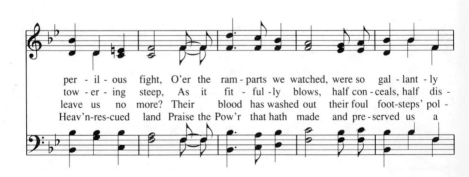

per - il - ous   fight, O'er the ram - parts we watched, were so   gal - lant - ly
tow - er - ing   steep, As it   fit - ful - ly   blows, half con - ceals, half dis -
leave us   no   more? Their   blood has washed out   their foul foot-steps' pol -
Heav'n-res-cued   land Praise the Pow'r that hath made   and pre-served us   a

stream-ing? And the rock-et's red glare, the bombs burst-ing in air, Gave
clos-es? Now it catch-es the gleam of the morn-ing's first beam, In full
lu-tion; No ref-uge could save the hire-ling and slave From the
na-tion! Then con-quer we must, when our cause it is just; And

proof through the night that our flag was still there. O say, does that
glo-ry re-flect-ed, now shines on the stream: 'Tis the Star-span-gled
ter-ror of flight or the gloom of the grave; And the Star-span-gled
this be our mot-to: "In God is our trust!" And the Star-span-gled

Star-span-gled Ban-ner yet wave O'er the land
Ban-ner; O long may it wave O'er the land
Ban-ner in tri-umph doth wave O'er the land
Ban-ner in tri-umph shall wave O'er the land

of the free, and the home of the brave?
of the free, and the home of the brave.
of the free, and the home of the brave.
of the free, and the home of the brave.

437   Battle Hymn of the Republic

JULIA WARD HOWE

WILLIAM STEFFE

1. Mine eyes have seen the glo - ry of the com - ing of the Lord; He is
2. I have seen Him in the watch-fires of a hun-dred cir-cling camps; They have
3. He has sound-ed forth the trum-pet that shall nev - er sound re - treat; He is
4. In the beau - ty of the lil - ies Christ was born a-cross the sea, With a

tram-pling out the vin-tage where the grapes of wrath are stored; He hath loosed the
build - ed Him an al - tar in the ev - 'ning dews and damps; I can read His
sift - ing out the hearts of men be - fore His judg-ment seat. O be swift, my
glo - ry in His bos - om that trans - fig - ures you and me; As He died to

fate-ful light-ning of His ter - ri - ble swift sword; His truth is march-ing on.
right-eous sen-tence by the dim and flar-ing lamps; His day is march-ing on.
soul, to an-swer Him! be ju - bi - lant, my feet! Our God is march-ing on.
make men ho - ly, let us die to make men free; While God is march-ing on.

Glo - ry! glo - ry, hal - le - lu - jah! Glo - ry! glo - ry, hal - le - lu - jah!
Glo - ry! glo - ry, hal - le - lu - jah! Glo - ry! glo - ry, hal - le - lu - jah!
Glo - ry! glo - ry, hal - le - lu - jah! Glo - ry! glo - ry, hal - le - lu - jah!
Glo - ry! glo - ry, hal - le - lu - jah! Glo - ry! glo - ry, hal - le - lu - jah!

Glo - ry! glo - ry, hal - le - lu - jah! His truth is march-ing on.
Glo - ry! glo - ry, hal - le - lu - jah! His day is march-ing on.
Glo - ry! glo - ry, hal - le - lu - jah! Our God is march-ing on.
Glo - ry! glo - ry, hal - le - lu - jah! While God is march-ing on.

My Country, 'Tis of Thee 438

SAMUEL FRANCIS SMITH

Anonymous
From "Thesaurus Musicus"

1. My coun - try, 'tis of thee, Sweet land of lib - er - ty,
2. My na - tive coun - try, thee, Land of the no - ble free,
3. Let mu - sic swell the breeze, And ring from all the trees
4. Our fa - thers' God, to Thee, Au - thor of lib - er - ty,

Of thee I sing: Land where my fa - thers died, Land of the
Thy name I love: I love thy rocks and rills, Thy woods and
Sweet free-dom's song: Let mor - tal tongues a - wake, Let all that
To Thee we sing: Long may our land be bright With free-dom's

pil - grims' pride, From ev - 'ry moun-tain side Let free - dom ring!
tem - pled hills; My heart with rap - ture thrills Like that a - bove.
breathe par-take; Let rocks their si - lence break, The sound pro - long.
ho - ly light; Pro - tect us by Thy might, Great God, our King!

439 Count Your Blessings

JOHNSON OATMAN, JR.

EDWIN O. EXCELL

1. When up-on life's bil-lows you are tem-pest-tossed, When you are dis-
2. Are you ev-er bur-dened with a load of care? Does the cross seem
3. When you look at oth-ers with their lands and gold, Think that Christ has
4. So, a-mid the con-flict, wheth-er great or small, Do not be dis-

cour-aged, think-ing all is lost, Count your man-y bless-ings, name them
heav-y you are called to bear? Count your man-y bless-ings, ev-'ry
prom-ised you His wealth un-told; Count your man-y bless-ings, mon-ey
cour-aged, God is o-ver all; Count your man-y bless-ings, an-gels

one by one, And it will sur-prise you what the Lord hath done.
doubt will fly, And you will be sing-ing as the days go by.
can-not buy Your re-ward in Heav-en, nor your Home on high.
will at-tend, Help and com-fort give you to your jour-ney's end.

Count your bless-ings, name them one by one; Count your
Count your man-y bless-ings, name them one by one; Count your man-y

bless-ings, See what God hath done; Count your bless-ings,
bless-ings, See what God hath done; Count your man-y bless-ings,

rit.   *a tempo*

Name them one by one: Count your man-y bless-ings, See what God hath done.

Thanks to God   440

From the Swedish
Translated by C. E. Backstrom

J. A. HULTMAN

1. Thanks to God for my Re - deem - er, Thanks for all Thou dost pro - vide!
2. Thanks for prayers that Thou hast an-swered, Thanks for what Thou dost de - ny!
3. Thanks for ros - es by the way-side, Thanks for thorns their stems con-tain!

Thanks for times now but a mem - 'ry, Thanks for Je - sus by my side!
Thanks for storms that I have weath-ered, Thanks for all Thou dost sup - ply!
Thanks for home and thanks for fire-side, Thanks for hope, that sweet re - frain!

Thanks for pleas - ant, balm - y spring-time, Thanks for dark and drear-y fall!
Thanks for pain, and thanks for pleas - ure, Thanks for com - fort in de - spair!
Thanks for joy and thanks for sor - row, Thanks for heav'n-'ly peace with Thee!

Thanks for tears by now for - got - ten, Thanks for peace with - in my soul!
Thanks for grace that none can meas-ure, Thanks for love be-yond com-pare.
Thanks for hope in the to - mor-row, Thanks through all e - ter - ni - ty.

441 Great Is Thy Faithfulness

THOMAS O. CHISHOLM

WILLIAM M. RUNYAN

1. "Great is Thy faith-ful-ness," O God my Fa-ther, There is no shad-ow of turn-ing with Thee; Thou chang-est not, Thy com-pas-sions, they fail not; As Thou hast been Thou for-ev-er wilt be.

2. Sum-mer and win-ter, and spring-time and har-vest, Sun, moon, and stars in their cours-es a-bove, Join with all na-ture in man-i-fold wit-ness, To Thy great faith-ful-ness, mer-cy and love.

3. Par-don for sin and a peace that en-dur-eth, Thy own dear pres-ence to cheer and to guide; Strength for to-day and bright hope for to-mor-row, Bless-ings, all mine, with ten thou-sand be-side!

"Great is Thy faith-ful-ness! Great is Thy faith-ful-ness!" Morn-ing by morn-ing new mer-cies I see; All I have need-ed Thy

Favorite song of Dr. Clyde Narramore.

hand hath pro - vid - ed — "Great is Thy faith-ful-ness," Lord, un -to me!

We Gather Together   442

Anonymous
Translated by Theodore Baker

Netherlands Folk Song
Arranged by Edward Kremser

1. We gath - er to - geth - er to ask the Lord's bless - ing,
2. Be - side us to guide us, our God with us join - ing,
3. We all do ex - tol Thee, Thou Lead - er in bat - tle,

He chas - tens and has - tens His will to make known;
Or - dain - ing, main - tain - ing His king - dom di - vine;
And pray that Thou still our De - fend - er wilt be.

The wick - ed op - press - ing cease them from dis - tress - ing,
So from the be - gin - ning the fight we were win - ning,
Let Thy con - gre - ga - tion es - cape trib - u - la - tion;

Sing prais - es to His name, He for - gets not His own.
Thou, Lord, wast at our side — the glo - ry be Thine!
Thy name be ev - er praised. O Lord, make us free!

443 Lead Me Gently Home, Father

WILL L. THOMPSON   WILL L. THOMPSON

1. Lead me gen-tly Home, Fa-ther, Lead me gen - tly Home,
2. Lead me gen-tly Home, Fa-ther, Lead me gen - tly Home,
3. Lead me gen-tly Home, Fa-ther, Lead me gen - tly Home,

When life's toils are end - ed, and part - ing days have come;
In life's dark - est hours, Fa - ther, when life's trou - bles come,
In temp - ta-tion's hours, Fa - ther, when sore tri - als come;

Sin no more shall tempt me, Ne'er from Thee I'll roam,
Keep my feet from wan - dering, Lest from Thee I roam,
Be Thou near to keep me, Take me as Thine own,

rit. **p**

If Thou'lt on - ly lead me, Fa - ther,
Lest I fall up - on the way-side, Lead me gen - tly Home.
For I can - not live with-out Thee,

Lead me gen - tly Home, Fa-ther, lead me gen - tly,
Lead me gen - tly Home, Fa-ther, Lead me gen - tly Home, Fa-ther,

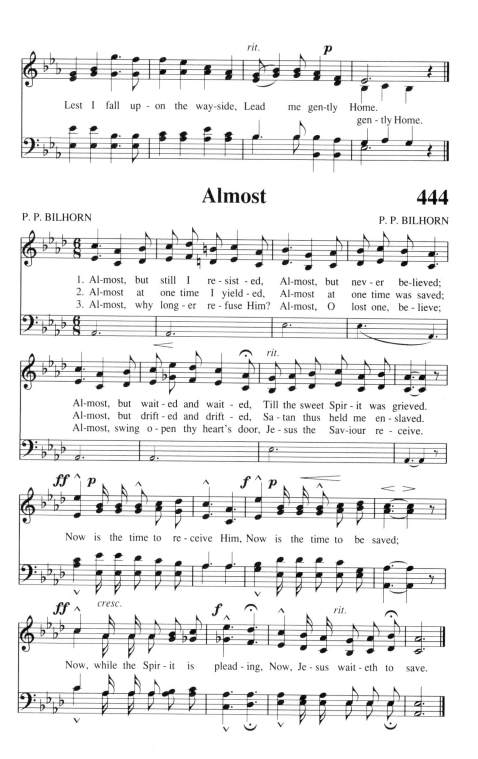

Lest I fall up - on the way-side, Lead me gen-tly Home.

gen - tly Home.

Almost

444

P. P. BILHORN

P. P. BILHORN

1. Al-most, but still I re - sist - ed, Al-most, but nev - er be-lieved;
2. Al-most at one time I yield - ed, Al-most at one time was saved;
3. Al-most, why long - er re - fuse Him? Al-most, O lost one, be - lieve;

Al-most, but wait - ed and wait - ed, Till the sweet Spir - it was grieved.
Al-most, but drift - ed and drift - ed, Sa - tan thus held me en - slaved.
Al-most, swing o - pen thy heart's door, Je - sus the Sav - iour re - ceive.

Now is the time to re - ceive Him, Now is the time to be saved;

Now, while the Spir - it is plead - ing, Now, Je - sus wait - eth to save.

445 Friendship With Jesus

J. C. LUNDGATE

S. FOSTER

1. A friend of Je - sus, oh, what bliss That one so weak as I
2. A Friend when oth - er friend-ships cease, A Friend when oth - ers fail;
3. A Friend to lead me in the dark, A Friend who knows the way;
4. A Friend when sick-ness lays me low, A Friend when death draws near;
5. A Friend when life's rough voyage is o'er, A Friend when death is past;

Should ev - er have a Friend like this To lead me to the sky.
A Friend who gives me joy and peace, A Friend who will pre - vail.
A Friend to steer my weak, frail bark, A Friend my debts to pay.
A Friend as thro' the vale I go, A Friend to help and cheer.
A Friend to greet on Heav-en's shore, A Friend when Home at last.

Friend - ship with Je - sus, Fel - low - ship di - vine;

rit.

Oh, what bless-ed sweet com - mun - ion, Je - sus is a Friend of mine.

Ivory Palaces

446

HENRY BARRACLOUGH

HENRY BARRACLOUGH

1. My Lord has gar-ments so won-drous fine, And myrrh their tex-ture fills;
2. His life had al - so its sor-rows sore, For al - oes had a part;
3. His gar-ments too were in cas - sia dipped, With heal - ing in a touch;
4. In gar-ments glo - ri - ous He will come, To o - pen wide the door;

Its fra-grance reached to this heart of mine, With joy my be - ing thrills.
And when I think of the cross He bore, My eyes with tear-drops start.
Each time my feet in some sin have slipped, He took me from its clutch.
And I shall en - ter my heav'n - ly Home, To dwell for-ev - er-more.

DUET - *Slowly, softly, and with much expression*

Out of the i - vo - ry pal - a - ces In - to a world of woe,

FULL CHORUS

DUET - *Very softly*

On - ly His great e - ter - nal love made my Sav-iour go.

447 Here Am I

JOHN R. RICE

JOHN R. RICE

1. We should pray the Lord of Har-vest, "Reap-ers send in-to Thy field."
2. Ho-ly Fa-ther, send a se-raph, From the al-tar take a coal.
3. Not four months a-way the har-vest, Fields are white: lift up your eyes.
4. Pluck as em-bers from the burn-ing Souls for whom the Sav-iour died.

Few are reap-ers; white and wast-ing Are the fields, How rich the yield.
Cleanse my lips, I hear "Whom shall I Send to gar-ner pre-cious souls?"
Fruit for life e-ter-nal gath-er, Rich the wag-es for such prize.
O then send me, Christ of mer-cy, To the doomed and lost out-side.

Here am I! (O Lord, send me) Here am I! (I wait on Thee) Send me

forth, O Lord of Har-vest, Breathe on me Thy Ho-ly Spir-it. Here am

I! (O Lord, send me) Here am I! (I wait on Thee) Send me

forth to win some pre - cious soul to - day.

Brethren, We Have Met to Worship 448

GEORGE ATKINS

*Attributed to William Moore
in "Columbian Harmony"*

1. Breth-ren,   we have met to   wor - ship   And a - dore the Lord our God;
2. Breth-ren,   see poor sin-ners   round   you   Slum-b'ring   on the brink of woe;
3. Sis - ters,   will you join and   help   us?   Mo - ses'   sis - ter aid - ed him;
4. Let   us   love our God su - preme - ly,   Let us   love each oth - er too;

Will you   pray with all your   pow - er,   While we   try to preach the Word?
Death is   com-ing, Hell is   mov - ing—   Can you   bear to   let them go?
Will you   help the trem-bling mourn - ers   Who are   strug-gling hard with sin?
Let us   love and pray for   sin - ners   Till our   God makes all things new.

All   is   vain un - less the   Spir - it   Of the Ho - ly   One comes   down;
See our   fa -thers and our   moth-ers   And our chil-dren   sink-ing   down;
Tell them all   a - bout the   Sav-iour —Tell them that He   will be   found;
Then He'll call us Home to   Heav-en.   At His ta - ble   we'll sit   down;

Breth-ren,   pray, and ho - ly   man - na   Will be   show-ered all   a-round.
Breth-ren,   pray, and ho - ly   man - na   Will be   show-ered all   a-round.
Sis - ters,   pray, and ho - ly   man - na   Will be   show-ered all   a-round.
Christ will   gird Him - self and   serve   us   With sweet   man - na   all   a-round.

449   Dwelling in Beulah Land

C. AUSTIN MILES   C. AUSTIN MILES

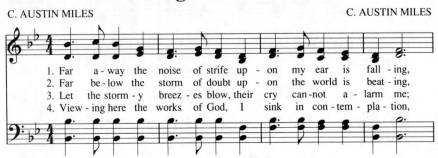

1. Far a-way the noise of strife up-on my ear is fall-ing,
2. Far be-low the storm of doubt up-on the world is beat-ing,
3. Let the storm-y breez-es blow, their cry can-not a-larm me;
4. View-ing here the works of God, I sink in con-tem-pla-tion,

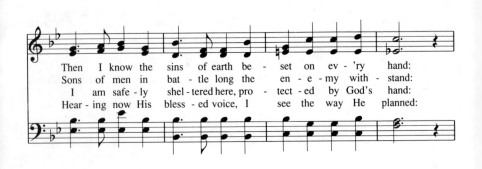

Then I know the sins of earth be-set on ev-'ry hand:
Sons of men in bat-tle long the en-e-my with-stand:
I am safe-ly shel-tered here, pro-tect-ed by God's hand:
Hear-ing now His bless-ed voice, I see the way He planned:

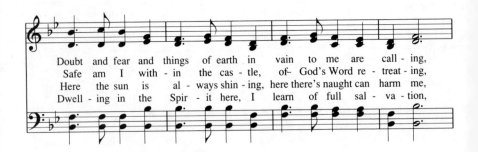

Doubt and fear and things of earth in vain to me are call-ing,
Safe am I with-in the cas-tle, of God's Word re-treat-ing,
Here the sun is al-ways shin-ing, here there's naught can harm me,
Dwell-ing in the Spir-it here, I learn of full sal-va-tion,

450 The Lights of Home

FANNY J. CROSBY

CHARLES H. MARSH

1. O the friends that now are wait - ing, In the cloud - less realms of day,
2. They have laid a-side their ar - mor For the robe of spot-less white;
3. On those dear fa-mil-iar fac - es There will be no trace of care;

Who are call - ing me to fol - low Where their steps have led the
And with Je - sus they are walk - ing Where the riv - er spark-les
Ev - 'ry sigh was hushed for-ev - er At the pal-ace gate so

way; They have laid a - side their ar - mor, And their earth - ly
bright. We have la - bored here to-geth - er, We have la - bored
fair. I shall see them, I shall know them, I shall hear their

course is run; They have kept the faith with pa - tience And their
side by side, Just a lit - tle while be - fore me They have
song of love, And we'll all sing hal - le - lu - jah In our

crown of life is won.
crossed the roll - ing tide. They are call - ing, gen - tly call - ing, Sweet - ly
Fa - ther's house a - bove.

call - ing me to come, And I'm look - ing through the

rit.

shad - ows For the bless - ed lights of Home.

Where Could I Go? 451

J. B. COATS   J. B. COATS

1. Liv - ing be - low in this old sin - ful world, Hard - ly a com - fort can af - ford;
2. Neigh - bors are kind, I love them ev - 'ry - one, We get a - long in sweet ac - cord;
3. Life here is grand, with friends I love so dear, Com - fort I get from God's own Word;

Cho.: Where could I go, O where could I go; Seek - ing a ref - uge for my soul?

D.C. for Chorus

Striv - ing a - lone to face temp - ta - tions sore,
But when my soul needs man - na from a - bove, Where could I go but to the Lord?
Yet when I face the chill - ing hand of Death,

Need - ing a friend to help me in the end, Where could I go but to the Lord?

© Copyright 1940, by Stamps-Baxter Co. in "Golden Key."

452 All I Need

Anonymous   Anonymous

1. Je - sus Christ is made to me, All I need, all I need,
2. He re-deemed me when He died, All I need, all I need,
3. He's the treas - ure of my soul, All I need, all I need,
4. Je - sus is my all in all, All I need, all I need,
5. Glo - ry, glo - ry to the Lamb, All I need, all I need,

He a - lone is all my plea, He is all I need.
I with Him was cru - ci - fied, He is all I need.
He hath cleansed and made me whole, He is all I need.
While He keeps I can - not fall, He is all I need.
By His Spir - it sealed I am, He is all I need.

Wis-dom, right - eous - ness and power, Hol - i - ness this ver - y hour,

My re - demp - tion full and free, He is all I need.

The Touch of His Hand on Mine 453

JESSIE BROWN POUNDS

HENRY P. MORTON

1. There are days so dark that I seek in vain For the face of my
2. There are times, when tired of the toil-some road, That for ways of the
3. When the way is dim, and I can-not see Through the mist of His
4. In the last sad hour, as I stand a-lone Where the pow-ers of

Friend Di - vine; But though dark-ness hide, He is there to guide
world I pine; But He draws me back to the up - ward track
wise de - sign, How my glad heart yearns and my faith re - turns
death com - bine, While the dark waves roll He will guide my soul

By the touch of His hand on mine. O the touch of His hand on

mine, O the touch of His hand on mine! There is grace and
on mine, on mine!

pow'r, in the try-ing hour, In the touch of His hand on mine.

454   He Will Hold Me Fast

ADA R. HABERSHON

ROBERT HARKNESS

1. When I fear my faith will fail, Christ will hold me fast;
2. I could nev-er keep my hold, He will hold me fast;
3. I am pre-cious in His sight, He will hold me fast;
4. He'll not let my soul be lost, Christ will hold me fast;

When the tempt-er would pre-vail, He can hold me fast.
For my love is oft-en cold, He can hold me fast.
Those He saves are His de-light, He can hold me fast.
Bought by Him at such a cost, He can hold me fast.

He will hold me fast, He will hold me fast;
hold me fast, hold me fast;

For my Sav-iour loves me so, He will hold me fast.

O Perfect Love

455

DOROTHY F. GURNEY

JOSEPH BARNBY

1. O per - fect Love, all hu - man thought tran - scend - ing,
2. O per - fect Life, be Thou their full as - sur - ance
3. Grant them the joy which bright - ens earth - ly sor - row,
4. Hear us, O Fa - ther, gra - cious and for - giv - ing,

Low - ly we kneel in prayer be - fore Thy throne,
Of ten - der char - i - ty and stead - fast faith,
Grant them the peace which calms all earth - ly strife,
Through Je - sus Christ, Thy co - e - ter - nal Word,

That theirs may be the love which knows no end - ing,
Of pa - tient hope, and qui - et, brave en - dur - ance,
And to life's day the glo - rious, un - known mor - row
Who, with the Ho - ly Ghost, by all things liv - ing

Whom Thou for - ev - er - more dost join in one.
With child - like trust that fears no pain and death.
That dawns up - on e - ter - nal love and life.
Now and to end - less a - ges art a - dored.

456 All Your Anxiety

E. H. JOY

E. H. JOY

1. Is there a heart o'er-bound by sor-row? Is there a life weighed
2. No oth-er Friend so keen to help you; No oth-er Friend so
3. Come then, at once, de-lay no long-er; Heed His en-treat-y,

down by care? Come to the cross, each bur-den bear-ing,
quick to hear; No oth-er place to leave your bur-den;
kind and sweet; You need not fear a dis-ap-point-ment,

All your anx-i-e-ty—leave it there.
No oth-er one to hear your prayer. All your anx-i-e-ty,
You shall find peace at the mer-cy seat.

all your care, Bring to the mer-cy seat, leave it

there; Nev-er a bur-den He can-not bear,

Nev - er a Friend like Je - sus.

Sing as You Ride

457

WILLIAM H. RICE

Anonymous
Arranged by Mrs. William H. Rice

Sing as you ride in the round-up of life. Sing as you ride through the day and the night. Sing as you ride, for with Christ by your side He will nev - er once fail to the end of the trail, So just sing as you ride.

458 The Church in the Wildwood

WILLIAM S. PITTS   WILLIAM S. PITTS

D.S. al fine

come to the church in the vale;

come, come, come, come, come, come, come,

Fairest Lord Jesus 459

4th Verse Tr. JOSEPH A. SEISS

Arr. by Richard S. Willis

1. Fair - est Lord Je - sus! Ru - ler of all na - ture!
2. Fair are the mead - ows, Fair - er still the wood - lands,
3. Fair is the sun - shine, Fair - er still the moon - light,
4. Beau - ti - ful Sav - iour! Lord of all the na - tions!

O Thou of God and man the Son! Thee will I cher - ish,
Robed in the bloom-ing garb of spring; Je - sus is fair - er,
And all the twin-kling star - ry host; Je - sus shines bright - er,
Son of God and Son of Man! Glo - ry and hon - or,

Thee will I hon - or, Thou, my soul's glo - ry, joy, and crown!
Je - sus is pur - er, Who makes the woe - ful heart to sing!
Je - sus shines pur - er, Than all the an - gels Heav'n can boast!
Praise, a - dor - a - tion, Now and for - ev - er - more be Thine!

Favorite song of Dr. William Culbertson.

460 From Every Stormy Wind

H. STOWELL

S. WILDER

1. From ev - 'ry storm - y wind that blows, From ev - 'ry swell - ing tide of woes, There is a calm, a sure re - treat: 'Tis
2. There is a place where Je - sus sheds The oil of glad - ness on our heads: A place than all be - sides more sweet: It
3. There is a scene where spir - its blend, Where friend holds fel - low - ship with friend; Though sun - dered far, by faith they meet A -
4. O let my hand for - get her skill, My tongue be si - lent, cold, and still, This bound - ing heart for - get to beat, If

found | be - neath | the | mer - cy | seat.
is | the | blood - bought | mer - cy | seat.
round | one com - mon | mer - cy | seat.
I | for - get | the | mer - cy | seat!

Resting in His Promise

461

JOHN R. RICE

JOHN R. RICE

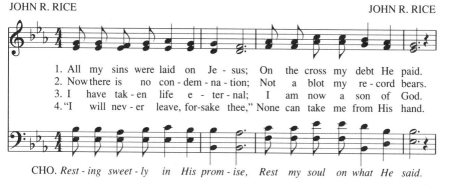

1. All my sins were laid on Je - sus; On the cross my debt He paid.
2. Now there is no con - dem - na - tion; Not a blot my re - cord bears.
3. I have tak - en life e - ter - nal; I am now a son of God.
4. "I will nev - er leave, for-sake thee," None can take me from His hand.

CHO. *Rest - ing sweet - ly in His prom - ise, Rest my soul on what He said.*

D.C.

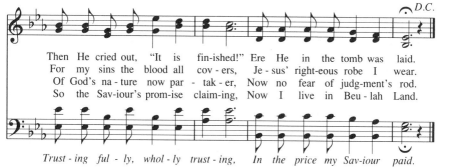

Then He cried out, "It is fin-ished!" Ere He in the tomb was laid.
For my sins the blood all cov - ers, Je - sus' right-eous robe I wear.
Of God's na - ture now par - tak - er, Now no fear of judg-ment's rod.
So the Sav-iour's prom-ise claim-ing, Now I live in Beu - lah Land.

Trust - ing ful - ly, whol - ly trust - ing, In the price my Sav-iour paid.

462   Christ Is King

CHARLES R. SCOVILLE   De LOSS SMITH

1. Come, friends sing, of the faith that's so dear to
2. Cru - ci - fied, thus He suf-fered and bled for
3. At His feet, on old Ol - i -vet's Hill they

me, Re - vealed through God's Son,
me, Death and the grave won
say Cloud char - iots halt - ed,

in Gal - i - lee; He brought peace on
sin's vic - to - ry; Then the sky grew
took Christ a - way; Then the an - gels

earth and good will to the sons of men,
dark and the tem - ple veil rent in twain,
came and to won-d'ring dis - ci - ples said

Go tell it to the world, her King reigns a -
Rocks rent, and an - gels came, for He lived a -
He'll come, and earth and sea shall yield up their

463   Awakening Chorus

CHARLOTTE G. HOMER   CHARLES H. GABRIEL

464 God So Loved the World

John 3:16, altered

JOHN STAINER

God so loved the world, God so loved the world,
that He gave His on - ly be - got - ten Son, that who - so be -
liev - eth, be - liev - eth in Him should not per - ish, should not
per - ish, but have ev - er - last - ing life. For God sent not His
Son in - to the world to con - demn the world, God sent not His Son in - to the
world to con - demn the world; But that the world through Him might be sav -

465 The Ninety and Nine

ELIZABETH C. CLEPHANE

IRA D. SANKEY

1. There were nine - ty and nine that safe - ly lay In the
2. "Lord, Thou hast here Thy nine - ty and nine; Are
3. But none of the ran - somed ev - er knew How
4. "Lord, whence are those blood - drops all the way That
5. But all through the moun - tains, thun - der - riv'n, And

shel - ter of the fold, But one was out on the
they not e - nough for Thee?" But the Shep - herd made an - swer:
deep were the wa - ters crossed; Nor how dark was the night that the
mark out the moun - tain's track?" "They were shed for one who had
up from the rock - y steep, There a - rose a glad cry to the

hills a - way, Far off from the gates of gold — A -
"This of Mine Has wan - dered a - way from Me, And al -
Lord passed through Ere He found His sheep that was lost.
gone a - stray Ere the Shep - herd could bring him back." "Lord,
gate of Heav'n, "Re - joice! I have found My sheep!" And the

rit.

way on the moun - tains wild and bare, A - way from the ten - der
though the road be rough and steep, I go to the des - ert to
Out in the des - ert He heard its cry — Sick and help - less, and
whence are Thy hands so rent and torn?" "They're pierced to - night by
an - gels ech - oed a - round the throne, "Re - joice, for the Lord brings

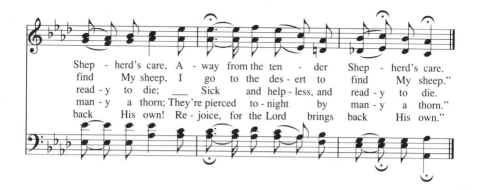

Shep - herd's care, A - way from the ten - der Shep - herd's care.
find My sheep, I go to the des - ert to find My sheep."
read - y to die; ___ Sick and help - less, and read - y to die.
man - y a thorn; They're pierced to - night by man - y a thorn."
back His own! Re - joice, for the Lord brings back His own."

Breathe on Me, Breath of God   466

EDWIN HATCH

ROBERT JACKSON

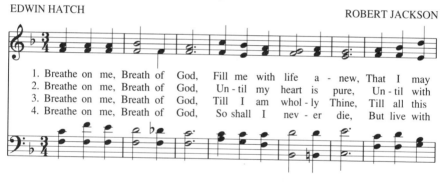

1. Breathe on me, Breath of God, Fill me with life a - new, That I may
2. Breathe on me, Breath of God, Un - til my heart is pure, Un - til with
3. Breathe on me, Breath of God, Till I am whol - ly Thine, Till all this
4. Breathe on me, Breath of God, So shall I nev - er die, But live with

love what Thou dost love, And do what Thou wouldst do.
Thee I will one will, To do or to en - dure.
earth - ly part of me, Glows with Thy fire di - vine.
Thee the per - fect life Of Thine e - ter - ni - ty.

467

The B-I-B-L-E

Anonymous

Anonymous

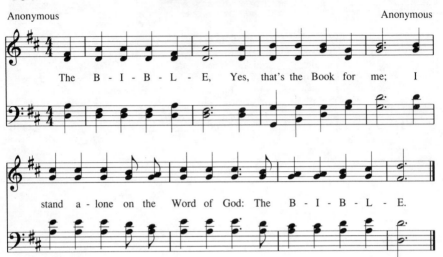

The B - I - B - L - E, Yes, that's the Book for me; I

stand a - lone on the Word of God: The B - I - B - L - E.

468

Isn't He Wonderful?

S. JONES

Arranged

Is - n't He won - der - ful, won - der - ful, won - der - ful? Is - n't

Je - sus my Lord won - der - ful? Eyes have seen; ears have heard; It's re -

cord - ed   in God's Word.   Is - n't   Je - sus   my   Lord   won-der - ful?

Jesus Bids Us Shine

469

SUSAN WARNER

EDWIN G. EXCELL

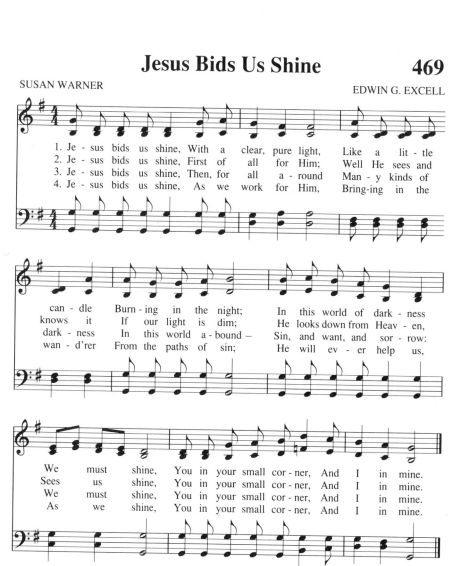

1. Je - sus bids us shine, With a clear, pure light,
2. Je - sus bids us shine, First of all for Him;
3. Je - sus bids us shine, Then, for all a - round
4. Je - sus bids us shine, As we work for Him,

Like a lit - tle
Well He sees and
Man - y kinds of
Bring-ing in the

can - dle Burn - ing in the night; In this world of dark - ness
knows it If our light is dim; He looks down from Heav - en,
dark - ness In this world a - bound — Sin, and want, and sor - row:
wan - d'rer From the paths of sin; He will ev - er help us,

We must shine, You in your small cor - ner, And I in mine.
Sees us shine, You in your small cor - ner, And I in mine.
We must shine, You in your small cor - ner, And I in mine.
As we shine, You in your small cor - ner, And I in mine.

470 Come Unto Me

ELIZA E. HEWITT

D. WARD MILAM

Solo or Unison

1. Come, all ye wea - ry and op-pressed, O come and I will
2. Come, ye that feel the weight of sin, And I will breathe sweet
3. So ten - der - ly my Sav - iour pleads, For all His own He

give you rest; I'll bid your anx - ious fears de - part, For
peace with - in; I'll lift the bur - den from your heart, For -
in - ter - cedes; And still He's call - ing, Come to Me, And

I am meek and low - ly in heart, For I am meek and
give - ness I will free - ly im - part, For - give - ness I will
ye shall find rest un - to your soul, For I am meek and

ad lib.

low - ly in heart, And I will give you rest.
free - ly im - part, And I will give you rest.
low - ly in heart, And I will give you rest. Ye that la - bor

471 Cleanse Me

J. EDWIN ORR

Maori Melody

1. Search me, O God, and know my heart to-day;
2. I praise Thee, Lord, for cleans-ing me from sin:
3. Lord, take my life, and make it whol-ly Thine:
4. O Ho-ly Ghost, re-viv-al comes from Thee:

Try me, O Sav-iour, know my thoughts, I pray:
Ful-fill Thy Word, and make me pure with-in;
Fill my poor heart with Thy great love di-vine;
Send a re-viv-al— start the work in me:

See if there be some wick-ed way in me:
Fill me with fire, where once I burned with shame:
Take all my will, my pas-sion, self and pride;
Thy Word de-clares Thou wilt sup-ply our need:

Cleanse me from ev-'ry sin, and set me free.
Grant my de-sire to mag-ni-fy Thy name.
I now sur-ren-der: Lord, in me a-bide.
For bless-ing now, O Lord, I hum-bly plead.

This Is My Father's World

MALTBIE D. BABCOCK

FRANKLIN L. SHEPPARD

1. This is my Fa-ther's world, And to my lis-t'ning ears, All
2. This is my Fa-ther's world, The birds their car-ols raise, The
3. This is my Fa-ther's world, O let me ne'er for-get That

na-ture sings, and round me rings The mu - sic of the spheres.
morn-ing light, the lil - y white, De-clare their Ma-ker's praise.
though the wrong seems oft so strong, God is the Rul-er yet.

This is my Fa-ther's world, I rest me in the thought Of
This is my Fa-ther's world, He shines in all that's fair; In the
This is my Fa-ther's world, The bat-tle is not done, Je -

rocks and trees, of skies and seas, His hand the won-ders wrought.
rus-tling grass I hear Him pass, He speaks to me ev-'ry-where.
sus who died shall be sat-is-fied, And earth and Heav'n be one.

473 Ship Ahoy!

M. J. CARTWRIGHT

D. B. TOWNER

Effective Solo

1. I was drift-ing a-way on life's pit-i-less sea, And the
2. 'Twas the "old ship of Zi-on," thus sail-ing a-long, All a-
3. The good Cap-tain com-mand-ed a boat to be low'red, And with
4. O soul, sink-ing down 'neath sin's mer-ci-less wave, The strong

an-gry waves threat-ened my ru-in to be, When a-way at my
board her seemed joy-ous, I heard their sweet song; And the Cap-tain's kind
ten-der com-pas-sion He took me on board; And I'm hap-py to-
arm of our Cap-tain is might-y to save; Then trust Him to-

side, there I dim-ly de-scried A state-ly old ves-sel, and
ear, ev-er read-y to hear, Caught my wail of dis-tress, as I
day, all my sins washed a-way In the blood of my Sav-iour, and
day, no lon-ger de-lay, Board the old ship of Zi-on, and

loud-ly I cried: "Ship a-hoy! Ship a-hoy!"
cried out in fear: "Ship a-hoy! Ship a-hoy!"
now I can say: "Bless the Lord! Bless the Lord!"
shout on your way: "Je-sus saves! Je-sus saves!"

And loud-ly I cried: "Ship a-hoy!"
As I cried out in fear: "Ship a-hoy!"
From my soul I can say: "Bless the Lord!"
Shout and sing on your way: "Je-sus saves!"

Though Your Sins Be As Scarlet 474

FANNY J. CROSBY

WILLIAM H. DOANE

475 Jesus, Lover of My Soul

CHARLES WESLEY

REFUGE

JOSEPH P. HOLBROOK

1. Je - sus, Lov - er of my soul, Let me to Thy bos-om fly, While the
2. Oth - er ref - uge have I none; Hangs my help-less soul on Thee; Leave, O
3. Thou, O Christ, art all I want; More than all in Thee I find: Raise the
4. Plen-teous grace with Thee is found, Grace to cov - er all my sin; Let the

near - er wa - ters roll, While the tem - pest still is high!
leave me not a - lone, Still sup - port and com - fort me:
fall - en, cheer the faint, Heal the sick, and lead the blind.
heal - ing streams a - bound; Make me, keep me pure with - in.

Hide me, O my Sav - iour, hide, Till the storm of life is past;
All my trust on Thee is stayed, All my help from Thee I bring;
Just and ho - ly is Thy name, I am all un-right-eous-ness;
Thou of life the foun - tain art, Free - ly let me take of Thee.

Safe in - to the ha - ven guide, O re - ceive my soul at last.
Cov - er my de - fense - less head With the shad - ow of Thy wing.
Vile, and full of sin I am, Thou art full of truth and grace.
Spring Thou up with - in my heart, Rise to all e - ter - ni - ty.

My Plea

J. L. BAKER

J. L. BAKER

1. Should I at the gates of Heav-en ap-pear To an-swer the chal-lenge, "What claim hast thou here, What hast thou to of-fer, yea, what is thy plea?" With bless-ed as-sur-ance my an-swer would be,

2. Of all earth-ly treas-ures no-thing I've brought; No great deeds of mer-it have I ev-er wrought. Tho vile and un-worth-y as mor-tal could be, I've no-thing to of-fer but this is my plea,

3. My sins, they are man-y, my vir-tues are few. The blood of my Sav-iour will car-ry me through. When Christ in my place died on Cal-va-ry's tree, Hal-le-lu-jah, that o-pened God's Heav-en to me!

All that I have is Je - sus, All that I claim is Je - sus, All that I want, All that I need, All that I plead is Je - sus.

477 Jesus in My Heart

J. L. BAKER

J. L. BAKER

1. You may won-der why it is I'm al-ways hap-py, You may
2. You may won-der why I seek no earth-ly treas-ure, And the
3. It is Je - sus who has pur-chased my re - demp - tion, It was

won - der why I'm sing - ing all day long, You may won - der at the
lux - ur - y that gold a - lone can buy, You may won - der why I
Je - sus who trans-formed this heart of mine, He who loved me and from

joy with - in my be - ing That can on - ly find ex - pres-sion in my song.
crave no world-ly pleas - ure. If you lis - ten I will tell the rea - son why.
all my sin has washed me In the foun-tain of His pre-cious blood di - vine.

It is Je - sus, on - ly Je - sus; It is Je - sus in my

heart. It is Je - sus, on - ly Je - sus; It is

1. Je - sus in my heart. 2. in my heart.

Onward, Christian Soldiers

478

SABINE BARING-GOULD

W. H. JUDE

Tempo di marcia

Unison

1. On - ward, Chris - tian sol - diers! March - ing as to war, With the cross of Je - sus Go - ing on be - fore. Christ, the roy - al Mas - ter, Leads a - gainst the foe; For - ward in - to bat - tle, See, His ban - ner

2. On - ward, then, ye peo - ple! Join our hap - py throng, Blend with ours your voic - es In the tri - umph song; Glo - ry, laud, and hon - or Un - to Christ the King, This through count - less a - ges Men and an - gels

479 Hallelujah Chorus

(The vocal score is complete and uniform with the Messiah edition)

GEORGE FREDERICK HANDEL

TOPICAL INDEX

ASSURANCE

A Mighty Fortress Is Our God 144

A Shelter in the Time of Storm 146

All I Need 452

Anywhere With Jesus 126

Blessed Assurance 143

Blest Be the Tie That Binds 154

Christ Is All I Need 131

Constantly Abiding 336

Each Step I Take 128

He Hideth My Soul 102

How Firm a Foundation 153

I Do Believe 151

I Know I Am Saved 135

I Know Whom I Have Believed 139

In Times Like These 137

It Is Well With My Soul 145

Jesus, I Am Resting 201

Jesus, Lover of My Soul 90

Jesus Never Fails 101

Jesus, Only Jesus 148

Leaning on the Everlasting Arms 147

Like a River Glorious 121

Master, the Tempest Is Raging 136

Moment by Moment 222

My Anchor Holds 134

My Faith Has Found a Resting Place 150

My Plea 476

Near to the Heart of God 118

Never Alone! 132

Resting in His Promise 461

Safe Wherever I Go 133

Security 152

The Haven of Rest 138

The Old-Time Religion 142

The Solid Rock 125

Tis So Sweet to Trust in Jesus 127

Trusting Jesus 149

Under His Wings 103

We Have an Anchor 140

What Will You Say Then? 141

Yesterday, Today, Forever 130

BIBLE

Break Thou the Bread of Life 365

Holy Bible, Book Divine 368

I Know the Bible Is True 369

My Mother's Bible 367

Standing on the Promises 364

The B-I-B-L-E 467

The Old Book and the Old Faith 366

Wonderful Words of Life 363

CHOIR AND SPECIAL

All Hail the Power of Jesus' Name 167

All Hail the Power of Jesus' Name (Diadem) ... 168

All I Need 452

All Your Anxiety 456

Almost 444

Awakening Chorus 463

Breathe on Me, Breath of God 466

Brethren We Have Met to Worship 448

Christ Is King 462

Cleanse Me 471

Come Unto Me (Milam) 470

Dwelling in Beulah 449

Each Step I Take 128

Fairest Lord Jesus 459

Friendship With Jesus 445

From Every Stormy Wind (Wilder) 460

From Every Stormy Wind (Hastings) 353

God So Loved the World 464

Hallelujah Chorus 479

He Will Hold Me Fast 454

Here Am I 447

Isn't He Wonderful 468

Ivory Palaces 446

Jesus Bids Us Shine 469

Jesus in My Heart 477

Jesus, Lover of My Soul (Marsh) 90

Jesus, Lover of My Soul (Refuge) 475

Lead Me Gently Home 443

Master, the Tempest Is Raging 136

My Plea 476

O Perfect Love 455

Onward, Christian Soldiers (Jude) 478

Onward, Christian Soldiers (Sullivan) 412

Resting in His Promise 461

Ship Ahoy 473

Sing As You Ride 457

Sweet Will of God 302

The B-I-B-L-E 467

The Church in the Wildwood 458

The Lights of Home 450

The Ninety and Nine 465

The Old Book and the Old Faith 366

The Touch of His Hand 453

This Is My Father's World 472

Though Your Sins Be as Scarlet 474

What Did He Do? 268

Where Could I Go? 451

Wonderful Grace of Jesus 210

Wonderful Peace 113

Yes, I Know! 267

Christian Warfare

As a Volunteer 416

Am I a Soldier of the Cross? 418

Faith Is the Victory! 410

Faith of Our Fathers 407

Hold the Fort 411

Loyalty to Christ 408

Onward, Christian Soldiers (Jude) 478

Onward, Christian Soldiers (Sullivan) 412

Sound the Battle Cry 419

Stand Up, Stand Up for Jesus (Webb) 413

Stand Up, Stand Up for Jesus (Geibel) 414

The Banner of the Cross 405

The Fight Is On 409

True-Hearted, Whole-Hearted 417

Victory Through Grace 415

When the Battle's Over 404

Who Is on the Lord's Side? 406

Christmas

Angels, From the Realms of Glory 432

Away in a Manger 433

Hark! the Herald Angels Sing 429

I Heard the Bells on Christmas Day 426

It Came Upon the Midnight Clear 428

Joy to the World! 423

No Room in the Inn 425

O Come, All Ye Faithful 424

O Little Town of Bethlehem 434

Silent Night! Holy Night! 431

The First Noel 421

There's a Song in the Air 420

Thou Didst Leave Thy Throne 422

We Three Kings of Orient Are 427

While Shepherds Watched Their Flocks 430

Comfort and Guidance

Abide With Me 106

All That Thrills My Soul 105

All the Way My Saviour Leads Me 110

Art Thou Weary, Art Thou Languid? 93

Be Still, My Soul 112

Come, Ye Disconsolate 99

Day by Day 100

Does Jesus Care? 89

God Leads Us Along 96

God Will Take Care of You 124

He Hideth My Soul 102

He Leadeth Me 116
Hiding in Thee 91
How Can I Be Lonely? 92
I Need Thee Every Hour 97
In the Garden 86
Jesus Never Fails 101
Jesus! Jesus! Jesus! 85
Jesus, Lover of My Soul (Marsh) 90
Jesus, Saviour, Pilot Me 120
Just When I Need Him Most 87
Lean on His Arms 104
Like a River Glorious 121
Near to the Heart of God 118
Never Alone! 132
No One Ever Cared for Me Like Jesus 115
O God, Our Help 122
Praise the Saviour 107
Safe in the Arms of Jesus 117
Saviour, Like a Shepherd Lead Us 109
Security 152
Some Time We'll Understand 88
Stand by Me 94
Sun of My Soul 108
Sweet Peace, the Gift of God's Love 111
The Christian's Good-Night 123
The Great Physician 114
The Lord Is My Shepherd 95
The Name of Jesus 98
Till the Storm Passes By 119
Under His Wings 103
Wonderful Peace 113

Consecration

All for Jesus 311
Ashamed of Jesus 300
Back to Bethel 295
Channels Only 332
Christ Is All 326
Close to Thee 297
Dare to Be a Daniel 309
Draw Me Nearer 324

Follow On 296
Footprints of Jesus 310
Give Me Jesus 333
Give Me Thy Heart 318
Have Thine Own Way, Lord! 306
Higher Ground 327
His Way With Thee 292
I Have Decided to Follow Jesus 316
I Surrender All 308
I Want That Mountain! 328
I Would Be Like Jesus 330
I'll Be True, Precious Jesus 313
I'll Live for Him 317
If Jesus Goes With Me 335
Is Your All on the Altar? 293
Jesus Calls Us 307
Just a Closer Walk With Thee 319
Living for Jesus 322
Make Me a Blessing 334
More About Jesus 323
More Like the Master 298
More Love to Thee 314
My Faith Looks Up to Thee 303
Near to the Heart of God 118
Nothing Between 304
O to Be Like Thee! 320
Open My Eyes, That I May See 312
Something for Thee 299
Stepping in the Light 294
Sweet Hour of Prayer 301
Sweet Will of God 302
Take My Life, and Let It Be 315
Take Time to Be Holy 329
Trust and Obey 325
Where He Leads I'll Follow 321
Wherever He Leads I'll Go 331
Yield Not to Temptation 305

Consolation

Come, Ye Disconsolate 99
Does Jesus Care? 89

He Is So Precious 234

He the Pearly Gates Will Open 58

Just When I Need Him Most 87

Meet Me There 49

Saved By Grace 62

Shall We Gather at the River? 64

Sweet By and By 41

Sweet Will of God 302

Tell It to Jesus 351

The Pearly White City 67

There'll Be No Dark Valley 37

Till the Storm Passes By 119

Turn Your Eyes Upon Jesus 261

Under His Wings 103

What a Day That Will Be 63

When We All Get to Heaven 56

When We See Christ 81

Wonderful Peace 113

Zion's Hill 52

CROSS

Alas! and Did My Saviour Bleed? 28

And Can It Be That I Should Gain? 24

Are You Washed in the Blood? 22

At the Cross 29

Beneath the Cross of Jesus 6

Blessed Redeemer 12

Glory to His Name 2

Hallelujah for the Cross! 26

He Died for Me 11

I Am Coming to the Cross 8

I Gave My Life for Thee 7

Jesus, I My Cross Have Taken 1

Jesus Paid It All 3

Kneel at the Cross 14

Lead Me to Calvary 15

Majestic Sweetness Sits Enthroned 16

Must Jesus Bear the Cross Alone? 13

Near the Cross 10

Nothing But the Blood 30

One Day! 17

Rock of Ages 129

Room at the Cross for You 9

Take the Name of Jesus With You 18

The Old Rugged Cross 27

The Way of the Cross Leads Home 4

There Is a Fountain 19

There Is Power in the Blood 23

What a Wonderful Saviour! 21

When I See the Blood 20

When I Survey the Wondrous Cross 5

Wounded for Me 25

DUET

Ask and Seek and Knock 357

Away in a Manger 433

Blessed Quietness 340

Come and Dine 255

Count Your Blessings 439

Day by Day 100

God Leads Us Along 96

God Will Take Care of You 124

Have You Any Room For Jesus? 283

He the Pearly Gates Will Open 58

Heaven Came Down and
        Glory Filled My Soul 215

Here Am I 447

How Can I Be Lonely? 92

I Gave My Life For Thee 7

I Know That My Redeemer Liveth 34

I Love Him 181

I'm Going Higher 83

In the Garden 86

It Is Well With My Soul 145

Jesus in My Heart 477

Jesus, Lover of My Soul (Refuge) 475

Jesus, Lover of My Soul (Marsh) 90

More Like the Master 298

My Mother's Bible 367

My Plea 476

No One Ever Cared For Me Like Jesus 115

Pray About Everything 360

Some Golden Daybreak 73

When I See the Blood 20

Yes, I Know! 267

Faith and Trust

Faith of Our Fathers 407

I Know Whom I Have Believed 139

My Faith Has Found a Resting Place 150

My Faith Looks Up to Thee 303

Rock of Ages 129

The Old-Time Religion 142

Tis So Sweet to Trust in Jesus 127

Trust and Obey 325

Trusting Jesus 149

Whosoever Will 254

Grace

Amazing Grace 244

Grace Greater Than Our Sin 208

Only a Sinner 207

Saved By Grace 62

Victory Through Grace 415

Wonderful Grace of Jesus 210

Heaven

At Calvary 66

Beulah Land 53

Caught Up Together 59

Face to Face 60

He the Pearly Gates Will Open 58

How Beautiful Heaven Must Be 39

I'll Be So Glad 48

Just Over in the Glory Land 65

Let the Sun Shine Again in My Heart 47

Meet Me There 49

My Latest Sun Is Sinking Fast 42

My Saviour First of All 46

No Disappointment in Heaven 40

O That Will Be Glory 54

Peace, Perfect Peace 50

Remembering in Heaven 68

Saved by Grace 62

Shall We Gather at the River? 64

Sweet By and By 41

The Pearly White City 67

We'll Never Say Good-bye 61

We'll Work Till Jesus Comes 44

We're Marching to Zion 43

What a Day That Will Be 63

When I Can Read My Title Clear 45

When the Roll Is Called Up Yonder 55

When They Ring the Golden Bells 57

When We All Get to Heaven 56

Where We'll Never Grow Old 51

Zion's Hill 52

Holy Spirit

Blessed Quietness 340

Breathe on Me 345

Bring Your Vessels, Not a Few 346

Come, Holy Spirit 348

Constantly Abiding 336

Fall Fresh on Me 344

Fill Me Now 347

Ho! Every One That Is Thirsty 337

Holy Ghost, With Light Divine 338

Old-Time Power 342

Pentecostal Power 341

Revive Thy Work 350

Revive Us Again 343

Spirit of God, Descend Upon My Heart 339

The Comforter Has Come 349

Invitation

Almost Persuaded 275

Come Unto Me (Jones) 274

Come Unto Me (Milam) 470

Come, Sinner, Come! 289

Have You Any Room for Jesus? 283

I Am Coming, Lord 291

I Am Resolved 288

Into My Heart 285

Jesus Is Calling 278

Jesus, I Come 272

Just as I Am 270

Let Him In 290

Let Jesus Come Into Your Heart 279

Lord, I'm Coming Home 271

Only Trust Him 277

Open Your Heart's Door 287

Pass Me Not, O Gentle Saviour 281

Softly and Tenderly Jesus Is Calling 280

The Nail-Scarred Hand 286

What Will You Do With Jesus? 273

Where He Leads Me 276

Who at My Door Is Standing? 284

Why Do You Wait? 269

Why Not Now? 282

JOY AND SINGING

He Keeps Me Singing 205

He's a Wonderful Saviour to Me 200

I Will Sing of the Mercies 195

I Will Sing the Wondrous Story 196

In My Heart There Rings a Melody 191

Jesus, I Am Resting 201

Joy Unspeakable 198

Let the Joy Overflow 199

My Redeemer 202

O! Say, But I'm Glad 206

Ring the Bells of Heaven 192

Since Jesus Came Into My Heart 194

Singing I Go 197

Songs in the Mountains 204

The Windows of Heaven 203

Wonderful, Wonderful Jesus 190

You May Have the Joy-bells 193

LOVE

I Love Him 181

I Love Thee, My Jesus 184

I Never Will Cease to Love Him 189

Isn't the Love of Jesus
    Something Wonderful? 180

It's Just Like His Great Love 175

Jesus Loves Even Me 178

Jesus Loves Me (Rice) 186

Jesus Loves Me (Bradbury) 187

Jesus Loves the Little Children 176

Jesus! the Very Thought of Thee 171

Love Divine, All Loves Excelling 172

Love Lifted Me 173

My Jesus, I Love Thee 174

My Saviour's Love 185

O How I Love Jesus 183

Such Love 179

The Love of God 188

When Love Shines In 177

Wonderful Story of Love 182

PATRIOTIC

Battle Hymn of the Republic 437

My Country, 'Tis of Thee 438

O Beautiful for Spacious Skies 435

The Star-Spangled Banner 436

PRAISE

A Mighty Fortress Is Our God 144

All Hail the Power of Jesus' Name 167

All Hail the Power of Jesus' Name (Diadem) ... 168

Blessed Be the Name 159

Come, Thou Almighty King 157

Come, Thou Fount 169

Crown Him With Many Crowns 160

Doxology 155

Hallelujah, What a Saviour! 170

I Will Praise Him 166

Jesus Is the Sweetest Name I Know 156

O for a Thousand Tongues to Sing 158

O Worship the King 165

Our Great Saviour 161

Praise Him! Praise Him! 164

To God Be the Glory 162

When Morning Gilds the Skies 163

PRAYER

Ask and Seek and Knock 357

Did You Think to Pray? 361

From Every Stormy Wind (Hastings) 353

From Every Stormy Wind (Wilder) 460

Have You Prayed It Through? 352
I Am Praying for You 354
I Must Tell Jesus 356
I'm Leaning on Jesus 362
Near to the Heart of God 118
Pray About Everything 360
Tell It to Jesus 351
Thy Word Have I Hid in My Heart 359
Tis the Blessed Hour of Prayer 358
What a Friend We Have in Jesus 355

RESURRECTION

Christ Arose! 36
Christ the Lord Is Risen Today 33
Hallelujah, We Shall Rise 38
He Lives 31
He Lives on High 32
I Know That My Redeemer Liveth 34
There'll Be No Dark Valley 37
When I See My Saviour 35

SALVATION

Christ Receiveth Sinful Men 258
Come and Dine 255
He Is Able to Deliver Thee 260
Honey in the Rock 266
If I Gained the World 251
Jesus Saves 259
Look and Live 257
Look to the Lamb of God 256
Once for All 264
Someone's Last Call 265
The Light of the World Is Jesus 262
Turn Your Eyes Upon Jesus 261
Verily, Verily 263
What Did He Do? 268
Whiter Than Snow 252
Whosoever Will 254
Ye Must Be Born Again 253
Yes, I Know! 267

SECOND COMING

Behold, He Comes! 77

Christ Returneth 74
Coming Today? 80
I'm Going Higher 83
Is It the Crowning Day? 72
Jesus Is Coming 78
Jesus Is Coming Again 84
On Jordan's Stormy Banks 75
Some Golden Daybreak 73
There's a Great Day Coming 71
We Shall Shine As the Stars 69
What if It Were Today? 76
When He Cometh 82
When Jesus Comes to Reign 79
When We See Christ 81
Will Jesus Find Us Watching? 70

SOUL WINNING AND SERVICE

A Passion for Souls 378
A Soul Winner for Jesus 392
Bringing in the Sheaves 379
Bring Them In 389
Fight the Good Fight 381
Go Ye Into All the World 385
Have I Done My Best for Jesus? 390
He Was Not Willing 380
Help Somebody Today 395
I'll Wish I Had Given Him More 400
In Christ There Is No East or West 376
In the Service of the King 384
It Pays to Serve Jesus 386
Let the Lower Lights Be Burning 372
Little Is Much When God Is in It 397
Make Me a Channel of Blessing 383
Must I Go, and Empty-Handed? 387
O Bring Your Loved Ones 371
O Zion, Haste 393
Our Best 402
Ready 391
Rescue the Perishing 377
Seeking the Lost 382
Send the Light 374

Set My Soul Afire 401

Shall I Empty-Handed Be? 399

So Little Time 396

So Send I You 373

Speak, My Lord 388

Tell It Again 398

The Call for Reapers 403

Throw Out the Life-Line 370

To the Work! 394

Work, for the Night Is Coming 375

TESTIMONY

A Child of the King 221

All I Need 452

Amazing Grace 244

Builded on the Rock 214

Burdens Are Lifted at Calvary 250

Christ Liveth in Me 238

Each Step I Take 128

Grace Greater Than Our Sin 208

Hallelujah, 'Tis Done 218

He Included Me 217

He Is So Precious to Me 234

Heaven Came Down and
      Glory Filled My Soul 215

Heavenly Sunlight 230

I Know I Am Saved 135

I Know I Love Thee Better, Lord 235

I Love to Tell the Story 228

I've Found a Friend 226

It Took a Miracle 242

Jesus Is All the World to Me 220

Moment by Moment 222

My Burdens Rolled Away 219

No, Not One! 236

Nor Silver Nor Gold 225

Now I Belong to Jesus 248

O Happy Day 212

O It Is Wonderful! 241

Only a Sinner 207

Redeemed 246

Saved! 249

Saved by the Blood 227

Saved, Saved! 247

Seeking for Me 239

Since I Have Been Redeemed 229

Springs of Living Water 223

Sunlight 231

Sunshine in the Soul 209

Surely Goodness and Mercy 216

Tell Me the Old, Old, Story 233

Tell Me the Story of Jesus 232

The Cleansing Wave 237

The Lily of the Valley 240

The Old Account Was Settled 245

The Old-Time Religion 142

There Is Glory in My Soul 213

There Shall Be Showers of Blessing 224

Victory in Jesus 243

Whosoever Meaneth Me 211

Wonderful Grace of Jesus 210

THANKSGIVING

Count Your Blessings 439

Great Is Thy Faithfulness 441

Thanks to God 440

We Gather Together 442

YOUTH

A Soul Winner For Jesus 392

All for Jesus 311

All I Need 452

As a Volunteer 416

Ask and Seek and Knock 357

Christ Is All I Need 131

Cleanse Me 471

Dare to Be a Daniel 309

Each Step I Take 128

Fall Fresh on Me 344

Go Ye into All the World 385

Hallelujah, We Shall Rise 38

Have I Done My Best for Jesus? 390

Have Thine Own Way, Lord! 306

He Keeps Me Singing 205

He Will Hold Me Fast 454

He's a Wonderful Saviour to Me 200

Heaven Came Down and
Glory Filled My Soul 215

Heavenly Sunlight 230

Hold the Fort 411

Holy Bible, Book Divine 368

I Am Resolved 288

I Have Decided to Follow Jesus 316

I Never Will Cease to Love Him 189

I Want That Mountain! 328

I Will Sing of the Mercies 195

I Would Be Like Jesus 330

I'll Be So Glad 48

I'll Be True, Precious Jesus 313

In My Heart There Rings a Melody 191

Into My Heart 285

Isn't He Wonderful 468

Jesus Is Coming 78

Jesus Loves Even Me 178

Jesus Loves Me (Rice) 186

Jesus Loves Me (Bradbury) 187

Jesus Loves the Little Children 176

Living for Jesus 322

More Like the Master 298

No One Ever Cared for Me Like Jesus 115

Now I Belong to Jesus 248

O! Say, But I'm Glad 206

Onward, Christian Soldiers (Jude) 478

Onward, Christian Soldiers (Sullivan) 412

Saved, Saved! 247

Saviour, Like a Shepherd Lead Us 109

Set My Soul Afire 401

Sing As You Ride 457

Springs of Living Water 223

Stand Up, Stand Up for Jesus (Webb) 413

Stand Up, Stand Up for Jesus (Geibel) 414

Sunlight 231

Surely Goodness and Mercy 216

Take My Life, and Let It Be 315

The B-I-B-L-E 467

The Fight Is On 409

The Windows of Heaven 203

Turn Your Eyes Upon Jesus 261

Victory in Jesus 243

We'll Never Say Good-bye 61

When He Cometh 82

When the Battle's Over 404

Where Could I Go? 451

Who Is on the Lord's Side? 406

Yes, I Know! 267

Yield Not to Temptation 305

You May Have the Joy-bells 193

GENERAL INDEX

A

A Child of the King 221

A Mighty Fortress Is Our God 144

A Passion for Souls 378

A Shelter in the Time of Storm 146

A Soul Winner for Jesus 392

Abide With Me 106

Alas! and Did My Saviour Bleed? 28

All for Jesus 311

All Hail the Power of Jesus' Name 167

All Hail the Power (Diadem) 168

All I Need 452

All That Thrills My Soul 105

All the Way My Saviour Leads Me 110

All Your Anxiety 456

Almost 444

Almost Persuaded 275

Am I a Soldier of the Cross? 418

Amazing Grace 244

And Can It Be That I Should Gain? 24

Angels, From the Realms of Glory 432

Anywhere With Jesus 126

Are You Washed in the Blood? 22

Art Thou Weary, Art Thou Languid? 93

As a Volunteer 416

Ashamed of Jesus 300

Ask and Seek and Knock 357

At Calvary 66

At the Cross 29

Awakening Chorus 463

Away in a Manger 433

B

Back to Bethel 295

Battle Hymn of the Republic 437

Be Still, My Soul 112

Behold, He Comes! 77

Beneath the Cross of Jesus 6

Beulah Land 53

Blessed Assurance 143

Blessed Be the Name 159

Blessed Quietness 340

Blessed Redeemer 12

Blest Be the Tie That Binds 154

Break Thou the Bread of Life 365

Breathe on Me 345

Breathe on Me, Breath of God 466

Brethren, We Have Met to Worship 448

Bring Them In 389

Bring Your Vessels, Not a Few 346

Bringing in the Sheaves 379

Builded on the Rock 214

Burdens Are Lifted at Calvary 250

C

Caught Up Together 59

Channels Only 332

Christ Arose! 36

Christ Is All 326

Christ Is All I Need 131

Christ Is King 462

Christ Liveth in Me 238

Christ Receiveth Sinful Men 258

Christ Returneth 74

Christ the Lord Is Risen Today 33

Cleanse Me 471

Close to Thee 297

Come and Dine 255

Come, Holy Spirit 348

Come, Sinner, Come! 289

Come, Thou Almighty King 157

Come, Thou Fount 169

Come Unto Me (Jones) 274

Come Unto Me (Milam) 470

COME, YE DISCONSOLATE 99

COMING TODAY? 80

CONSTANTLY ABIDING 336

COUNT YOUR BLESSINGS 439

CROWN HIM WITH MANY CROWNS 160

D

DARE TO BE A DANIEL 309

DAY BY DAY 100

DID YOU THINK TO PRAY? 361

DOES JESUS CARE? 89

DOXOLOGY 155

DRAW ME NEARER 324

DWELLING IN BEULAH LAND 449

E

EACH STEP I TAKE 128

F

FACE TO FACE 60

FAIREST LORD JESUS 459

FAITH IS THE VICTORY! 410

FAITH OF OUR FATHERS 407

FALL FRESH ON ME 344

FIGHT THE GOOD FIGHT 381

FILL ME NOW 347

FOLLOW ON 296

FOOTPRINTS OF JESUS 310

FRIENDSHIP WITH JESUS 445

FROM EVERY STORMY WIND (HASTINGS) 353

FROM EVERY STORMY WIND (WILDER) 460

G

GIVE ME JESUS 333

GIVE ME THY HEART 318

GLORY TO HIS NAME 2

GO YE INTO ALL THE WORLD 385

GOD LEADS US ALONG 96

GOD SO LOVED THE WORLD 464

GOD WILL TAKE CARE OF YOU 124

GRACE GREATER THAN OUR SIN 208

GREAT IS THY FAITHFULNESS 441

H

HALLELUJAH CHORUS 479

HALLELUJAH FOR THE CROSS! 26

HALLELUJAH, 'TIS DONE 218

HALLELUJAH, WE SHALL RISE 38

HALLELUJAH, WHAT A SAVIOUR! 170

HARK! THE HERALD ANGELS SING 429

HAVE I DONE MY BEST FOR JESUS? 390

HAVE THINE OWN WAY, LORD! 306

HAVE YOU ANY ROOM FOR JESUS? 283

HAVE YOU PRAYED IT THROUGH? 352

HE DIED FOR ME 11

HE HIDETH MY SOUL 102

HE INCLUDED ME 217

HE IS ABLE TO DELIVER THEE 260

HE IS SO PRECIOUS TO ME 234

HE KEEPS ME SINGING 205

HE LEADETH ME 116

HE LIVES 31

HE LIVES ON HIGH 32

HE THE PEARLY GATES WILL OPEN 58

HE WAS NOT WILLING 380

HE WILL HOLD ME FAST 454

HE'S A WONDERFUL SAVIOUR TO ME 200

HEAVEN CAME DOWN AND GLORY FILLED MY SOUL 215

HEAVENLY SUNLIGHT 230

HELP SOMEBODY TODAY 395

HERE AM I 447

HIDING IN THEE 91

HIGHER GROUND 327

HIS WAY WITH THEE 292

HO! EVERY ONE THAT IS THIRSTY 337

HOLD THE FORT 411

HOLY BIBLE, BOOK DIVINE 368

HOLY GHOST, WITH LIGHT DIVINE 338

HONEY IN THE ROCK 266

HOW BEAUTIFUL HEAVEN MUST BE 39

How Can I Be Lonely? 92
How Firm a Foundation 153

I

I Am Coming to the Cross 8
I Am Coming, Lord 291
I Am Praying for You 354
I Am Resolved 288
I Do Believe 151
I Gave My Life for Thee 7
I Have Decided to Follow Jesus 316
I Heard the Bells on Christmas Day 426
I Know I Am Saved 135
I Know I Love Thee Better, Lord 235
I Know That My Redeemer Liveth 34
I Know the Bible Is True 369
I Know Whom I Have Believed 139
I Love Him 181
I Love Thee, My Jesus 184
I Love to Tell the Story 228
I Must Tell Jesus 356
I Need Thee Every Hour 97
I Never Will Cease to Love Him 189
I Surrender All 308
I Want That Mountain! 328
I Will Praise Him 166
I Will Sing of the Mercies 195
I Will Sing the Wondrous Story 196
I Would Be Like Jesus 330
I'll Be So Glad 48
I'll Be True, Precious Jesus 313
I'll Live for Him 317
I'll Wish I Had Given Him More 400
I'm Going Higher 83
I'm Leaning on Jesus 362
I've Found a Friend 226
If I Gained the World 251
If Jesus Goes With Me 335
In Christ There Is No East or West 376

In My Heart There Rings a Melody 191
In the Garden 86
In the Service of the King 384
In Times Like These 137
Into My Heart 285
Is It the Crowning Day? 72
Is Your All on the Altar? 293
Isn't He Wonderful 468
Isn't the Love of Jesus Something Wonderful? 180
It Came Upon the Midnight Clear 428
It Is Well With My Soul 145
It Pays to Serve Jesus 386
It Took a Miracle 242
It's Just Like His Great Love 175
Ivory Palaces 446

J

Jesus Bids Us Shine 469
Jesus Calls Us 307
Jesus, I Am Resting 201
Jesus, I Come 272
Jesus, I My Cross Have Taken 1
Jesus Is All the World to Me 220
Jesus Is Calling 278
Jesus Is Coming 78
Jesus Is Coming Again 84
Jesus Is the Sweetest Name I Know 156
Jesus In My Heart 477
Jesus! Jesus! Jesus! 85
Jesus, Lover of My Soul (Marsh) 90
Jesus, Lover of My Soul (Refuge) 475
Jesus Loves Even Me 178
Jesus Loves Me (Rice) 186
Jesus Loves Me (Bradbury) 187
Jesus Loves the Little Children 176
Jesus Never Fails 101
Jesus, Only Jesus 148
Jesus Paid It All 3

Jesus Saves 259

Jesus, Saviour, Pilot Me 120

Jesus! the Very Thought of Thee 171

Joy to the World! 423

Joy Unspeakable 198

Just a Closer Walk With Thee 319

Just as I Am 270

Just Over in the Glory Land 65

Just When I Need Him Most 87

K

Kneel at the Cross 14

L

Lead Me Gently Home 443

Lead Me to Calvary 15

Lean on His Arms 104

Leaning on the Everlasting Arms 147

Let Him In 290

Let Jesus Come Into Your Heart 279

Let the Joy Overflow 199

Let the Lower Lights Be Burning 372

Let the Sun Shine Again in My Heart 47

Like a River Glorious 121

Little Is Much When God Is in It 397

Living for Jesus 322

Look and Live 257

Look to the Lamb of God 256

Lord, I'm Coming Home 271

Love Divine, All Loves Excelling 172

Love Lifted Me 173

Loyalty to Christ 408

M

Majestic Sweetness Sits Enthroned 16

Make Me a Blessing 334

Make Me a Channel of Blessing 383

Master, the Tempest Is Raging 136

Meet Me There 49

Moment by Moment 222

More About Jesus 323

More Like the Master 298

More Love to Thee 314

Must I Go, and Empty-Handed? 387

Must Jesus Bear the Cross Alone? 13

My Anchor Holds 134

My Burdens Rolled Away 219

My Country, 'Tis of Thee 438

My Faith Has Found a Resting Place 150

My Faith Looks Up to Thee 303

My Jesus, I Love Thee 174

My Latest Sun Is Sinking Fast 42

My Mother's Bible 367

My Plea 476

My Redeemer 202

My Saviour First of All 46

My Saviour's Love 185

N

Near the Cross 10

Near to the Heart of God 118

Never Alone! 132

No Disappointment in Heaven 40

No One Ever Cared for Me Like Jesus 115

No Room in the Inn 425

No, Not One! 236

Nor Silver Nor Gold 225

Nothing Between 304

Nothing But the Blood 30

Now I Belong to Jesus 248

O

O Beautiful for Spacious Skies 435

O Bring Your Loved Ones 371

O Come, All Ye Faithful 424

O for a Thousand Tongues to Sing 158

O God, Our Help 122

O Happy Day 212

O How I Love Jesus 183

O It Is Wonderful! 241

O Little Town of Bethlehem 434

O Perfect Love 455
O! Say, But I'm Glad 206
O That Will Be Glory 54
O to Be Like Thee! 320
O Worship the King 165
O Zion, Haste 393
Old-Time Power 342
On Jordan's Stormy Banks 75
Once for All 264
One Day! 17
Only a Sinner 207
Only Trust Him 277
Onward Christian Soldiers (Jude) 478
Onward, Christian Soldiers (Sullivan) .. 412
Open My Eyes, That I May See 312
Open Your Heart's Door 287
Our Best 402
Our Great Saviour 161

P

Pass Me Not, O Gentle Saviour 281
Peace, Perfect Peace 50
Pentecostal Power 341
Praise Him! Praise Him! 164
Praise the Saviour 107
Pray About Everything 360

R

Ready 391
Redeemed 246
Remembering in Heaven 68
Rescue the Perishing 377
Resting in His Promise 461
Revive Thy Work 350
Revive Us Again 343
Ring the Bells of Heaven 192
Rock of Ages 129
Room at the Cross for You 9

S

Safe in the Arms of Jesus 117

Safe Wherever I Go 133
Saved! 249
Saved by Grace 62
Saved by the Blood 227
Saved, Saved! 247
Saviour, Like a Shepherd Lead Us 109
Security 152
Seeking for Me 239
Seeking the Lost 382
Send the Light 374
Set My Soul Afire 401
Shall I Empty-Handed Be? 399
Shall We Gather at the River? 64
Ship Ahoy 473
Silent Night! Holy Night! 431
Since I Have Been Redeemed 229
Since Jesus Came Into My Heart 194
Sing as You Ride 457
Singing I Go 197
So Little Time 396
So Send I You 373
Softly and Tenderly Jesus Is Calling 280
Some Golden Daybreak 73
Some Time We'll Understand 88
Someone's Last Call 265
Something for Thee 299
Songs in the Mountains 204
Sound the Battle Cry 419
Speak, My Lord 388
Spirit of God, Descend Upon My Heart ..339
Springs of Living Water 223
Stand by Me 94
Stand Up, Stand Up for Jesus (Webb) 413
Stand Up, Stand Up for Jesus (Geibel) 414
Standing on the Promises 364
Stepping in the Light 294
Such Love 179
Sun of My Soul 108

Sunlight 231	The Old-Time Religion 142
Sunshine in the Soul 209	The Pearly White City 67
Surely Goodness and Mercy 216	The Solid Rock 125
Sweet By and By 41	The Star-Spangled Banner 436
Sweet Hour of Prayer 301	The Touch of His Hand 453
Sweet Peace, the Gift of God's Love 111	The Way of the Cross Leads Home 4
Sweet Will of God 302	The Windows of Heaven 203

T

Take My Life, and Let It Be 315	There Is a Fountain 19
Take the Name of Jesus With You 18	There Is Glory in My Soul 213
Take Time to Be Holy 329	There Is Power in the Blood 23
Tell It Again 398	There Shall Be Showers of Blessing 224
Tell It to Jesus 351	There'll Be No Dark Valley 37
Tell Me the Old, Old, Story 233	There's a Great Day Coming 71
Tell Me the Story of Jesus 232	There's a Song in the Air 420
Thanks to God 440	This Is My Father's World 472
The B-I-B-L-E 467	Thou Didst Leave Thy Throne 422
The Banner of the Cross 405	Though Your Sins Be As Scarlet 474
The Call for Reapers 403	Throw Out the Life-Line 370
The Christian's Good-Night 123	Thy Word Have I Hid in My Heart 359
The Church in the Wildwood 458	Till the Storm Passes By 119
The Cleansing Wave................................. 237	'Tis So Sweet to Trust in Jesus 127
The Comforter Has Come 349	'Tis the Blessed Hour of Prayer 358
The Fight Is On 409	To God Be the Glory 162
The First Noel 421	To the Work! 394
The Great Physician 114	True-Hearted, Whole-Hearted 417
The Haven of Rest 138	Trust and Obey 325
The Light of the World Is Jesus 262	Trusting Jesus............................... 149
The Lights of Home 450	Turn Your Eyes Upon Jesus 261

U

The Lily of the Valley 240	Under His Wings 103
The Lord Is My Shepherd.......................... 95	

V

The Love of God 188	Verily, Verily 263
The Nail-Scarred Hand 286	Victory in Jesus 243
The Name of Jesus 98	Victory Through Grace 415
The Ninety and Nine 465	

W

The Old Account Was Settled.................. 245	We Gather Together 442
The Old Book and the Old Faith 366	We Have an Anchor 140
The Old Rugged Cross 27	We Shall Shine As the Stars 69

We Three Kings of Orient Are 427
We'll Never Say Good-bye 61
We'll Work Till Jesus Comes 44
We're Marching to Zion 43
What a Day That Will Be 63
What a Friend We Have in Jesus 355
What a Wonderful Saviour! 21
What Did He Do? 268
What if It Were Today? 76
What Will You Do With Jesus? 273
What Will You Say Then? 141
When He Cometh 82
When I Can Read My Title Clear 45
When I See My Saviour 35
When I See the Blood 20
When I Survey the Wondrous Cross 5
When Jesus Comes to Reign 79
When Love Shines In 177
When Morning Gilds the Skies 163
When the Battle's Over 404
When the Roll Is Called Up Yonder 55
When They Ring the Golden Bells 57
When We All Get to Heaven 56
When We See Christ 81
Where Could I Go? 451
Where He Leads I'll Follow 321
Where He Leads Me 276

Where We'll Never Grow Old 51
Wherever He Leads I'll Go 331
While Shepherds Watched Their Flocks 430
Whiter Than Snow 252
Who at My Door Is Standing? 284
Who Is on the Lord's Side? 406
Whosoever Meaneth Me 211
Whosoever Will 254
Why Do You Wait? 269
Why Not Now? 282
Will Jesus Find Us Watching? 70
Wonderful Grace of Jesus 210
Wonderful Peace 113
Wonderful Story of Love 182
Wonderful Words of Life 363
Wonderful, Wonderful Jesus 190
Work, for the Night Is Coming 375
Wounded for Me 25

Y

Ye Must Be Born Again 253
Yes, I Know! 267
Yesterday, Today, Forever 130
Yield Not to Temptation 305
You May Have the Joy-bells 193

Z

Zion's Hill 52

Favorite Songs of Christian Leaders

Jesus, I My Cross Have Taken	Dr. John R. Rice	1
	Dr. Arthur DeMoss	
When I Survey the Wondrous Cross	Dr. Bill Rice	5
	Composer John W. Peterson	
Must Jesus Bear the Cross Alone?	Dr. Oliver B. Greene	13
Majestic Sweetness Sits Enthroned	Dr. Robert G. Lee	16
One Day!	Dr. Glen H. Schunk	17
There Is a Fountain	Dr. Tom Malone	19
	Dr. Harold Sightler	
And Can It Be That I Should Gain?	Dr. Bob Jones III	24
	Dr. Rod Bell	
The Old Rugged Cross	Dale Evans Rogers	27
He Lives	Evangelist Bud Lyles	31
What a Day That Will Be	Dr. Ron Schaffer	63
When We See Christ	Bill Gothard	81
Just When I Need Him Most	Dr. Lee Roberson	87
Come, Ye Disconsolate	Dr. Bob Jones, Jr.	99
'Til the Storm Passes By	Dr. David A. Cavin	119
	Dr. John Rawlings	
The Solid Rock	Dr. Curtis Hutson	125
Never Alone	Evangelist Hyman J. Appelman	132
The Haven of Rest	Singer Ray Hart	138
I Know Whom I Have Believed	Dr. Dwight Gustafson	139
Blessed Assurance	Dr. Jack Hyles	143
	Singer Jerome Hines	
	Dr. Clarence Sexton	
	Dr. Bruce Cummons	
How Firm a Foundation	Dr. G. Archer Weniger	153
	Dr. Noel Smith	
O for a Thousand Tongues	Dr. Monroe Parker	158
Our Great Saviour	Dr. J. R. Faulkner	161
	Dr. Bob Gray	
My Jesus I Love Thee	Dr. Alfred B. Smith	174
Only a Sinner Saved by Grace	Dr. Ed Nelson	207
	Dr. G. B. Vick	
Amazing Grace	Dr. Harold Henniger	244
	Dr. Ford Porter	
	Dr. Dallas Billington	
Once for All	Dr. Hugh Pyle	264
Pass Me Not, O Gentle Saviour	Dr. Charles Billington	281
I Surrender All	Dr. Fred D. Jarvis	308
What a Friend We Have in Jesus	Dr. Al Janney	355
I Must Tell Jesus	Dr. Lindsay Terry	356
Great Is Thy Faithfulness	Dr. Clyde M. Narramore	441
Fairest Lord Jesus	Dr. William Culbertson	459